Grave Expectations

THE MINISTRY OF CURIOSITIES SERIES
#4

C.J. ARCHER

Series by C.J. Archer:

The Emily Chambers Spirit Medium Trilogy

The 1st Freak House Trilogy

The 2nd Freak House Trilogy

The 3rd Freak House Trilogy

The Ministry of Curiosities

Lord Hawkesbury's Players

The Assassins Guild

The Witchblade Chronicles

Stand-alone books by C.J. Archer:

Redemption

Surrender

Courting His Countess

The Mercenary's Price

DEDICATION

Thank you to reader Michelle S. for the wonderful title suggestion.

CHAPTER 1

Paris, autumn 1889

"Ah, Mademoiselle Holloway, Monsieur Fitzroy. I have been expecting you. Please come in. Sit." The matron's accent sounded like a cat's purr with its rolling Rs and softly tumbling consonants. Her kind smile rippled across her face and reached her gray eyes. Eyes that looked at me with as much wonder as I had looked at Paris through the coach window.

"Thank you for seeing us," Lincoln said, holding a chair out for me.

"Would you mind continuing to speak in English," I said. "I'm afraid I know very little French." Since docking at Calais several hours ago, I'd learned the words for yes, no, thank you, please and hat, after it blew off in the wind. I'd also discovered that a *pâtisserie* was heaven in a shop.

"Not at all." The matron clasped her knotty hands on the desk in front of her. "You look like her. Your face, your chin, nose, hair. So pretty."

A blush crept up my throat and threatened to engulf my cheeks. I was acutely aware of Lincoln sitting beside me. I didn't need to see him to know that he watched me. His warm gaze made my skin tingle.

"Thank you." In an effort to shift the focus off me, I leaned forward. "Please tell me about her, Matron."

"I will try."

The matron of the St. Madeleine orphanage in Paris had sent Lincoln a letter after he'd learned that I'd been adopted from that institution as a baby. She had provided him with brief details about my mother, and she now repeated these facts. Ellen Mercier had been unwed when she gave birth to me. She was educated and most likely from a good family but had perhaps been cast out when she became pregnant. She'd been gravely ill and had given me to the orphanage in desperation. She'd asked them to find me a nice home, so when the English vicar and his wife inquired about a child to raise as their own, I'd been handed over to them and whisked away to London. The woman I'd grown up believing was my mother was now dead, buried in Highgate Cemetery, and the man I'd called Father had disowned me when I'd raised her spirit at the age of the thirteen. Despite calling myself Charlotte Holloway, I was not a Holloway. Nor was I really a Frankenstein, after my real father. I was Charlie. Just Charlie. That was enough—for now.

"I would like to have known her in happier times," the matron concluded. "She had a quick...what do you English say? Witty?"

"Wit," I said. "A quick mind."

"A quick mind, yes, and a good heart. She had two pair of shoes, and gave her spare to a girl here. A poor girl, so thin and cold with no shoes. Ellen, your mother, insist. She was kind." But instead of smiling at the thought of my mother's kindness, she frowned and shook her head. "Perhaps that is why she find herself in trouble."

"Did she tell you anything about my father?"

"No. We begged her to tell us. We would write to him, you see, and ask that he give you his name, or money if he had any. But she refuse, most strongly. I do not think he was a good man."

"I met him," I told her. "He's dead. And you're correct—he wasn't a good man."

Her eyebrow inched up her forehead, but I didn't elaborate. Victor Frankenstein was dead, and I didn't want to waste my breath on him. He may have been my real father but he didn't care for me as a father ought. He only wanted me for my necromancy and to fulfil his mad medical dreams.

"Is there anything else you can tell me about her, Matron?"

She sighed. "That is all, I am sorry to say. But!" Her face folded into a map of crinkles. "I have something for you. Something she wanted you to have."

"Your letter to Linc—Mr. Fitzroy—mentioned it." I felt myself rising from the chair in anticipation and firmly clasped the chair arms to ground myself. "What is it?"

She flattened her hands on the desk, and that's when I noticed an envelope sealed with a plain red wax seal. She handed it to me.

The envelope bulged in one corner. "Thank you," I heard myself murmur. I stared at the envelope. It was the first thing I'd held that my mother's hands—my *real* mother—had also touched. It was such a small thing, so insignificant, but it felt more wondrous than all the artifacts in the British Museum.

Lincoln touched my arm. "Charlie?"

"I'll open it at the hotel." I clasped the envelope tightly in my gloved hand and rose. My legs felt unsteady but I stood without assistance. Lincoln moved closer, as if to support me if I stumbled. "Thank you, Matron," I said. "You've been very kind. Thank you for your care all those years ago, of both my mother and myself. It is very much appreciated."

She came around the desk and took my hand. "You are welcome, *mademoiselle*. It is a joy to see you grown and in good health. It fills my heart to know that we gave you to a good family."

I didn't correct her. She didn't need to know about the cruel words Anselm Holloway had flung at me as he forced me out of the house I'd called home. She didn't need to hear how he'd almost killed me in an attempt to 'cure' me of my necromancy. Besides, my adopted mother had been good to me. She, at least, had loved me. Of course, she hadn't learned of my strangeness during her lifetime.

"We will be in Paris for a few more days," Lincoln said in his brisk but bland tone. "Would you mind drafting a letter stating that Charlotte Holloway, now of London, was left here as a baby eighteen years ago by Ellen Mercier and given to Mr. and Mrs. Holloway."

"Whatever for?" I asked.

"It may be required for legal reasons."

"What legal reasons?"

His gaze turned cool. The topic was not up for discussion. Or so he thought. I would finish the discussion out of the matron's hearing.

"*Bien sur*," she said.

"Send it to *Le Grand Hôtel,* on the *Boulevard des Capucines.*"

Her eyes flared ever-so slightly at the salubrious address. "I'll write it today. Goodbye, *monsieur et mademoiselle*. Good fortune to you both."

She escorted us through the orphanage's labyrinth of stone corridors to the front door, but Lincoln paused before passing through the giant arched doorway. "Do you know where Ellen Mercier went after she left here?" he asked.

"I am afraid I do not," the matron said. "She was too ill and would not have survived long." She gave me a pitying look.

"Why did you ask that?" I whispered to Lincoln as he escorted me down the orphanage steps. "Do you want to make sure she's dead?"

"Yes."

His bluntness shouldn't have surprised me. He was, after all, not only here for me, but as the leader of the Ministry of Curiosities. The file on Ellen Mercier was open. Until we had proof of her death, he couldn't close it.

Lincoln spoke to the coachman who'd waited for us and paid him. I took Lincoln's offered hand and climbed into the hackney. Our fingers lingered longer than necessary, the touch sending a tiny shockwave through my body.

"Why did you ask for a letter of...?" What was such a letter called?

"Authenticity?"

I swear the corners of his mouth kicked up in a smile, even though his lips didn't seem to move at all. I laughed. "I suppose it could be called that. But why?"

The contours of his face changed, and a small line appeared between his brows. "Holloway made it seem as though he is your real father. When he brought you to England as a baby, he pretended you were their natural child, born in France. As far as English law is concerned, he is your legal guardian. A letter from the matron will go some way to proving that you are not his legitimate child. You do not wish him to be your legal guardian, do you?"

"No, certainly not. But he has disowned me. Surely any legal claim on me is now irrelevant."

"What if he decides to no longer disown you? What if he exerts his legal right, perhaps in the hope of curing you?" His jaw hardened. "I can't risk it."

"I see," I murmured. "Do you think the matron's letter will stand up in court, if it came to that?"

"If not, I will bring the matron herself to England to testify on your behalf."

"Failing that?"

His gaze shifted to the window. "I will do anything in my power to insure you are not under that man's guardianship."

I didn't ask how he would accomplish that; I didn't want to hear the answer. Hopefully, it could be settled legally and without violence. "Unless Holloway demands I return home with him, there is no need for my guardianship to become an issue at all. And I cannot imagine he wants me near him now. I'm quite sure I terrify him."

Lincoln frowned again. "Charlie, I don't think you understand."

"I do. I understand that he can exercise his legal claim over me, but only for three years. Two, in fact. I will be nineteen soon. But why would he? I have no fortune and nothing of value for him to take from me. If he wishes to remove my freedom, I will simply run away again, and you can hide me. Besides, he's in jail. He can do no harm from there."

The coach rolled to a stop outside our hotel. Instead of alighting, Lincoln leaned forward and grasped my hand in both of his. His dark, earnest gaze penetrated mine. "Charlie—"

He was cut off by the driver's barked order. With a pursing of lips, he got out and assisted me down the step. The hotel porter gave me a friendly smile and asked, in terrible English, how I had enjoyed Paris.

"Very much, thank you, but I have not seen a great deal yet. Hopefully tomorrow."

"You did not see my beautiful city?" He clicked his tongue. "But you must!"

"We had an errand to run this afternoon."

"It is late. Mademoiselle is tired, *oui*?"

"*Oui*. It's been a long day."

He went on to recommend some eateries to Lincoln in French, giving me an opportunity to admire the *Boulevard des Capucines* in the late afternoon. Despite the shadows, it was a pretty thoroughfare with its slender trees, now bare of leaves, and grand buildings with bright awnings. People walked quickly past, wrapped in furs against the cold wind, and coaches, omnibuses and carts jostled one another in their hurry to reach their destinations before dark.

Before Lincoln and I left London, my traveling guide told me that Paris was the city for love and lovers. A city "bursting with vibrancy," he'd said. "A delicious confection that teases, is never coy, and is always fresh." Considering my traveling guide had been Seth, I probably should have known his perception of the city would be influenced by his roguish escapades with the ladies of Paris.

While the city wasn't quite as he'd described, it wasn't like Lincoln's version either. When I'd asked him for his impressions of the city, as we waited for the boat to depart at Dover, he'd told me it was "much like London" and left it that. He'd not been overly talkative, and it wasn't until we settled on the boat and his jaw turned green that I remembered why. Seasickness kept him in his cabin the entire crossing, and it wasn't until we were an hour into the train journey from Calais to Paris that his color returned. He refused to discuss his wellbeing with me, despite my numerous questions. It would seem the topic of his weakness, as he thought of it, was off-limits.

I took his offered arm and we entered the hotel together. My mother's letter felt like a lead weight in my reticule, and I could hardly wait to reach my room to open it.

"Sit with me," I urged Lincoln at the door to the small sitting room that adjoined my bedroom. "I might need your support as I read it."

He followed me inside and stoked the coals in the grate as I sat at the table by the window for the light. I opened the envelope with shaking fingers and peered inside.

"It's a necklace." I tipped out the silver chain and pendant onto my palm. The pendant consisted of two circular rings, one inside the other, which could swivel independently. A spherical orange-brown stone was inset into the smaller ring. It could also swivel on its axis, like a globe. "It's quite pretty."

Lincoln held out his hand and I laid it on his palm. "It's amber." He turned it over, rubbed his thumb around the sphere, and held it up to the light. "No inclusions. It would be worth a small sum." He handed it back to me. "Is there a letter?"

I checked inside the envelope and my heart leapt into my throat. I removed the piece of paper and my heart dove a little. "Will you read it? It's in French."

He sat and took the paper. The letter wasn't long, but he took some time reading it first before he translated.

"'To my dearest daughter.

It is my greatest regret that we will never meet again, but I hope this letter will in some way give you comfort as you grow into a woman. Matron assures me you will be given to a good family, and I pray that you are greatly loved, as I love you.

I cannot write much as my body is too weak. I will die very soon, but I go to my afterlife in peace knowing you are in good health and with good people at the orphanage. Do not be sad. Death is nothing to be sad about or to fear, as you may know.

My daughter, I write this letter to you to tell you what I can about who you are and where you come from. My family name is Mercier, from Normandy. They will not welcome you and will only blacken my name. Forget them.

I will not tell you your father's name. He is a dangerous man, and does not love you, or me. I made a mistake to trust him and give him my heart. He only wanted me for my power over death.'"

"I suppose she means necromancy," I said lamely. I felt somewhat numb listening to her words, written so long ago. It must have felt quite strange for her too, writing to a baby. *Her* baby. I swallowed past the lump in my throat. "Please go on."

"'I will keep his name from you to protect you, Daughter. If he learns of your existence, he will pursue you relentlessly and use you in his experiments as he tried to use me. If you have not yet discovered your power over death, then I don't want to frighten you, but I must warn you. Like me, you are a witch who can raise the dead. When a spirit leaves its lifeless body, you can see it and speak to it, and even tell it to re-enter its body. Do not fear this power, but do not tell others. Most will not understand. They will fear you and perhaps harm you.

The necklace I am giving to you will protect you from your father and others who wish to harm you. Wear it always and when you are in danger, hold the orb and summon the imp with three words: 'I release you.'"

"Imp?" I echoed.

"That is the closest English word," Lincoln said.

"Do you think it's an actual, living...thing?"

"It's unclear. She could simply mean a childlike spirit."

"I don't see how a spirit could help me if I am in danger, but I quite like the idea of being protected." I slipped the necklace over my head and tucked it beneath my bodice. "Does it say how she came across it?"

"No." He continued to read:

"'The imp will protect the wearer from evil. I have not used it, and I caution you to only summon the imp if necessary. As with all witchcraft, be careful.

And now, dear Daughter, I grow too weak to continue. If you need to know more, call my spirit. It will be my greatest joy to meet you again. I will be at your side in a moment, but be assured, you are always in my heart. Always.

Your loving mother,

Ellen Marie Mercier.'"

He folded the letter and handed it back to me without a word.

I tucked it into my reticule and blinked away hot tears. It was a long time before I found my voice again, and he didn't try to rush me. "That was quite an experience," I murmured.

He reached across the table and took both my shaking hands in his. The gentle rubbing of his thumbs over my knuckles soothed my jangling nerves, but not my thumping heart. "Do you require a strong drink?"

I smiled. "No, thank you. Your presence is fortifying enough."

"I assume that's a compliment."

I squeezed his hands. "Most certainly." We stayed like that for an age, as I thought through the contents of the letter. I only let him go to inspect the pendant again.

"May I have it?" he said. "To keep it safe."

I closed my fist around it. "My mother wanted me to wear it for protection."

"*I'm* here to protect you now, you don't need a device." He nodded at the pendant. "Its power is unknown, perhaps dangerous itself if unleashed. Until we learn more about it, it should be locked away."

I studied the orb. It felt warm, as if it had been sitting by the fire. Then it throbbed.

I gasped and quickly unclasped the necklace. I thrust it toward him. "I think...I think it's alive."

Lincoln held it up to the light. "Amber sometimes has dead insects trapped inside from when it was a sticky tree resin. This one appears to have something very small in the center, but I can't make it out with the naked eye."

"I felt it beat, like a heart."

He tucked it into his inside jacket pocket. "We'll see what we can learn about it when we return home."

I stared out the window at the street below, where the lamp lighter climbed his ladder to light the nearest streetlamp. My mother's words tumbled through my mind, and while it was wonderful to have that connection with her, I wanted more. I couldn't hear her voice; I wanted so desperately to know its timbre and to see what she looked like. I had only matron's description of her. It wasn't enough.

Lincoln's hand on my cheek startled me. He'd not displayed much tenderness toward me since the kiss in his room back at Lichfield, so his gesture was a surprise, though not an unwelcome one.

But instead of kissing me, or stroking my cheek, he withdrew. He began to pace the small room, his hands at his back.

"I know what you're thinking," I said, also rising.

He stopped and looked at me. "You do?"

"You think I'll raise my mother's spirit. And since she's a necromancer, she might know the same spell that Estelle Pearson knew and override my power. You're worried she'll escape and I won't be able to send her back."

The memory of Estelle Pearson's decaying body getting away from me in Highgate Cemetery still haunted me. I'd gone against Lincoln's wishes and summoned her, but she'd been a witch and spoken a spell to override my commands. Knowing that she could have caused great harm to others still sickened me. I wouldn't summon a spirit again unless I knew they had been powerless in life.

"No," he said quietly. "That is not what I was thinking."

"Then what is it?" I touched his face as he had touched mine. He'd shaved that morning, but dark stubble already shadowed his jaw and roughed my palm. I stroked the smooth skin above it with my thumb. "What troubles you?"

He placed his hand over mine and drew it away. He kissed my wrist, but not passionately, and let me go. "Now is not the time. You're tired and your mind is occupied with thoughts of your mother. I'll have some supper sent up for you. Goodnight, Charlie. Tomorrow we will talk."

"But we're meeting Monsieur Fernesse, the decorator, tomorrow."

"After that." He kissed my forehead. "I will not be far away."

"Will you come to me if I have bad dreams?"

"Of course."

I smiled. I thought he'd be more concerned about someone seeing us. It was one thing to come to my room at night at Lichfield, where it was only us and our three friends, but now we were in public at an exclusive hotel. Perhaps being in a strange city, surrounded by strangers, eased his conscience. I was glad of it. I liked that he didn't care about propriety. Liked it very much.

***

Monsieur Fernesse occupied a gallery sandwiched between a wine shop and a cabaret on a sloping Montmartre street. Seth had told me all about the artists' corner of Paris before we left, describing its freedom, creativity and madness as if those three things could not be separated. On a frosty November morning, however, there was no sign of the previous night's revelries. Aside from a few souls braving the icy wind that swept down the hill, we were the only ones about.

"I hope he's in," I said to Lincoln as we waited for his knock to be answered.

He knocked again, and this time a man dressed in a long purple and gold smoking jacket unlocked the door. He barked out a string of French words I suspected weren't terribly welcoming, from the way Lincoln went very still beside me. He spoke back to the man in that quiet yet commanding tone he used when he was angry, then handed him Seth's letter of introduction.

The Frenchman read it. Then he burst out laughing and ushered us inside. I lifted my brows at Lincoln, and he held out his hand for me to go ahead of him. Seth must have been quite popular with Monsieur Fernesse to change his response from savage to solicitous with a mere letter.

It was just as cold inside the gallery as out, thanks to its cavernous nature and high ceiling. A staircase at the back led up, and an alcove beneath the stairs was occupied by a table covered in swathes of colorful fabrics, sewing tools, and a lamp. The rest of the gallery was set up like a crowded drawing room. Sofas, armchairs, wing chairs, tables, cushions, vases and artwork filled every space, allowing only a narrow path for walking. Each piece was unique and displayed to exquisite perfection. A flash of gold beading, a delicate tassel, a heavy strip of elaborate embroidery...nothing looked ordinary, simple.

"Come, mademoiselle," Monsieur Fernesse said, taking my hand in his long, slender fingers. He led me through the maze to a sofa. He plumped the cushions then insisted I sit. "I will warm your cold hands, mademoiselle. Please, a moment."

He set about lighting the fire. Once it blazed to his satisfaction, he summoned Lincoln. "Help me, young man. My knees, you know, they are old, like me."

Lincoln assisted him to his feet, and the little man gave him a small bow of thanks. He stroked his hands over his gray hair but it remained a tangled mess that fell to his shoulders. He had a beard to match, and it was difficult to tell where beard ended and hair began. He rather resembled an aging lion with a mane of gray.

"You are friends of my boy, Seth, eh?"

His boy? "He's a very dear friend," I said. "When we told him we wanted to redecorate and were coming to Paris, he insisted we seek your advice. You're the best decorator in the world, he claimed." Those weren't quite his words, but close to it.

Monsieur Fernesse glowed. His grin split his face. "Ah, that boy. Always the sweet one, always so good to old Fernesse. Of course, I was not so old when I lived in London, not so gray." He stroked his beard. "They were good days, very good, but good days must end, no? How is my boy?"

"Seth's very well and sends his fondest regards."

"Fond?" He chuckled. "I do so wish to see him again, but alas, I do not like to travel now. You tell him, mademoiselle, to come to Paris and see me. Tell him I long to see his beautiful face again."

"I will."

He insisted on making us tea because, "You English cannot do a thing without tea first." Lincoln and I took the opportunity to inspect the items in the gallery.

"I do hope he's not too expensive," I whispered as I ran my hand along the curved back of a chair.

"The expense is not important."

I'd been brought up never to discuss money. My mother had claimed it was vulgar to speak about the cost of things or how much a man earned. I'd never asked Lincoln who paid him or where he got his money from. I assumed the ministry itself had funds. If that were the case, he must be in charge of finances, because he had not asked the committee's permission to spend it. They weren't even aware we were in Paris.

Monsieur Fernesse directed us to sit again and handed us a cup each, served with airy little cakes that were as delicious as anything Cook made. We spent the next two hours choosing furniture, curtains and lampshades, to drag Lichfield's parlor and drawing room into a modern era. While I wanted to keep the parlor cozy, I allowed Monsieur Fernesse full reign in the drawing room. It currently stood empty and unused, but I wanted to turn it into a spectacular showcase. Lincoln was a gentleman, and the son of someone important, and he ought to take his place in London society. This could help launch him. All we would require would be some visitors other than the committee members. I wasn't yet sure how to go about encouraging callers, or if any would come to Lichfield, but there would be time to think about it back in London.

Monsieur Fernesse certainly had a lovely eye, and he was an excellent artist. He drew his plans for the rooms based on the dimensions Lincoln gave him.

We had everything settled for the two rooms when Lincoln suddenly said, "We also require the ballroom to be transformed."

"We're going to hold a ball?" I asked, unable to keep the excitement from my voice. I'd never been to a ball before, and the thought of hosting one was both thrilling and dreadful.

"In time," was all he said.

Once everything was settled upon, right down to the last tassel, Monsieur Fernesse assured us he would place orders for things he couldn't make himself and have it all shipped to England as soon as possible. We thanked him and left after promising to pass on his regards to "his dearest boy."

"He seemed very fond of Seth," I said as we walked away from the misty-eyed Frenchman.

"Very." Lincoln tucked my hand into the crook of his elbow.

"They must have been great friends, despite the age difference. I wonder why Seth warned me not to believe everything Monsieur Fernesse told us. Do you think he worried that his friend would regale us with the wild parties they attended together when Fernesse lived in England?"

"Perhaps."

"Considering we know many of the escapades Seth got up to, and still does, his concern is baffling. What could they possibly have done that Seth is too embarrassed for us to find out?"

"I suggest you don't ask him for fear of offending him."

"Oh."

After a moment, he added, "The curiosity is going to torture you, isn't it?"

I glanced up to see mischief dancing in his eyes. "I'll manage, thank you. And if not, I'll see what I can learn from Gus. They tell one another everything."

I was about to ask him for his theories when he suddenly stopped and turned to me. We were outside the bulky stone gate of a cemetery. Why did cemeteries always seem to feature in my life?

"We need to finish the discussion we began last night." He sported a peculiar look on his face, one that I'd never seen before. It was a mixture of earnestness and something I couldn't identify.

"Yes, of course. Go ahead."

"Charlie..." The fingers of one hand tapped against his thigh and the other rubbed his thumbnail over and over.

I caught the tapping hand in mine and he stilled. Swallowed. Was he nervous? "Lincoln, what is it? What's wrong?"

"Yesterday, when we were discussing your legal guardianship, I don't think you quite understood the implications of Holloway retaining that power over you."

"What more is there to understand? I have no possessions to hand over to him. I suppose I ought to give him a portion of the wages you pay me, but since I'll no longer be a maid at Lichfield, what does that matter?"

"He can control more than your financial matters. He can legally separate us."

Is that what worried him? Being separated? The thought warmed my heart. I liked that he was worried about losing me. "We won't let that happen. If necessary, I will go into hiding until I turn twenty-one. He can't force me to live with him unless he finds me, and then he'll have to lock me in my room. I doubt a lock has ever defeated you."

"Two years is a long time. Two years and a month, if I'm not mistaken." He opened his hands and pressed his palms to mine. "I don't want to wait that long. It's torturous enough."

I narrowed my gaze. Was he referring to intimacy? "What do you mean?"

"Do I need to spell it out to you?"

My face heated. "I, er, no. But...we don't need to wait until I'm twenty-one to do that." I looped my arms around his neck. My blood throbbed when he enveloped me in return and held me close. I touched my lips lightly to his. "We can begin tonight," I murmured against his mouth.

He pulled back, leaving me with pursed lips, kissing the air. "No, we cannot. And don't ask me to take you out of wedlock again."

I choked on my gasp. "You're talking about waiting for *marriage*? Lincoln, do you mean to *marry* me?"

CHAPTER 2

Lincoln's brows crashed into a frown. "I thought I made that clear before we left London. I remember the conversation in your room the night we freed Buchanan from Bedlam."

"It wasn't entirely clear to me." My voice sounded more rigid than I intended. I was thrilled, and yet...was this real? It felt like something I'd dreamed up. "I thought that night you were talking about me becoming your mistress."

He bristled. "You...think *that* of me? That I would destroy your virtue?"

"I...no. I suppose you wouldn't. You're an honorable man."

He grunted. "If it were honor that drove me to propose, then I would have asked many women to marry me out of concern for their reputations. I haven't. Only you."

I arched my brow. "Many?"

"Don't change the subject. I thought you knew I meant marriage."

"No. You have not *asked* me to marry you."

His frown deepened. "You require a formal proposal."

"That is generally how these things happen, so I'm told. Otherwise, how am I to know that it's what you want?" Where did I get such audacity? My heart hammered so hard that I felt like my entire body throbbed. I should be a trembling, blubbering mess. He wanted to *marry* me!

"Do you not know how I feel about you?"

"Lincoln..." I drew in a deep breath in an attempt to settle my raging blood. It didn't work. "You are the most complicated person I've ever met, and you usually hide what you're feeling. It's almost impossible to know your thoughts at any given time."

"It is?"

I thumped him lightly on the arm. He caught my hand and drew it to his lips. He kissed only my glove, but I felt his warmth through to my skin.

"You understand me more than anyone I've ever met, Charlie." His dark gaze locked onto me, trapping me as thoroughly as his hand trapped mine. "You care for me when no one else does. You saw the good in me when I couldn't see it myself. You make me a better man."

"You do that all on your own."

He shook his head. "My life changed immeasurably when you tumbled into it, with your big eyes and fierce determination."

Those were hardly qualities that led to love. Indeed, he did not mention love at all. Perhaps it was too soon for him to express it. He had, after all, never known it in his life.

"I tried to fight my feelings," he went on. "I tried to set them aside, but it couldn't be done. You have occupied my thoughts almost constantly since then.

You have changed how I work, what I think and do. You've changed everything. You have affected me in ways you may never know. The thought of giving you up or of seeing you with another man..." He shook his head and his deep, dark eyes shuttered but did not close. "I'm afraid of what will become of me if you're not there."

I stroked his cheek and wished I could say something, but my throat ached and no words came out.

To my surprise, he continued on. The man who was usually so reluctant to express himself, seemed to have a lot to say, all of a sudden. "I no longer have it in me to resist you *or* my feelings." His lips kicked up into a crooked smile. "Besides, I want the world to know that you're mine. And I want to know you, in every way. So you see, there is nothing to be done except marriage. It's the only solution."

It wasn't the most romantic proposal. It certainly wasn't the way it had unfolded in the countless imaginary proposals I'd dreamed up. But it was honest and raw, and I couldn't tease him about it. He appeared anxious enough as it was, waiting for me to respond.

Anxiety. Yes, that was the expression I'd not been able to identify in his face when we stopped. He was worried that I would turn down his proposal, or perhaps mock him. That could be why he hadn't actually asked me directly, but decided *for* me.

I cupped his cheek, to capture that uncertain look, and stroked the tiny line bracketing the corner of his mouth until it smoothed away. "Yes, Lincoln. With all my heart, I will marry you."

"Good." He took my hand in his so hard that I sucked in a breath. He loosened his grip and said, "Good" again. "We'll purchase a ring after luncheon."

We strolled on, hand-in-hand, and I began to wonder if we would walk all the way back to *Le Grand Hôtel*. Perhaps walking was a good idea. I had dozens of things to say and the cold air helped clear my head so that I could make sense of them all. Yet, I suddenly felt shy. Too shy to say what was on my mind. We'd gone from the occasional stolen kiss to engaged in a matter of moments, and I'd not seen it coming. I felt like I'd been swamped by an avalanche.

His grip tightened on my hand, anchoring me at his side. "You wish to ask me something?"

"I...yes." I cleared my throat. "Forgive me, I'm somewhat stunned. I wasn't expecting this."

"It will take some getting used to. For both of us." His thumb stroked my hand. "Charlie...if it's not what you want—"

"It is!" I hauled him to a stop. "Oh, Lincoln, yes it is what I want, very much. But it has come so soon after you declared you wouldn't marry anyone. That's why I thought you wished to take me as your mistress."

He flinched, as if my words stung him. "I'm prepared to take a risk and see if marriage agrees with me."

A laugh bubbled out of me, even though I didn't find his words amusing. He was *prepared* to take a *risk*? It was hardly a convincing argument. I supposed I should be glad that he thought me worthy of a risk at all. "Perhaps we should wait for you to become used to the idea of us being together."

He circled his arm around my back and drew me to his side as we continued to walk. It was very intimate, but I'd noticed the French cared less about such things than the English. I'd seen many couples walk together in this manner, and even seen them kissing without a care who saw them. If cities were people, then Paris was a dancer where London was a vicar's wife.

"I've waited long enough," he said. "As soon as we get permission from Holloway, we'll wed. I don't care where. I'll leave the arrangements to you. Leave Holloway to me."

The steely undercurrent in his tone chilled me. "I'm sure he'll give his permission," I said quickly. "He'll probably be glad to hand me over to someone else."

"Let's hope it's as simple as that."

We caught a hansom out of Montmartre almost back to the hotel, but alighted on the Rue de la Paix. We dined inside, at the Café de la Paix, since it was too cold to sit at one of the pavement tables.

The realization that I would marry Lincoln finally sank in after I finished the last of the delectable pastries. I felt positively giddy with the notion. Or perhaps that was the two glasses of champagne taking effect.

"Seth, Cook and Gus won't believe it," I told him, unable to hold back my grin.

"They will when they see the ring."

I stared at my fingers. I'd never worn a ring before, or jewelry of any kind. "Will we purchase one this afternoon?"

"If they have any in stock that fit and you like, otherwise we'll order it. I'm sure you'll have it by the end of the week, unless the diamond you want is too large."

Diamond! He wanted to give me a *diamond* ring!

"Expect some resistance from the committee," he said.

I blinked until his words sank in. "Oh, yes. I imagine they'll oppose the marriage quite vehemently."

He reached across the table and took my hand. His touch was warmer without gloves, and more thrilling. "They have no real power over me, Charlie, or you. If we want to marry, it's nothing to do with them."

"Not directly, I suppose."

The committee members considered me a danger. They claimed evil people would want to use my power, and although I hated admitting it, they were right. Twice now, mad scientists had tried to capture me and use my necromancy. But it wasn't only my attraction to those people that the committee feared. It was the amount of time and effort Lincoln had wasted to keep me safe. It was my distracting influence on him they didn't like. As the leader of the ministry, he couldn't afford such a distraction. It didn't help that part of me agreed with them, and I worried about that very thing too.

"Charlie." His quiet purr coaxed a small smile from me. "I'm in charge and always will be while I am alive. They have to accept my decisions."

"Can they remove you from the leadership?"

"They wouldn't go against the prophecy. There may be consequences. Supernatural ones."

I'd forgotten about the prophecy. A seer who lived many centuries ago foresaw Lincoln would become the ministry's leader. When the man in the prophecy was linked to baby Lincoln, he'd been taken in by General Eastbrooke and given tutelage in a wide range of subjects as he grew up. Now that I thought about it, the committee had invested quite a lot in him without really knowing how he would turn out. Clearly they were very certain they had the right person.

"You've told me so little about the prophecy," I said. "Now that you are to be my husband, will you tell me more?"

He glanced toward the window and the street beyond, where well-heeled Parisians hurried between shops to get out of the cold. "I'll tell you everything I know, but not here and not now. The weather is turning. I'd like to see the jeweler then return to the hotel. You don't have a warm enough coat to be out in this."

"I'm used to the cold." I'd survived bitter London winters in clothes so thin they were worn out in places and with one coat to share between a dozen boys in my gang. We'd huddled together in our bunker for warmth and somehow survived. At least some of us had. Those days had passed, thank God.

At my shiver, he rose and held out his hand. "You'll never be cold again." He drew me into his side, where it was warm and safe and felt so very good. So right.

He paid for our meal before we headed back outside and strolled along the Rue de la Paix to a fine jewelry shop. I ordered a diamond—*diamond!*—ring, and Lincoln insisted I also needed a sapphire necklace and earrings "to match your eyes." He wanted to take me back to the hotel, but I insisted we finish our shopping today to leave us the rest of the week for sightseeing. We continued on to Worth's, where I was measured and prodded until the small army of *modistes* were satisfied they had enough to assemble a new wardrobe of day gowns, riding habits, evening dresses and a fur-lined coat.

Upon our return to *Le Grand Hôtel*, I flopped onto the sofa and removed my boots. "Is this real?" I murmured to the ceiling as I lay back on the cushions. "Surely I'm dreaming."

Lincoln's face appeared above me. He stood behind the sofa, his arms resting on the back. One dark, twisting strand of hair tumbled forward, having escaped from the tie. The muscles in his face relaxed so that he no longer looked like the formidable gentleman who'd had the *modistes* running hither and thither with a mere look.

"Are you tired?" he asked.

"Not at all. I feel like I could climb that new tower I keep seeing everywhere I turn."

"Eiffel's Tower, they're calling it. We'll visit it tomorrow, weather permitting."

I sat up and caught the front of his shirt as he went to move away. He'd discarded jacket and waistcoat already and looked delectably casual. "Kiss me," I murmured.

He cupped my face in both hands. His long fingers teased the hair at the nape of my neck, and his lips touched mine in a light, lingering kiss that promised more would come.

But it didn't. He drew back and let me go with a heaving sigh. "I need to exercise."

I caught his hand before he could pull away from me entirely. I rose to my knees on the sofa and tugged him back. He offered no resistance. Only the sofa back separated our hips, and nothing but a few layers of fabric separated our chests. My heart thudded against his, strong and erratic.

I went to kiss him, and whispered against his lips. "Lie with me."

The muscles around his mouth tightened and the sharp focus of his eyes returned. He drew back. Shook his head.

"I don't see why we can't," I said, holding onto his shoulders so that he wouldn't walk away. "We're engaged now."

"Charlie." My name rumbled from the depths of his chest. He unclasped my fingers and held them in front of him the way an uncle would his niece. It was all very civilized, when I wanted to be anything but. "Don't."

"You're a cruel man."

"You're the cruel one for teasing me like this when you know I want you." He walked off toward the door that led to his adjoining room.

"Then take me!"

"You can be sure that I will," he tossed over his shoulder. "When we are wed."

I slumped down onto the sofa, my nerves twitching and jangling. He was being unnecessarily and unfairly protective of my so-called virtue. It was ridiculous, considering my background. While I might be a virgin, I was no innocent flower. I knew there were ways of pleasuring one another that didn't involve actual coupling.

I padded over to his door and flung it open, only to stop dead upon seeing him entirely naked. I'd already seen his body, back when he thought I was a boy, but now *all* of him was on display as he faced me. And he didn't bother to cover himself up. He merely stood there with his feet a little apart, his hands by his sides. Only his impressively muscular chest rose and fell with his heavy breathing.

"You should have knocked," he said, as calmly as ever.

My face flamed, but I couldn't look away from his, er...masculine parts. "I'm rather glad that I didn't. I'm sure you'll admonish me now, but I really don't care."

His low chuckle rolled around the bedroom. I dragged my gaze up to his face to see what he looked like when he laughed, and was rewarded with a flash of white teeth and a gleam in his eyes. I'd never seen him look so happy. I lowered my gaze again. Nor had I seen him look so magnificent.

He prowled toward me with the powerful grace of a lion. If I really were a virtuous woman, I ought to run from the room, or at least avert my gaze. I had no intention of doing either.

He closed the gap between us and kissed me. Thoroughly. Completely. It was the sort of kiss we'd shared in London—heated and possessive and more intoxicating than champagne. He scooped one arm around my waist and I clung to him, one hand on his shoulder, the other shamelessly grasping one muscular buttock. Part of me couldn't believe I was touching him there. The other part of me couldn't believe how silken his skin was and how firm the muscle.

He suddenly let me go. It wasn't until that moment that I realized he'd lifted me up and deposited me on the other side of the door. I'd been too distracted to notice.

"Out, vixen, before I break my vow and give in." He stepped back, smiled the most wickedly delicious smile, and shut the door in my face.

"That wasn't fair!" I called out, hands on hips.

"That's the pot calling the kettle black. You haven't played fair since the moment you walked into Lichfield."

"I never *walked* into Lichfield. I was dragged there, kicking and screaming, right after you almost suffocated me."

As soon as I said it, I regretted it. Lincoln's methods to capture me and keep me at Lichfield still troubled him, even though I'd forgiven him, and he didn't like talking about it. When he didn't respond, I worried that I'd offended him. I didn't want him thinking I still harbored a grudge.

"Lincoln?" I said to the door. "I'm sorry. I shouldn't have brought that up. It was a silly joke and—"

The door opened and he stormed past me. "Don't apologize." He dragged the sofa to the window and moved one of the occasional tables to the wall. "Go and change. It's time to resume your training."

"Here? Now?"

"Yes."

"You were going to tell me about the prophecy."

"I will, after training."

With a sigh, I headed to my bedroom and changed into my exercise clothing of loose men's pants and shirt. We exercised together until my skin became slick. Lincoln didn't look like he'd lifted a finger, whereas I had to gulp in every breath.

"Good," he said, with curt indifference when our session ended. "But you require more practice. We'll set aside time every afternoon."

"Even while in Paris?"

"Why waste the opportunity?"

"But I want to see as much of the city as possible. I may never come back here again."

"If you wish to return, we'll return." He strode to his bedroom and shut the door. The lock tumbled.

After I washed and changed into evening clothes, we headed to the hotel dining room where I felt quite under-dressed. The French ladies all wore gowns in the height of fashion, with jewels dripping from their ears, fingers and throats. My blue and white striped dress was reasonably pretty but quite ordinary by comparison, and I wore no jewelry.

Lincoln asked for a secluded table and we were led to an unoccupied corner. After ordering wine, he brought up the topic of the prophecy without prompting. "You know that I was chosen to be leader because the timing of my birth was right, and because of who my parents were," he said with a lift of his brow.

"Yes, but I know little about them except that your mother is a gypsy seer and your father is someone important. Is he a nobleman?"

"He is more than that."

"More?"

"Do you remember that night I went to the ball?"

"Very clearly. You were in a foul temper when you returned." We'd argued, but not about anything in particular. He'd wanted to pick a fight, and I'd simply been there at the wrong time.

His gaze shifted to the white tablecloth. "I was drunk and angry after seeing him there."

"Your father?"

"I only know that my mother is a gypsy because of that pendant she gave me. Like you, I researched it and discovered the eye was a symbol the gypsy clans use to ward off curses."

"What pendant?" I said weakly.

His gaze narrowed. "I know you found it in my desk drawer, Charlie. I also know you read all about it in my books."

"You do? Why didn't you tell me you knew I'd seen it?"

"I hoped you would come to me of your own volition and ask me about it."

"Oh. Right." I cleared my throat. "I...I suppose I should have, but I didn't want to be chastised for it."

His silence drew my gaze up to his. He was watching me with unnerving intensity. "Was I that bad?" he murmured.

I reached for his hand and gave him what I hoped was a reassuring smile. "That's in the past. Let's move forward."

His fingers clutched mine. "The point I'm trying to make is that I knew my mother was—is—a gypsy. I'd learned her name from my file in the ministry archives and learned that she still lives. The night of that ball, I had not seen my father in a long time, and never up close. When Julia told me he would be there, I couldn't help myself. I had to go. Not because I thought I'd get close enough to speak with him, but because I..." He shook his head. "I suppose I just wanted to see what he was like."

I remembered Lady Harcourt had manipulated Lincoln into going to the ball so that he could meet eligible young ladies. Knowing he hated balls, she'd needed another incentive to get him there. But I couldn't recall who she mentioned would be attending in particular.

"What I learned about my father that night is the reason I returned home angry. He knew my mother, his lover, was a gypsy. He must have known. And yet he disparaged them cruelly to his friends that night, all for a few laughs."

"What did he say?"

His eyes turned hard, cold, and not even stroking his hand chased the dark shadows away. "He said the women were all whores and the men their minders."

I winced. What a horrid thing to say, particularly since he must have cared for one of the women enough to bed her. Or...perhaps he hadn't cared for her at all. Perhaps he'd tricked her by pretending he had. Or perhaps he'd raped her.

I felt sick. "Oh, Lincoln. No wonder you were furious." His emotions must have been boiling over by the time he got home and he was too inexperienced to suppress them, and so he'd simply let them out.

"I'm sorry I wasn't able to confine my anger to him. I should never have made you suffer."

Our wine arrived and we let go of one another's hands and waited for the waiter to leave again.

"Our mothers had something in common," I told Lincoln. "Both got themselves into trouble with men who didn't love them." I sipped my wine and watched him over the rim of the glass. I was very aware that he had not yet told me his father's name. It couldn't have been a committee member if he needed to attend a ball to see him. "Who is he?" I asked, setting my glass down.

His fingers tightened around the wine stem. "Albert Edward Saxe-Coburg-Gotha."

"Bloody hell," I said a little too loudly. One of the ladies three tables away shot a flinty glare my way. I lowered my voice. "The Prince of Wales!"

He nodded.

"Are you sure?"

"It was listed on my file in the archive, and the prophecy states that the leader of the order would be the son of a king. He'll be king when his mother, the queen, dies."

"That's why your name is Fitzroy." It was so obvious now. I couldn't believe I hadn't put the pieces of the puzzle together before. "It means son of the king. Who named you?"

"The committee. Lincoln after Lincolnshire, the county where General Eastbrooke lived as a child, and Fitzroy for the reason you stated. When I saw his name on my file, I confronted the committee and they told me it was true. I was the son of the prince, but I wasn't to tell a soul."

"I suppose a scandal like that would undermine the monarchy."

"I'm not so sure it would be much of a scandal now. The Prince of Wales is well known for his philandering. His relationship with my mother—if it could even be called that—occurred before his marriage, when he was only your age, but that is no excuse to speak of her or her people dishonorably. I was extremely disappointed that night. I'd hoped he'd loved her—or at least cared for her. After hearing him say that, and worse, I knew he hadn't."

"How did the committee members learn about you?"

"I suspect they had spies watching the prince. From the dates in the prophecy, they could be quite certain he would father the ministry's future leader. It was only then a matter of watching the women he consorted with. Being with a gypsy seer would have certainly raised their interest. It fits with the prophecy."

I digested his news as we ate, but by the time it came to return to our rooms, my mind still reeled. Royal blood flowed through Lincoln's veins—and he wanted to marry *me*.

"If he acknowledged you as his son," I said as we approached our suite, "you would be accepted into the highest, most exclusive circles."

"You know that doesn't interest me."

"But it's your birthright, Lincoln."

"The ministry is my birthright." He opened the sitting room door and followed me inside.

"You would be introduced to powerful people from all over the world. Opportunities would come your way that you could never gain otherwise."

"I want none of those things." He frowned and closed the door. The click sounded loud in the heavy silence. I turned away, but he caught my arm and gently pulled me against him. "Charlie, I know that look. Tell me what's wrong."

"You're a prince, Lincoln."

He grunted. "I am nothing of the sort. The man who fathered me is a prince."

"But it changes everything!"

He stroked my hair back. "It changes nothing. I've known for some time, and decided after the ball, that he's not a man I want to get to know better. Even if he did acknowledge me, it still changes nothing. I will always be the leader of the ministry and you will be my wife."

"But...I'm a gutter rat."

"You are *my* gutter rat."

I spluttered a watery laugh and lay my head against his chest. He enveloped me in a hug and kissed the top of my head. "You're overwhelmed," he said. "The journey was long and tiring, and we've been busy since our arrival."

"Not to mention I got engaged to the man I fell in love with some months ago."

"I'd like to remind you that we've been engaged since the evening we rescued Buchanan from Bedlam."

"Not to my mind."

I felt him smile into my hair. "We'll slow down, now that everything is settled."

"Does that mean no more training?"

"Your training will continue in the afternoons. The way your saddle was cut worries me, and I want you to be as prepared as possible for whatever may come when we return." His arms tightened. "Finding who cut it will be my priority."

"*Our* priority. You do not work alone."

"You won't be helping if your life is in danger."

I sighed. I'd been expecting that response ever since he'd found the strap on my sidesaddle had been cut in the days before we left London. While the sabotaged strap had been easy to spot, it didn't mean the attacker wouldn't try again. Although Lincoln hadn't mentioned it since, I suspected it had been playing on his mind. Returning to London would see a return of the steely ministry leader who'd all but disappeared since arriving in Paris.

He pulled away first and set me at arm's length. "Goodnight, Charlie."

"Not even a goodnight kiss?"

He considered this for a moment then leaned in and pecked my cheek. "That will have to do."

I sank into a curtsey and lowered my head. "As you wish, your highness."

"I wondered how long it would be before you mocked me."

I straightened and squared up to him. His lips quirked but did not break into a smile. "If only the others knew what a good sport you were."

"They wouldn't believe you. Besides, I wouldn't allow anyone but you to mock me."

"I feel so fortunate."

"Goodnight, Charlie."

I caught his hand as he walked off and he stopped, brows raised, that mischievous smile still playing on his lips. He'd never looked more handsome. Relaxation suited him. "I *do* feel fortunate, Lincoln. I am the luckiest girl in the world."

CHAPTER 3

Seth, Gus and Cook were pleased to see us. At least, they were pleased to see *me*. They embraced me, in turn, with brotherly hugs and broad grins. They merely nodded at Lincoln, or muttered a half-hearted "Welcome back, sir." Despite knowing him for longer, they did not yet feel altogether comfortable with their leader. My fiancé.

"We are engaged," I blurted out before we'd even reached the front steps of Lichfield Towers. I thrust out my hand to prove it.

"Blimey," Gus muttered, inspecting the diamond from all angles. "That'd be worth a sum."

Seth jabbed him in the ribs. "A gentleman never discusses money. It is quite impressive, Charlie, but I think you could have held out for a larger one." We were out of earshot of Lincoln who was assisting the driver to remove our luggage, but Seth leaned closer to me anyway. "He would have given you Everest if you'd asked for it."

"She ain't that kind of lass," Cook snapped, putting his meaty arm around my shoulders and kissing the top of my head. "I be pleased for you, Charlie. But..." He glanced over his shoulder at Lincoln. "Are you sure? He be difficult."

"I know that as well as anyone, but I love him anyway." I kissed his soft cheek. "Thank you for your concern."

We all looked to Lincoln. The hackney that had brought us from the station drove off, leaving him glaring at his men, the bags at his feet.

"I think he wants your assistance," I whispered.

Gus trotted back down the steps, but the other two walked with me into the house.

Seth took my cloak and hung it on the coat stand. "One of us ought to pull Fitzroy aside and have *that* discussion with him."

"What discussion?" I asked, unpinning my hat.

"The one where we threaten him if he doesn't treat you well."

I laughed. "I'd like to see that discussion."

"Ain't be me," Cook said, folding his arms.

Seth shot a glance through the open door, where Gus and Lincoln were climbing the steps, cases under each arm and in each hand. "I nominate Gus."

"For what?" Gus said, edging sideways through the door.

"Later," Seth muttered through a clenched-teeth smile for Lincoln's benefit. "Congratulations, sir. Charlie is a fine choice for you."

I slapped my gloves into his chest, forcing him to take them. "I am not a horse, nor am I for sale."

"Take Charlie's luggage upstairs," Lincoln said coolly. "Cook, prepare tea to be served in the parlor. We're having a meeting."

"All of us?" Cook asked.

"All of us."

I followed Gus up to my rooms and pulled out my new clothes once he'd gone. After freshening up and changing into a smart dark green day dress and a matching fitted jacket with brass epaulettes on the shoulders, I returned to the parlor where the four men in my life waited for me. Three of them smiled at me. Lincoln did not, but his sharp gaze followed me until I sat on the sofa. He had not smiled since leaving France. I'd not seen him at all on the boat as he battled seasickness, but even when we'd touched land, he continued to look a little ill and had been quiet. When I'd asked him on the train back to London what was the matter, he'd simply said he was being vigilant. It took a moment for me to realize he was worried about someone attacking me.

Lincoln handed me a cup of tea and a slice of cake then sat beside me. "Eat. Drink. It's been a long day."

"I'm not tired." I drank the tea until the cup was almost empty then set it aside with a satisfied sigh. I'd not had a decent cup of tea since leaving England. The French did food, wine and fashion better than us, but they didn't know how to brew good tea.

"Does our news surprise you?" I asked, since no one had begun a conversation. I felt rather conspicuous in my new dress with the diamond on my ring finger. It was as if they all saw me differently now, like a grown woman and not the girl who'd first disrupted their lives. Or perhaps that had more to do with how *I* felt than how they saw me.

"Yes," Seth said as the other two muttered, "Aye."

"It does?"

While Cook's already florid complexion flushed more, the other two averted their gazes. "We didn't think you would, er, formalize your relationship," Seth said.

Lincoln set his cup down with a loud clank in the saucer. He blinked at each of them in turn, but since they were studying their slices of cake with great interest, none noticed. I resisted the childish urge to utter, "See, it wasn't just me," to him. I simply cleared my throat and smiled into my teacup.

"Tell us how you liked Paris, Charlie," Gus said, smiling. He had a rather gruesome smile, with his broken teeth and the scar that made one eyelid droop, but it warmed my heart to see it. I'd missed him. Missed them all. "Were it like you expected?"

"Better. It's a beautiful city. We saw everything there is to see, and ate the most delicious dishes. Except for the snails." I pulled a face. "Your friend Fernesse sends his warmest regards," I said to Seth. "He wants you to visit him."

"I'm unlikely to travel to Paris in the near future," he mumbled.

When he didn't continue on, I added, "He's quite well."

"I'm pleased to hear it." He turned to Lincoln. "You'll be wanting a report, sir?"

"Did something happen in our absence?" Lincoln asked.

"Nothing out of the ordinary. We've had no callers, not even committee members."

"I informed them all that I would be away until further notice."

"Will you send word tonight that we're back?" I asked.

"I prefer to wait until the morning."

"I prefer you never tell them, but I suppose it must be done." I stroked my thumb over the gold band of my engagement ring. "They will be surprised."

"They'll be bloody shocked," Gus said. "It ain't goin' to be a fun meetin', that one."

I gave Lincoln a grim smile. "Thank you for waiting until tomorrow. I'm not sure I can face them after such a long day."

"You don't have to face them," he said. "Leave them to me."

"It involves both of us. We'll do it together." I held up my hand when he protested. "Together, Lincoln, and that's final."

I wasn't aware of how forceful I'd sounded until I saw Gus's eyes widen in alarm, and Seth's worried gaze shift to Lincoln.

Lincoln, however, didn't bat an eyelid. "I'll summon them to a meeting tomorrow afternoon. That gives me the morning to speak with Holloway."

"Holloway!" Gus frowned. "He's in prison. What you want to speak to him for?"

"They need Holloway's permission to marry, dolt." Seth rolled his eyes.

"But he ain't her real father. Can't the courts place her under your guardianship, sir?"

"They may, but the process will take time." Lincoln seemed disinclined to elaborate, so I explained to them that Holloway was my father in the eyes of English law because he'd pretended I was born to his wife in France all those years ago. "We have a letter from the matron at the orphanage stating that he isn't my real father. If we need to go to court, we have that in our favor as well as his conviction. The courts move slowly, however. If we can get Holloway's permission now, we won't have to wait." I closed my hand over Lincoln's. "We don't want to wait."

Cook cleared his throat. "I hate to say it, but who'll be doin' maid's work now?"

Gus groaned. "I ain't cleanin' out the fireplaces no more. Soot gets into everything. Last time I was wipin' it out of the creases of my eyelids for days."

"Soft," Seth muttered.

"We'll place advertisements in the morning, one for an experienced housekeeper and another for a butler," Lincoln said. "Once those positions are filled, they will hire other staff as required."

"You're not worried about them learning ministry secrets?" Seth asked.

"All ministry documents will be locked away. Any meetings will be held with the door closed. No one will mention the ministry, our work, or supernaturals except in private."

Gus and Cook exchanged glances. I understood their concern. No matter how careful we were, a nosy maid could discover secrets if she wanted to.

"I will make it clear to the staff that there will be consequences if they are not discreet," Lincoln went on.

"Try not to use your threatening voice," I told him.

"My threatening voice?"

"Or that look."

"What look?"

"The one you use when you're trying to scare people into doing your bidding. I know now that it's just a look, and doesn't mean anything, but newcomers won't. We don't want to frighten the poor maids away before they even start."

Seth bit his lip but it didn't stop his smile. Fortunately Lincoln was too busy staring at me to notice. "I will not use my threatening voice or look." He said it without moving his jaw which made me think he hadn't understood what I meant at all.

"Seth, will you help me word an advertisement later?" I asked. "You must know how these things are done."

"My mother was in charge of the staff," he said. "But I'll do my best. In fact, I know an experienced butler in need of employment. He was our butler for almost two decades, until Mother fired him."

"Before or after she ran off with the second footman?" Gus asked with such an innocent expression that I had to smother my giggle.

Seth stabbed Gus with a pointed glare. "She fired him for drinking his way through my father's cellar. It was after Doyle left that everything fell to pieces. I had no idea how much he kept the other staff in order until the second footman moved into Mother's bedchamber the same day Doyle departed. By the time the new butler arrived, the damage had been done."

"Perhaps that's the real reason your mother fired Doyle," I said. "And not because of the drinking."

"Undoubtedly. Shortly after that, we lost everything to pay my father's gambling debts, and Mother left the country altogether in defiance." He flattened his tie and stretched his neck out of his collar. "Speaking of my mother, I received a letter from her."

"Is this relevant?" Lincoln asked.

"I'm interested," I said.

"The second footman died," Seth went on. "Mother is returning to England on a permanent basis."

"Oh? Her re-entry into society will be...interesting."

Gus snickered.

"That's not why I'm bringing it up." Seth cleared his throat. "She has requested to stay at Lichfield until she can secure herself a more permanent residence."

"Of course," I said at the same time that Lincoln growled a protest. "She's welcome to stay as long as she needs."

"Thank you, Charlie. Her stay will be brief, I'm sure."

"She doesn't have any money or possibility of an income," Lincoln said in the boldest fashion. "How will she secure herself a house?"

"She receives an annuity from her father's estate and still has friends in London. She'll persuade one of them to take her on as a companion. You'll find she's very good at getting her way," he muttered into his cup.

"Hire your butler tomorrow," Lincoln said. "As to your mother, she can stay here as long as she doesn't get in the way."

"Thank you."

"When do you expect her?" I asked.

"In two weeks."

"Speaking of mothers," Gus said to me. "Did you find out more about yours?"

"A little. The matron told me what she remembered, but it wasn't much." I relayed what the matron had said, and it wasn't until Lincoln's fingers closed over mine that I realized how forlorn I sounded.

"You didn't raise her spirit?" Gus asked.

"No."

"Why not?"

"I'm reluctant, after what happened with Estelle Pearson. My mother was a necromancer, so she may know the same spell to overrule my control. We can't risk that happening again."

"She won't do that to her own daughter," Gus said.

I shrugged. "That's not something we can know beforehand."

"Summon her," Lincoln said quickly. "Speak to her spirit but don't allow her to leave Lichfield and enter a body."

"I'm not sure," I hedged. "What if her powers can be used in spirit form?"

"She's your mother, Charlie," Gus said. "She won't cause you problems like the Pearson woman did."

"Mothers don't always put their children's interest above their own," Seth grumbled into his chest.

"Summon her," Lincoln said again with a nod.

I blinked at him. "Now?"

"Whenever you're ready."

"I...I suppose I'm ready now." I looked at each of them and met only encouraging nods. It would seem my mind had been made up for me. If they all thought it was safe, then perhaps I was worrying over nothing. I blew out a deep breath, but my nerves still felt tighter than bow strings. "Ellen Marie Mercier, I call your spirit to me. Ellen Marie Mercier, please return to the world of the living to—"

The mist rushed toward me from the corner of the ceiling and rolled to an abrupt stop near the table where I'd set down my cup and plate. With what felt like an excruciatingly slow pace, the white cloud formed into the shape of a face.

A face remarkably similar to mine, yet hollow in the cheeks and eyes from illness.

I gripped Lincoln's hand hard as the ghost said something in French. "Do you speak English?" I whispered. "Mother."

Her slender brows drew together. Two ghostly arms stretched forward, as if to embrace me, but went right through. "My little girl?" she said in a musical English accent.

I nodded. It was all I could manage with my full eyes and tight throat.

She bit her wobbling lip, and I noticed that I was doing the exact same thing. It made me smile. "My name is Charlotte. My friends call me Charlie."

She glanced at the others in the room before her gaze settled on my hand linked with Lincoln's. Her small frowned deepened. "And your family?"

"I have no family," I told her. "They're...gone." It seemed easier to let her think they were dead. Easier and kinder. She had, after all, been desperate for me to be given to a *good* family. It would be cruel to disturb her afterlife with the truth.

"Have you been happy, my daughter?"

I nodded and smiled. "Yes. I am happy."

She didn't seem to notice my use of the present tense, but Lincoln did. His thumb drew little circles on my knuckle.

My mother approached and knelt in front of me, the way one does to speak to a small child. "I have waited for you to call me and now you are grown. How old are you, Charlotte?"

"Almost nineteen. I only learned about you after visiting St. Madeleine's in Paris this week."

Shock rippled through the mist, distorting her features before they came together again. "Why?"

"The couple that took me from the orphanage as a baby didn't tell me anything about my past. I have only recently learned that they were not my real parents."

Her fingers brushed my throat, but I felt nothing. "The necklace?"

"Matron gave it to me a week ago. It's in safekeeping."

"But you must wear it!"

I glanced at Lincoln. His fingers squeezed mine, but he didn't ask me to repeat my mother's words. "Why must I wear it?" I said for his benefit.

"To protect you from him. From your father."

"Victor Frankenstein is dead. He can no longer harm me."

Her hand clasped her throat. There were no ghostly tears in her eyes, no trembling fingers. "Good," she spat. "I hope he is in hell."

I wanted to ask her about their relationship, but it felt too awkward and personal, particularly with the others in the room. "He tried to use my necromancy to reanimate his creatures," I told her. "He was unsuccessful."

"Thank God. That man...he tried to use me too. He tricked me. I'm glad you are not sorry he is dead."

"I'm not."

"Even so, you must wear the necklace. The pet will keep you safe."

"Pet?"

She waved a hand in a typical French gesture. "I do not know the correct English word."

"Lincoln translated it as imp, a sort of mischievous creature."

"That is as good a word as any." Her gaze shifted to our linked hands again then slid back to me. "Where is the necklace?"

"Lincoln has it."

"Why?"

"We were unsure of its power. We were going to research it, but since you're here, is there anything you can tell us?" Perhaps I should have asked my mother more personal questions, but I couldn't bring myself to do so. Somehow it seemed easier to speak about the necklace.

"It holds an imp that is released when you speak three words while wearing it." She frowned. "I paid a French witch to make it, and the words are French. You must have the accent just so. Try for me please: *Je libère toi.*"

"*Je libère toi.*"

"Good. Now put on the necklace today, now, and remember those words. The pet will help you when you call it, but you must not call it unless necessary. It likes mischief, and may run away if there is no present danger."

"How can an uncontrollable, mischievous creature save me?"

"I don't know. I did not create it. Be assured, it will save you. But if you call it without reason, it will go in search of excitement."

"How do I get it back into the amber?"

"It tires quickly. After it saves your life, it will want to go back to sleep in the amber. At such times, it is easy to control. At others it is not so easy. You must catch it and order it back."

"It sounds unpredictable."

"Magic often is."

"Do you know many supernaturals? Witches," I added when her brow creased in confusion.

She shook her head. "So few remain, and most do not wish to be found."

"Was your family magical?"

"My mother was a necromancer, but she died when I was very small. My father remarried to a devout woman. She detested me, feared me. Do not go to them. They will not treat you as a granddaughter ought to be treated."

I knew enough about devout people to know the horrible truth in her words. "I won't seek them out," I assured her.

"I am sorry, dear Charlotte, but you are all alone now that your adopted parents died, yes?"

"Not at all. Lincoln and I are recently engaged."

Her wispy form shimmered, as if she were cold. "I see." She studied him carefully, drifting around his head twice, before settling once more in front of me. "He looks strong."

"He is."

"There is another English word." She clicked her tongue as she searched for it. "Int... Intimid...?"

"Intimidating." I suddenly felt awkward discussing him like this while he was in the room.

Lincoln must have known that I was talking about him because he once again squeezed my hand.

"You think he loves you?" my mother asked.

"I know it."

She stood and smoothed her ghostly skirts. "Charlotte, it is my duty as your mother to warn you that men are not like us. They do not have soft hearts. To them, love is a way to get something else they want."

"You're wrong, Mother," I said very firmly. "I'm sorry your experience was unfavorable, but I know some very good, kind men. The ones in this room, for example."

"You are a young woman," she said gently. "And sheltered too."

"Not as much as you may think."

"You must listen to me when I tell you to be careful. I am your mother and I wish you to be happy. Find a man who is not so...strong. Find one less intimidating, who will do *your* bidding."

I pressed my lips together. This meeting was taking a turn in a direction I didn't like, yet I didn't have the heart to continue to disagree with her. "I will consider your advice. Thank you, Mother. Mama. May I call you that?"

"Of course." Her sweet smile momentarily filled out the hollowed contours of her cheeks and chased away the dark shadows circling her eyes. "That is a word I hoped to hear one day from your lips. I wish I were alive to hold you, dearest daughter, but this spirit form must do for now."

"We'll see one another again, won't we?" I asked, my tears once more close.

"Of course. You may summon my spirit whenever you need me. I am here for you, Charlotte. Always."

I nodded, no longer able to speak through my tears.

"Promise me you will get your necklace from him." She angled her head at Lincoln. "If he refuses, steal it. Listen to me, your mother, not him. I know what is best for you. You are always in my heart. Do you understand?"

I nodded again.

"*Bon.* Now, we must say farewell." She kissed her fingertips and held them up. I kissed mine and touched them to hers, although I felt nothing.

"Goodbye, Mama," I whispered. "I release you."

She slipped away, gliding up to the ceiling then disappearing altogether.

"She's gone?" Lincoln asked.

I nodded.

"Well?" Gus prompted. "What did she say?"

"Gus," Seth hissed. "That's private."

"I was askin' about the un-private bits."

"She spoke about the amber pendant," I told them. "She said I should wear it at all times." I mentioned how she'd commissioned it, and why, and how to release the imp from the amber. "The words must be spoken in French while I wear it."

Lincoln withdrew his hand from mine. "The creature sounds too unpredictable. We can't risk it escaping."

"She wanted me to steal it back if you didn't return it to me."

He refilled my teacup and handed it to me. "Research it further. There might be something in the library."

"You've read every book in the library and you have a fantastic memory. Do you recall reading about an imp?"

If he heard the challenge in my voice, he gave no indication. "All sorts of creatures are mentioned, but nothing trapped in amber. Perhaps that's a new technique."

"Very well, I'll see what I can find." I didn't tell him that I would have it back, one way or another. If my mother thought it important then I would wear it. I didn't want to argue with Lincoln. Not when everything was so lovely between us.

***

Lincoln finally gave in and allowed me to go to the prison with him after I caught him at a rare weak moment—he was in the middle of kissing me.

With my back to his door, his hands on my waist, I gently pushed him away and simply told him I was going too. With a resigned sigh, he said, "I suspected as much."

What followed was a list of rules, most of them boiling down to staying vigilant and staying close to him. I did as told because his commands were entirely sensible—and he said please.

The entrance gate of Surrey House of Correction rose out of the landscape like a grim, austere medieval castle presiding over its subjects. Lincoln and I were shown into the governor's office in the heart of the complex. The prison was designed like an octopus with four tentacles; the central office windows overlooked each yard between the tentacles. A smattering of prisoners huddled in the corners out of the wind, but otherwise the yards were barren.

"He's in the infirmary," Governor Crease said upon our inquiry. "You can't visit him." He was a tall, imposing man with impressive muttonchops and moustache but no beard. Small, round eyes peered back at us with intense focus that seemed to be searching our souls for our crimes.

Lincoln passed a fat envelope across the desk. Crease peered inside and, without so much as a blink, opened the top drawer of his desk and dropped it inside. He locked the drawer with a key that he slipped into his watch pocket.

"I'll have one of the guards escort you."

A few minutes later we were shown into another building that reminded me of the wards at the Bedlam asylum. Men dressed in shapeless, drab prison garb lay on beds divided into two rows. There were no blankets to cover them and no nurses to tend to them. Some watched us warily, but others were either asleep or too sick to open their eyes.

Only one guard stood at the door. He directed us to the bed three down on the left. It took me a moment to recognize the figure lying there, curled over and clutching his stomach. Holloway was so changed. He'd lost weight and the usually neat man had grown a patchy beard. Without Macassar oil, his hair hung loose and lank past his nape. The blue spidery veins on his closed eyelids stood out alarmingly against pale, glistening skin.

"Holloway," Lincoln said. "Are you awake?"

The man I'd affectionately called Father for thirteen years, and less affectionately for another five, cracked open his eyes. Whatever ailed him clearly didn't affect his mind because he took us both in then grunted.

"The devil child." His voice was as fragile as the rest of him. "Come to take me to the pits of hell?"

"You're not dead yet," I said, feeling bold now that I saw how sick he was. I thought I'd feel anger and hatred, but I felt neither of those. Indeed, I felt nothing for him except a small kernel of nostalgia that took little effort to quash.

"What do you want?"

The prisoner in the next bed began coughing uncontrollably. The warden and other prisoners took no notice.

"Sign these papers." Lincoln produced a folded document from his inside jacket pocket. He'd come prepared.

"What papers?" Holloway asked.

"Charlie is going to wed."

Holloway pushed himself up on his elbow with effort. I stepped forward to help him, but he flinched and gave me a look of such horror that I hung back. "She needs my consent." He chuckled and lay down again. "How ironic."

"Sign it," I said, "and I will be out of your way forever. You'll never have to see me again."

"No."

I exchanged a glance with Lincoln. He looked like he wanted to thump Holloway. "Why not?" I asked. "Why do you care what I do?"

"Marriage is a sacred endeavor in the eyes of God. I cannot allow a creature like yourself to enter a house of God and speak vows meant for good, Christian folk. What sort of vicar would that make me? What sort of man?"

"A forgiving one. A kind one." But the more I spoke, the more I saw how hopeless it was. Holloway wasn't the sort of man who feared death, or Lincoln, or me. He thought he was in the right, and nothing could sway him.

"I tried to save you," he said to me. "I tried to remove the devil from you—"

"By digging it out of me with a knife!"

"If I were in better health, and not confined to this hell, I would try again. Now it's up to you to fight the devil alone. If this man you wish to marry truly loved you, he would help you fight it." He sighed and seemed to sink further into the bed. "Be gone, Devil. Get away from me."

I moved off, but Lincoln did not. He leaned down to the figure in the bed and whispered something in his ear. Holloway's eyes widened. His Adam's apple bobbed.

"What did you say to him?" I asked as we followed the warden back to the governor's office.

"I told him that he will die soon, and that he'd better hope his treatment of you does not go against his God's wishes. I may have recited a few lines of the testament that counsel compassion to everyone."

"How do you know he'll die soon? He might recover."

We arrived in the governor's office and he didn't have a chance to answer me. Nor did he respond as we drove off, and I didn't ask again. Neither of us mentioned Holloway or his refusal to grant his permission.

I knew from Lincoln's rigidity that he was seething. His black fathomless eyes stared out the window, and the muscles in his jaw stretched taut.

"We'll speak with a lawyer," I said quietly. "It will all work out, Lincoln. You'll see." A small, cold place inside me hoped that Holloway would die, handing over my guardianship to the state, but it was not the sort of thing I could admit out loud.

Seth drove us to the newspaper offices of *The Times,* where we placed our advertisement for a housekeeper, then drove home. I felt flat, restless, and it only grew worse as the hour for the committee meeting approached. As the first arrival rolled along the drive, I began to regret my insistence that I face them too. While I wanted to present a united front with Lincoln, I was in no mood for their snobbery and, in the case of Lady Harcourt, jealousy.

The first to arrive was General Eastbrooke with Lord Marchbank close behind. They eyed me with curiosity as we sat in the library and waited for the others to arrive. I folded my hand over my engagement ring to hide it until they were all present.

"What's *she* doing here?" Lord Gillingham asked before he'd even fully entered the library. "Get rid of her."

"Charlie is staying," Lincoln said blandly.

"Why?" Lady Harcourt asked, with a defiant tilt of her chin. She looked lovely in a lavender gown, cinched at the waist to show off her feminine figure, her hair arranged in a style that must have taken her maid an age to do. "Are you still insisting we call her your assistant? That's all well and good, but Lichfield needs maids for now."

"We've placed an advertisement in *The Times* for a housekeeper."

Her face froze. "We?"

"Where did you go, Fitzroy?" Lord Gillingham cut in.

"On holiday," Lincoln said.

Gillingham snorted a laugh but when no one else joined in, he said, "To where?"

"That is none of your affair."

"It damned well is, man." Whenever Gillingham grew angry, his face turned the same reddish hue as his hair. He was well on the way to that color already and the meeting had only just begun.

Lincoln said nothing. He stood by the fireplace, a severely drawn frown on his brow. I sat in the only vacant armchair, and he switched to the other side of the hearth to be closer to me.

"You're the ministry's leader," Gillingham went on. "It's your *raison d'être* and ought to be your priority. It's not work from which you can come and go. It's your life."

I took a breath to counter him, but Lincoln put his hand on the back of my chair. I would stay silent if he wanted me to—for now.

"Gilly is correct," Eastbrooke said. The general's physical presence always commanded attention when he entered a room, but it was his military authority that made him the unspoken leader of the four-person committee. That and his age. At sixty-odd, he was the eldest. "Holidays are not for the likes of you, Lincoln. Do not disappear like that again."

"Stop it, both of you," Lady Harcourt hissed. "Of course he should be allowed to get away, from time to time. As long as it's not in the middle of an investigation, or for long, what's the harm in it?"

"What's the harm?" Gillingham echoed in a high-pitched voice. "Julia, in light of what's happened in his absence—"

"What happened?" Lincoln snapped.

"Two supernaturals are dead."

"Murdered," Lord Marchbank added.

I gasped. "How?"

"You don't ask the questions," Gillingham sneered.

"Both shot." Marchbank was the least talkative of the lot, but when he did speak, his words had far more impact than anyone else's. "It appears the killer was the same man."

"Or woman," Lady H added. Why did she look at me when she said it?

"How do you know they were supernaturals?" Lincoln asked.

"They had files in our archives."

"You've memorized the names on file?" Disbelief edged the blandness.

She stiffened. "I looked through them during the investigation into my stepson's disappearance in the hope a name from my late husband's journal would match one on file. I remembered Reginald Drinkwater, since it's an unusual name. When his death was reported in the papers, I checked the address and it turned out to be the same one in our files. The second victim, Joan Brumley, died in the exact same way as Drinkwater, and it was the newspapers that linked the two deaths as having been committed by the same killer. If it weren't for that, we would never have realized she was a supernatural too."

"What was Drinkwater's magical ability?" Lincoln asked.

"It's listed as levitation, but we now believe it was something more."

"According to the police and the papers, Drinkwater was a scientist," Eastbrooke said, folding his hands over his considerable girth. "He was involved in the area of mechanics. Specifically, mechanical limbs for people who've lost them through accident or birth defect."

Another scientist in the medical field. My stomach rolled.

"His devices were very good, apparently," Lady Harcourt said. "They worked well, but only while Drinkwater was in the room. Based on that information, we think he was using his magic to make the mechanical limbs work like real ones, seemingly of their own volition."

"The man was a charlatan," Gillingham said. "The limbs never could have operated without him present. They needed his magic."

"Indeed." Eastbrooke nodded. "Very devious practice, if you ask me."

"He hadn't sold any," Marchbank pointed out.

"I'm sure he would have, if he hadn't died first."

"Perhaps that was why he was killed," I said. "Perhaps one of the trial patients found out that the limb didn't really work and was so angry that he killed Drinkwater."

"Your opinion was not sought, Charlotte," Eastbrooke intoned. "If Lincoln insists that you're an assistant now, and not a maid, then make yourself useful and fetch the tea or take notes instead of espousing on things you know nothing about."

Lincoln's cool fingers skimmed the hot skin at the back of my neck. "You'll refrain from speaking to Charlie in such a manner in this house."

Eastbrooke spluttered a protest, but the rest was cut off by Gus and Seth's arrival with trays.

"The second victim, Joan Brumley, was an historian whose opinions were often controversial," Marchbank went on, setting his teacup aside.

"Why?" Lincoln asked.

"She claimed to have spoken with the spirits of historical figures in person."

"Bloody hell," Gus muttered, earning a glare from all four committee members. He went back to serving tea then sank into the shadows near the door.

"It was a recent claim," Lady Harcourt added, "and not made in one of the respectable academic periodicals. She was soundly ridiculed of course, and there was even discussion of having her committed to Bedlam."

"But we believe her," Marchbank said.

My chest constricted. My heart stilled. A woman in communication with dead historical figures could only be one thing.

"She must be a necromancer." Lady Harcourt turned hard, glittering eyes onto me as she accepted a cup from Seth.

I arched my brow at her in what I hoped was defiance, when all I felt was cold through to my bones.

A necromancer...dead. And someone had tried to kill me too.

CHAPTER 4

"Stupid woman," Gillingham muttered. "Joan Brumley could have caused panic on a grand scale with her claims."

"Not to mention drawing attention to herself," Eastbrooke said. "There are enough madmen in this country who would believe her and try to use her necromancy for their own ends, as they tried to do with Charlotte."

"It's just as well she died then." Gillingham sipped his tea, oblivious to my shocked gasp and Lady Harcourt's quiet chiding.

Lincoln shifted his weight from one foot to the other. "Aside from them both dying in the same manner, and both being magical, did you discover any other links?"

"What more do you need?" Eastbrooke asked. "They both have the potential to use their magic for harm."

"But did they?"

"That isn't the point."

"I think it is."

"The point is," Eastbrooke ground out, "that if they fell into the wrong hands, they would have been very dangerous tools."

Like me, he could have said. The look he gave me from beneath his bushy eyebrows implied he was thinking it.

"What were they like?" I asked suddenly.

"Pardon?" Lady Harcourt said.

"It seems to me that neither of them were doing anything harmful. Giving working limbs to those who have none is charitable, and historical research is benign enough. Drinkwater and Brumley don't sound like people who want to use their magic for ill. No one can force them."

"We don't know that for certain," she said. "Everyone has a price."

"Not everyone," Lincoln said.

She bristled. "And if money fails, then blackmail or a threat to a loved one will work. Even a saint can turn bad if the right sort of pressure is applied to the right place."

She sounded ruthless. Knowing her background as a dancer, I almost understood why, except that she continued to want to climb higher up the social ladder and grow richer, despite being rich and powerful now. She'd even admitted as much when she claimed she couldn't marry Lincoln. Even though she knew he was the son of a prince, she also knew that could never be publicly acknowledged. Lincoln was a step down from her previous husband, and she wouldn't have that.

"We've seen what can happen," Gillingham said with a nod at me. "The girl was kidnapped for just such a reason."

"I helped neither Frankenstein nor Jasper," I snapped. "Nor would I, under any circumstances."

"Do you think so?" Lady Harcourt's flinty gaze slipped to Lincoln. "What if they'd captured someone you love?"

I swallowed. There was no winning against that argument. Everyone in that room knew I would do anything to save Lincoln, even if it meant jeopardizing others.

His hand rested on my shoulder, but it wasn't very reassuring. "Leave Charlie out of this."

"We can't," Eastbrooke said. "It's as simple as that. Which brings me to my next suggestion."

"*No.*" Lincoln growled the word with all the force of a blunt hammer.

"You must go somewhere safe, Charlotte. Somewhere that no one will look for you. I know just the place. Leave it to me."

Lincoln's fingers dug into my shoulder. I wasn't certain he knew how hard he was holding me. "She's not leaving."

"We're being extra vigilant," I said. "Once this killer is found—"

"There will be another," Gillingham said. "Then another and another. There will always be someone after you."

"He's right," Lady Harcourt said, in a tone that was a little too silky to be genuinely sympathetic. "Let us find you somewhere safer to live. London is too—"

"If Charlie leaves Lichfield then so do I," Lincoln growled. "We're engaged."

Dense silence filled the library. Seth and Gus exchanged glances, but otherwise, nobody moved. It was as if time had ceased, trapping us in that moment.

"What!" Eastbrooke's explosion shattered the eerie quiet.

"We are to be wed." Lincoln's voice was all calm authority, with a hint of steel that perhaps only I noticed.

"You bloody fool," Gillingham sneered.

Eastbrooke's hand curled into a fist on the chair arm. "We cannot allow it."

"Agreed."

"It's not up to you," Lincoln said.

"Think, man," Gillingham said. "Think what you're doing. You'll ruin yourself."

"Then I'll be a happily ruined man."

I touched Lincoln's hand at my shoulder and smiled up at him. His troubled gaze watched me intently, perhaps for signs that the tirades upset me. They did not. I didn't care what these people thought.

"You can't," Eastbrooke stated with an emphatic shake of his head. "We forbid it."

"You have no power to forbid me to do anything."

"You're the head of the ministry and we're the committee—"

"I'm the leader because of the prophecy, not because you *chose* me. The committee has no power over Charlie or me."

Eastbrooke hauled himself to his feet and took a step toward us. I felt Lincoln's fingers tense again. "I raised you," the general snarled. "I took you into my home and treated you like a son, and this is how you repay me! By going behind my back to court this...this..."

"Tutors raised me, and occasionally the housekeeper. Granted, you provided a roof over my head, for which I am grateful, although I hold no illusions that you did it out of the goodness of your heart. You never treated me like a son, General. Don't pretend otherwise."

Eastbrooke sat down heavily. He stared at Lincoln, his mouth ajar, his chest heaving with his deep breaths.

"This is outrageous," Gillingham said. "I knew we should have gotten rid of her as soon as the matter with Frankenstein ended. None of this would have happened if you'd all listened to me."

"That's enough, Gilly," Marchbank said. To us, he added, "Your mind is made up?"

"It is," Lincoln said.

"Then we must live with it, I suppose, although I agree that there are some concerns."

"She's safer here with me to watch over her."

"I'm not referring to *her* safety, but to the ongoing effectiveness of the ministry, and yourself, Fitzroy. Hear me out. Say she is kidnapped again and forced to raise a witch with the power to overrule her commands. Say the only way to send the witch back is to kill Charlie. Will you do it?"

"That is an unlikely event."

"But not impossible."

"There will be other ways to send the witch back, we just don't know what they are yet."

Gillingham snorted.

Marchbank turned to Lady Harcourt. "Julia, what do you think?"

She had gone very pale. She hadn't moved a muscle or uttered a syllable since our announcement. It must be quite difficult for her to accept our relationship, since she believed Lincoln still loved her until quite recently. Her gaze shifted from Lincoln to mine then back again. "Do you have consent from her father?"

"Not yet," Lincoln said.

"If he doesn't give it, you'll have to wait until she's of age.

Lincoln said nothing. It would seem he wasn't going to tell them about our plan to get Holloway's guardianship overturned.

"Ha!" Gillingham slapped his hand down on the head of his walking stick. "Good point, Julia. It's unlikely he'll give it."

"He's ill," Marchbank said. "So Governor Crease from the House of Correction tells me. Perhaps he'll die."

Gillingham used his walking stick to push himself up and approached us. I steeled myself for more insults. Lincoln tensed. "This will pass, you know," he said to Lincoln. "What you think is love is just a passing...urge." He looked pleased with himself for choosing that word. "You're still young and ruled by your cock, but—"

Lincoln let me go, stepped forward, and punched Gillingham in the nose. Gillingham fell to the ground, clutching his face and choking out the vilest obscenities. Nobody went to his aid.

"Really, Lincoln," Lady Harcourt chided. "Was that necessary?"

"Get up, Gilly," Eastbrooke said. "It can't be that bad. He pulled back."

"I'm bleeding!" Gillingham lurched to his feet, one hand covering his nose, the other pulling out a handkerchief from his pocket. A trickle of blood seeped through the cracks of his fingers.

"Seth, Gus, show his lordship to the door." Lincoln held out his hand to me and I took it. "This meeting is over."

***

"Bloody...minded...*arses*." Cook interjected every word with a severe chop of his knife through an onion. "Don't listen to them, Charlie. Their hearts be cold."

"I don't care what they think," I assured him. "As Lincoln pointed out to them, they have no power to send me away. They'll grow used to our marriage, in time."

"Wish I'd seen Fitzroy clock Gillingham."

"It was rather satisfying." I smoothed my hand over the book in front of me on the kitchen table. It was a hefty tome about supernatural creatures, mostly demons. I'd found nothing yet on imps captured in amber, but I hadn't given up.

Lincoln had gone out after the meeting, taking Seth and Gus with him. They were hoping to learn more about the murders from the police, neighbors and other witnesses. I'd decided to read in the kitchen for company. I probably should have tackled some housework but it was almost dinnertime, and I really wanted to know more about the imp.

I'd found the necklace in Lincoln's desk drawer. It wasn't stealing, since it was mine anyway. I didn't put it around my neck but set it beside the book.

"Any luck?" Cook asked with a nod at the book.

"None." I sighed and slammed it closed.

"It be a pretty piece."

"It is, albeit somewhat peculiar with the creature inside. You can hardly see it with the naked eye, but it's in there."

He wiped his hands on his apron and picked up the pendant. He held it to the lamplight and squinted. "You should wear it, for safekeeping."

"It'll be safe in Lincoln's drawer."

"Not the imp's safety, yours. If your mama wants you to wear it, you should listen to her."

"She also said it was unpredictable and mischievous. I shouldn't risk it."

"Wear it, but don't let it out." He shrugged. "I don't see no harm in that. Your mama wouldn't give it to you if it be dangerous."

"No-o, I suppose not." I took the necklace and placed it around my neck, leaving the pendant exposed against my dress so that Lincoln could see it when he returned. I wasn't going to try and hide my actions from him. "He probably won't like it."

"If anyone can convince him it ain't a problem, it be you."

I smiled. "Thank you, Cook."

"Just don't tell him it were me who suggested it."

"I suppose there's no way of releasing it accidentally. I don't speak French, and I'm hardly about to say 'I release you' in a foreign language when I don't—Oh!"

The pendant glowed a bright orange and its warmth seeped through my dress above my breast. I fumbled with the clasp and threw the necklace on the table as if it were a spider that had fallen in my lap.

"What have I done?" I whispered.

"You weren't to know it be bilingual." Cook picked up his knife and raised it to strike at whatever came out of the amber.

A sudden blast of yellow light blinded me. When my vision returned, a small creature blinked back at me from the table. My rapidly beating heart calmed a little when the creature didn't move, and I was able to get a good look at it. It resembled a hairless cat, with long pointy ears and slanted green eyes that followed me as I edged around the table toward Cook.

"Do you understand me?" I said, speaking slowly.

It tilted its head to the side and the catlike mouth opened. A small mewling sound escaped as if it were trying to talk to me.

"I see why my mother called it a pet."

"It looks like a plucked chicken."

"I think it's rather adorable, with those eyes and the way the skin wrinkles above its nose like it's frowning at us."

"Touch it," Cook said.

"No! You touch it."

"I ain't going near that thing."

"Big baby." I shifted closer, smiled at the creature and made cooing sounds. I'd befriended alley cats when I lived on the streets. They were good at keeping the mice away. Perhaps the imp would respond to my soothing voice. "Come here, little one. Go back into your amber."

"It ain't moving."

I reached across the table, but it shifted back, out of my reach. Those large green eyes didn't leave mine the entire time. "Perhaps we should feed it." The alley cats had become more friendly if we spared them some of our food. "Pass me some beef."

"That be dinner!"

"This is an emergency, Cook. If Lincoln finds out I released it, he'll be furious with you."

"Me? Why me?"

"Because you didn't allow me any beef to coax it back into the amber."

He wiped his shiny brow and bald head with the back of his sleeve. "It can have some meat, but I ain't feeding it. It be your pet, you do it."

"Very well."

He chopped a slice of beef into small pieces and handed three to me. I put them down on the table and stood back. The imp crept on all fours to the beef, sniffed it, but didn't eat. It tilted its head and looked at me as if it were waiting for something.

"Go back into your amber," I urged. When nothing happened, I tried a different command. "Return, imp. I send you back."

It mewled again.

"It don't look magical," Cook said.

"What does a magical creature look like?"

"Don't know, but if I be a magical creature, I'd make meself prettier for a start, and bigger, with fur. Lots and lots of fur everywhere."

I kept my gaze strictly averted from his bald head and hairless face. Cook couldn't even grow eyebrows. "What shall we do?" Lincoln might walk in at any moment. I eyed the door and chewed my lip.

"Maybe it understands French for 'go back' better than English."

"That's all well and good, but I don't know the French for 'go back.' Do you?"

"I dozed off when me tutor were teaching them words in French lessons."

I gave him a withering glare. "This is not a time for jokes."

"I think you have to hold it and touch the amber too."

"Now you're just making things up." But I recalled my mother saying something similar. The suggestion was as good as any. "If it bites me, fetch the medical kit." I picked up the necklace and dangled the pendant where the creature could see it then caught the pendant in my hand. "Come here, little—"

The creature let out a squawk that seemed far too loud for its small size, then jumped off the table. It ran out of the kitchen before I'd registered that it had moved.

"It's escaping!" I lifted my skirts and sprinted after it.

"It can't get out," Cook said from directly behind me. "The doors and windows all be closed."

Thank goodness for that. I spotted the tip of its skinny pink tail as it turned a corner. It was heading toward the front of the house.

"Stop!" I shouted. "Get back here, you little rat!"

"Don't call it names or it might not want to come back."

Thank goodness the front door was closed, so we only had to corral it in one of the rooms and—

I skidded to a halt just as the creature leapt into the air. It was going to slam head first into the solid wooden door!

The imp stretched itself very thin. It resembled a stiletto dagger. Even the head was distorted. Then I saw why.

It squeezed through the keyhole and disappeared.

"*That* be its magic trick," Cook muttered.

"It's getting away!"

He flung open the door and pointed into the darkness ahead. "There! On the drive. It be normal shape again."

I ran down the steps and along the drive, flicking up clumps of damp gravel with every step. It wasn't until I was halfway to the gate that I realized Cook was no longer behind me. I turned to see him doubled over, holding his side.

"Go on," he puffed out between heavy breaths. "I'll catch it if it comes back."

Nearly three months ago I'd been known as fleet-foot Charlie, and for good reason, but my speed was not enough to close the gap between myself and the creature. It was as fast as any cat, and its magic trick, as Cook had called it, gave it an added advantage.

By the time I reached Lichfield's gates, I was in utter despair. The moonlight and street lamps weren't enough to reveal much in either direction, and the imp was nowhere to be seen. Once again I'd been responsible for releasing a supernatural creature with the potential to cause great harm.

The committee members would be gloating if they knew.

I stood on the pavement, hands on hips, and squinted into the darkness to left and right. It could be halfway to Clerkenwell by now.

Leaves in a nearby tree rustled. Thank goodness! "Come here, you little—"

The crack of a gunshot woke up the birds and deafened me.

And then everything became a blur.

CHAPTER 5

A blurry shadow slammed into my side, pushing me to the ground. I landed on my elbow and shoulder, the wind knocked out of me.

"Charlie!" Cook shouted. "Charlie, you hurt?" He appeared at the gate, his white apron making him look ghostly as he emerged out of the darkness. He sounded like a steam engine puffing up a hill.

"I don't think so," I gasped out.

As I said it, someone jumped out of the tree and ran off down the street. A gun dangled from his right hand. Cook made to go after him, but he could never have caught up to the nimble-footed man.

"Don't risk it," I told him as I got to my feet. "He's armed."

The imp sat on the ground beside me, panting steadily with its tongue out. Its green eyes watched my every move. It seemed to be waiting for something.

"It saved me," I murmured.

"That be its job," Cook said.

"Yes, but...it became something else, something large and strong that pushed me out of the way. How could it have done that in the moment between the shot being fired and the bullet hitting me?"

"Magic?"

"I suppose."

The imp suddenly lay down on its haunches and stretched its paws forward.

"Go after that man!" I ordered it. "Go!"

It lay its head on its paws and mewled.

"Maybe it only works when your life be in danger. The danger be over, now."

"Good point. I also think it might be tired. My mother said that happens after it does its duty." I knelt down on the pavement and patted my lap.

The imp lifted its head and, with a small mewl, got to its feet and padded over to me. It walked directly into my hands and allowed me to pick it up and cuddle it to my chest.

"Isn't it adorable?"

"It still be ugly." Cook glanced off in the direction the attacker had gone. "We better return to the house."

The imp snuggled into me all the way back to the kitchen. "It's quite a sweet little thing, when it's not running away." I held it tightly in one hand and patted its wrinkled head with the other. "You saved my life, little imp. Thank you."

It made a sound in its chest like a strangled version of a cat's purr and tucked its head beneath my chin. But, oddly, it thrust out its paw and tapped the table.

"I think it wants to go back now." Cook handed me the necklace that we'd left behind.

With the imp in one hand and the necklace in the other, I said, "Return, imp. Go back inside."

Both imp and amber glowed and grew warmer, then the blinding light forced me to turn my head away. When I opened them, the creature was gone.

I held up the necklace to the lamp. Now that I knew what it looked like, I could just make out the imp's tiny body curled into a ball, the two ears pointing straight up. "It's asleep."

Cook dragged over the stool from the stove and sat down. "Bloody hell, that were…" He shook his head.

"Interesting?"

"Not the word I were going to say."

Lincoln entered the kitchen and eyed each of us in turn. I'd not heard the door to the courtyard open or close. Cook stood quickly and resumed chopping vegetables, his head studiously down.

I gave Lincoln what I hoped was a cheerful smile. "Welcome back. Where's Seth and Gus?"

He whipped off his gloves and unbuttoned his jacket. "Coach house. What happened?"

"What makes you think something happened?"

"You look guilty."

"I do not!"

He tilted his head to the side. "You're neither dead nor injured, so I'll assume there is no immediate danger."

"Something did happen, and if you give me a chance, I'll tell you." I rose. "But first, may I make you tea? Or would you like something stronger?"

"Sit down."

I sat. "Very well, but I'm only thinking of your comfort." Where to begin? With the worst incident or best? Which one was the worst? "The imp escaped from the amber, but we caught it and returned it to the necklace where it fell asleep. Now, the tea…"

He perched on the edge of the table, his arms and ankles crossed, and watched me prepare a pot of tea. I tried not to feel awkward, but his silence eventually grew too taut and I felt compelled to break it.

"The imp understands English. Isn't that clever of it?"

"And you spoke the words in English to release it."

"Unintentionally, of course."

"Of course."

I handed a cup to him. "It then escaped from the house, despite the doors and windows being closed and locked."

"How?"

"It distorted itself to fit through the keyhole."

"Magic," Cook added with a knowing nod.

"Then it ran off. We chased it, caught it and said the words for it to return, which it did. Simple."

He set the teacup aside and picked up the necklace. The amber dangled from his fingers as he held it up to the light. "What did it look like?"

"Ugly," Cook said.

"Like a hairless cat," I added. "It moved like a cat too, and it sounded a little like one. It was quite a friendly little thing once it tired itself out."

He put the necklace down again and fixed me with one of his penetrating glares. "It was fast?"

"Very."

"And yet you caught it."

I sighed again. There was no point delaying the inevitable. "It grew very tired after it saved my life."

He stiffened. "Go on."

"Someone was in the tree near the front gate. I followed the imp to the street and the person shot at me. The imp pushed—"

"Shot at you!" He grasped my shoulders and searched my face.

"I'm unharmed, Lincoln. The imp pushed me out of the way and the man ran off without firing another shot."

His jaw set hard. "Did you see him?"

"No. It was dark, but I'm quite certain it was a man, and an agile one. He must have been camped out in that tree, waiting for me to reappear. I wonder how long he was up there."

"This reinforces my opinion that you must remain in the house."

"Only for the time being, until he's caught."

"As for the imp..." He collected the necklace again and frowned. For a moment, I thought he was going to pocket it so he could hide it from me, but instead, he held it out. "Store it somewhere safe."

"And don't speak the words to release it?"

"In any language." He stalked out of the kitchen and I had to run to catch up with him.

"Where are you going?"

"Outside to look for clues to the shooter's identity."

"I doubt he left a calling card."

He gave me a withering glare. "Lock the door behind me, and don't open it until you hear my voice. Lock all the doors."

By the time he returned, Seth and Gus had joined us. Lincoln checked that every door and window was locked before sitting us all down in the library and going through his new rules, most of which involved not letting me out of the house or leaving me on my own.

"Go and change into your exercise clothes, Charlie," he said once we'd all agreed. "We'll resume your training."

"Now?"

He gave me a blank look.

I pointed to the clock on the mantel. "It's almost eleven."

"Tomorrow morning then. Early." He once again strode out of the room, his hands behind his back. He took the stairs two at a time and disappeared. He didn't even say goodnight.

With a sigh, I followed him, only to find that he was waiting for me at my door. He leaned against the wall, arms crossed, apparently seeing something of interest on the floor at his feet.

"Lincoln? Are you all right?"

He watched me approach through his thick, dark lashes. "I believe that's *my* question." He opened his arms and folded me against his chest. "*Are* you all right?"

"I am. I wasn't hurt."

"You could have been." He rested his cheek on the top of my head and drew in a deep breath.

"Let's not dwell on that. The imp saved me." I'd slipped the necklace into the top drawer of my dresser, beneath my unmentionables. I didn't want to release it accidentally again, but if I felt threatened, I knew where to find it quickly. "It was quite a strange experience, and I still can't fathom it."

He held me without speaking for a moment, then kissed the top of my head. "Goodnight, Charlie. I hope you can sleep, in spite of everything."

"I'll sleep better if you're with me."

He kissed the tip of my nose. "You and the imp are well suited to one another."

***

Training was more intense than usual. There was no teasing, hardly any talking, and certainly no kissing. After two hours, my muscles ached and my knuckles sported a graze from punching the rice-filled bag. I was relieved when Seth interrupted us—until I saw his face. It was lined with worry.

"You have a visitor, sir." His gaze flicked to me then away. "It's Governor Crease."

"From the jail?" I looked to Lincoln, but he'd not reacted. "This can't be good if he's calling on us in person."

"Tell him I'll be down in a moment," Lincoln said.

I raced from the ballroom to my bedchamber and quickly washed and dressed in my deep green day dress. Although I hurried, Lincoln beat me to the parlor, where he was already deep in conversation with the governor of the Surrey House of Correction

"Good morning, Mr. Crease," I said.

The governor rose. "Miss...er...I didn't catch your name, last time."

"Charlotte is my fiancée." Lincoln sounded a little more distracted than usual. "You were just about to tell me why you're here, Crease."

Crease stroked his woolly sideburns. "It's with grave concern that I have to inform you that Holloway has escaped."

CHAPTER 6

My stomach flipped. I clutched my throat where Holloway's knife had nicked my skin the night he'd attacked me in the courtyard. In order to keep my name and identity out of the papers, Lincoln had told the police that Holloway attacked Cook but Cook had managed to capture him.

Lincoln placed a steadying hand at my lower back. "How?" he asked. "I thought he was too ill to move."

"The medic thought he was dead."

"Dead!" I echoed. "Didn't he check?"

Crease winced. "He claims he did and that there was no pulse. The body was removed to an outbuilding that isn't guarded. When the mortuary staff came for him in the morning, the body was gone."

"So he may indeed be dead," I said.

"You think body snatchers took him, Miss...Charlotte?"

"Oh, er, yes. The city is rampant with them. Didn't you know?" I wasn't sure which was worse—a living Holloway on the loose, or a resurrected one.

"Ordinarily I would agree with you, but the door was bolted from the outside and the windows are nailed permanently shut. The police surmise that someone opened the door, carried the ill Holloway out, and locked it again from the outside."

"And the lack of a pulse?"

He shrugged. "The medic was mistaken."

"That is quite a serious mistake."

"Quite," he said with a twitch of his sideburns. He cleared his throat and seemed to be waiting for something. "I thought you should know, since he was arrested here and you showed interest in him recently."

"Thank you," I said, because Lincoln had gone quiet. "It was good of you to inform us."

"It was, wasn't it? I doubt the police would have bothered." Crease did not move toward the door.

I was beginning to think we might have to offer him tea when Lincoln strode to the door and called for Seth. He whispered something and Seth disappeared, returning a few moments later with an envelope identical to the one Lincoln had handed to Crease when we'd visited Holloway in jail.

Crease tucked it into his jacket pocket. "Good morning, sir, miss." He put on his hat, touched the brim and saw himself out.

"Do you think he's alive or dead?" I asked as soon as Crease had climbed into the hackney waiting for him. "He can't be alive, surely. His health couldn't have improved enough for him to escape unassisted, and nobody cares enough about him to risk freeing him. He must be dead. But that throws up another horrible prospect."

"Who raised his spirit and helped him re-enter his body."

Seth and Gus joined us and I repeated what Crease had told us. "There must be another necromancer," Gus said with a shrug. "Someone we don't know about, like the Brumley woman. There ain't no other explanation."

Lincoln dragged his hand through his hair. "Either way, someone helped him. Are you certain no one cares about him enough to orchestrate an escape?"

"No," I said. "No one."

"A family member?" Seth asked.

"He has no family."

"A parishioner?"

"The only parishioners who ever visited us at home were a handful of old ladies, and I can't see them as the sort to assist in a prison escape." I began to pace back and forth across the entrance floor tiles. "This is a mystery. Perhaps we should double check the archives for necromancers. You may have missed one."

"I didn't," Lincoln said.

"There must be another. After all, you didn't know about Joan Brumley. Perhaps someone you thought didn't have children in fact did and their descendent has kept their magic a secret. Joan Brumley might have children."

"It's possible." From his tone, I think he meant it was also very unlikely. "If there is another necromancer, the ministry is not aware of her."

"Yes, you're right." I began pacing again. Lincoln watched me with a frown, but it was Gus who intercepted me by stepping in my way.

"It'll be all right, Charlie," he said gently.

"Will it? Because this morning I had only one killer to worry about, now I have two, one of whom may be dead."

"He won't kill you," Seth said. "He's your...*was* your father. I'm sure a part of him still cares for you."

"If he thinks killing me will save me, then he'd rather see me dead."

"We'll find him," Lincoln assured me. "But it may take time with only three of us."

I didn't tell him that we were four. There was no point trying to argue with him when he was entirely correct in keeping me in the house. I hated it, but I saw no other way—for now.

He lightly touched my fingers then drew away to bark orders to his men. It wasn't long before they headed out to investigate, although I wasn't sure how they were going to find Holloway. Without knowing whether they were even looking for a dead body or a live man, it was impossible to know where to begin.

The day wore on, as did the next and the next. By the third day, they'd learned that Holloway wasn't hiding out at his parishioners' homes, nor that of any acquaintances. As Gus had put it, it felt like they were wading through mud into a head wind.

There was a little more news about the murders of Drinkwater and Brumley. First of all, neither had any children recorded against their names, so I was able to complete their ministry files. Lincoln had managed to break into Joan Brumley's house and had brought home a stack of research papers for me to go through. While I learned much about several historical figures, there was no direct mention of her necromancy or any clues as to why she may have died. I could only guess that someone took offence to her suggestion that our national hero, the Duke of Wellington, had been a condescending bully.

Despite my thorough search through her documents, and Lincoln's search through her house, we'd found nothing to point the finger at a particular individual and no connection between the victims. Brumley had died a spinster and lived alone in the house that had once belonged to her parents. She had few friends, only one cousin, and no true enemies. She was considered a harmless crackpot by her fellow historians and was mostly ignored.

Drinkwater had left behind a widow but no children. Mrs. Drinkwater had departed London immediately after her husband's funeral to stay with a sister in Acton. It wasn't clear if that would be a permanent arrangement or if she would return to her own home. I supposed she must, at some point, if only to sort through his belongings. Her hurried departure meant Lincoln was easily able to get inside the house and the upstairs workshop to remove any paperwork.

I sifted through the records of Drinkwater's so-called patients and gave Lincoln their names and addresses. With the help of Seth and Gus, he learned as much as he could about their movements at the time of Drinkwater's death. After three days they'd not singled out a likely suspect. Indeed, since all patients lacked at least one limb, they were considered highly unlikely to have been able to kill Drinkwater. That didn't rule out their family members taking out their anger on him, however. The man had given those poor people false hope. While I was in no doubt he thought he was doing good, and he hoped to improve their situation, he should never had tried his magical limbs on real subjects until tests proved positive.

The arrival of Seth's butler was a welcome relief from the monotony. He was a distinguished looking fellow with gray flecks through his brown hair and a cleanly shaved face that bore few lines. After speaking with him for half an hour in the parlor, I began to wonder if the lack of lines was due to a lack of expression. Fortunately I was an expert at deciphering the meaning behind a mere lift of an eyebrow, and we got along quite well.

He moved into one of the attic rooms reserved for servants recently vacated by Seth and Gus. They now occupied the larger bedrooms on the second level. I hadn't discussed the change with Lincoln first, but he'd not objected when he found out. In fact, I was almost certain he was satisfied with the new arrangement.

With Doyle settled, and taking smoothly to his new position, I set about reading through the applications for housekeeper, but quickly realized I needed help. Doyle's first job as butler was to go through the references and pick out the applicants who had worked for London's best families. One stood clearly above the rest.

The following afternoon, Mrs. Webb arrived at Lichfield, bringing an air of grimness with her. Dressed in severe black, and with dark hair and smooth, marble-white skin, she reminded me of a photograph of a dead woman I'd once seen. It seemed rather serendipitous that Mrs. Webb would come to work in a place where the mistress was a necromancer.

Despite her macabre appearance, she moved with grace and poise, and spoke well.

"And why did you leave your previous position, Mrs. Webb?" I asked.

"I remarried, miss." Her face fell. "Sadly, he lived only a year after our wedding and recently passed away."

"Oh, I am sorry."

"I find myself in need of employment again. Your advertisement seemed like a gift when I saw it in *The Times*. I like the idea of finding my own maids. I can be sure of their character first, you see. A gentle, simple nature is very important in a maid, in my opinion. You don't want a girl with airs, and certainly none too pretty."

"You've had experience employing staff?"

"In my previous post, in the course of five years, I hired four maids, all of whom proved excellent workers. Would you like a list of my other duties?"

"Yes, please."

She proceeded to rattle off everything she did at her last placement, with a gleam of pride shining in her otherwise lackluster eyes.

"It will be a lot of hard work at first," I said, "getting yourself—as well as maids—settled. We've been short staffed for some time, and there's much to be done."

"I'm not afraid of hard work. It will help keep my mind off...recent events." She gave me wobbly smile.

Poor thing. The death of her husband must have been a blow. "Mrs. Webb, my fiancé and I will be very pleased if you can begin immediately."

"Fiancé?"

"Mr. Fitzroy. You'll meet him tomorrow, if you can start then." And if I could keep Lincoln in the house long enough.

"Miss Holloway, I...I'm a little nonplussed. I didn't know there was a gentleman living here. I assumed you were all alone. His name wasn't listed on the advertisement."

"Since you will report to me, we decided only my name was necessary. Is our situation here at Lichfield a problem for you?" If she turned out to be a prude then I would be sorely disappointed. She seemed suitable in every other way.

"No, but I must insist that propriety be observed. For the sake of the young maids, you understand."

"Let me assure you that propriety is very much on Mr. Fitzroy's mind." Too much, damn him. I was growing quite frustrated with merely kissing.

"Then I shall see you tomorrow. Is eight o'clock too early?"

"Not at all."

Doyle saw her out then offered to bring me tea.

"Serve it in the kitchen," I said.

His brows almost flew off his forehead. "The kitchen, miss?"

It was at that moment I realized our quiet, unconventional household was about to change, and I wasn't sure I would like everything about the new arrangement. "I need to speak to Cook about meals...and such." I needed to do no such thing. Cook decided what we ate and was given a weekly allowance with which to purchase whatever he needed. I'd never had cause to interfere. "Perhaps send him in here instead. With the tea."

I waited until Cook arrived, followed by Doyle carrying a tray. There was only one teacup on it. Cook watched Doyle pour the tea, his arms crossed, foot tapping on the carpet.

"Thank you," I said, accepting the cup from Doyle. "Now please bring another for Cook."

Doyle's eyes widened in horror. "Miss! That would be quite inappropriate."

"I say what is and is not appropriate here, not you. If you dislike the way I manage the household, you're free to leave."

Doyle's jowls shook. His eyes widened even more. I expected him to storm out and gather his things, but after a moment, the jowls settled and his eyelids lowered. "Of course, miss. I'll fetch another cup immediately."

"You summoned me, miss?" Cook asked once we were alone.

"Miss? It's still Charlie to you, Cook."

He held my gaze for a long time then sighed and sat without being asked. "I'll have to stop sometime."

"Perhaps, but not yet. We've been through too much together to become suddenly formal with one another."

"Aye, that be true. So, you want to discuss the menus, now Lichfield be getting all formal?"

"Not at all. I simply wanted to enjoy my tea with a friendly face. Doyle didn't like me going to the kitchen, so I decided to bring you out of it instead. You don't have something on the stove, do you?"

He grinned. "I only be cleaning up. Ain't no one to do it no more."

"That'll change very soon. We have a new housekeeper starting tomorrow. Her name is Mrs. Webb."

Doyle returned with the second cup, and I asked him to stay while I told them both about our new housekeeper. I also took the time to inform Doyle of how we did things at Lichfield. It was difficult to say whether he appreciated our informality or not. His face remained blank.

By the end, however, his shoulders were a little less rigid as he collected the cups. "Forgive me for my earlier outburst, miss. It's just that I am unused to such unconventional households. I am grateful to you for giving me this opportunity."

"It's not me you need to thank, but Seth."

He bowed. "I owe Lord Vickers much."

Cook snickered. Once Doyle left, he said, "Lord Vickers don't sound right."

"I think Seth would agree with you there."

Lincoln arrived home with Seth and Gus in time to dine with me in the dining room. After they told me about their progress, I informed them that we had a new housekeeper.

"She starts tomorrow."

"So early?" Lincoln said.

"Yes, why?"

"I need time to investigate her."

"But she answered our ad and her references are excellent. Doyle knows her previous employers."

"Did you check she isn't lying?"

"Why would she lie?"

He arched a brow.

"I suppose she might be the murderer, but it does seem like a convoluted way of getting to me. Besides, she could have killed me in the parlor."

"Were you alone?"

"Doyle remained."

"Then she couldn't have attacked."

I sighed. "I still think it's an overly obscure way to get to me, but you're right. She should be thoroughly checked first. I'll send word to put her off another day."

He shook his head. "I'll investigate her tonight. If you have an address for her previous employer, it won't take long."

I scrutinized him to see if there were any signs of exhaustion on his face, but he seemed perfectly fine, albeit somewhat gruffer than usual. I put that down to worry. "If you're sure."

"I am." His lips flattened into a kind of smile.

I smiled back at him, and after dinner, I took him in my arms before he went out again. "How long will you be gone?"

"No more than two hours. It's a simple matter of ensuring she worked where she claims, and that can be answered with a few questions of the present staff."

"I think I'll look up the name Webb in the files, just to be certain. It's a pity I didn't ask for her maiden name."

"Good idea. Perhaps I can learn the maiden name from the other servants."

He kissed me lightly then left in a carriage driven by Seth. I checked the ministry records kept in the attic, but found no information for Webb.

Upon his return, Lincoln confirmed that she had indeed worked at the Powell residence in Mayfair for several years before her marriage to Mr. Webb. Her name prior to her second marriage was Cotwell, so I searched the archives again while Lincoln returned to his rooms.

"Find anything?" he asked when he rejoined me in my sitting room.

"Nothing. Come sit by me near the fire. Your feet must be freezing."

He looked down at his bare feet. "They're a little cold."

"And you only just noticed?" I clicked my tongue and ordered him to sit. Then I sat on his lap. "We'll find him, won't we?"

"Holloway? Yes."

"And the other killer."

He circled his arms around me. "I suspect learning the identity of the killer will lead us to finding Holloway."

"You think the murderer helped Holloway escape?"

"They must be linked. I don't believe in coincidence."

I laid my head on his shoulder and enjoyed how his arms tightened around me and his body began to relax. "I hope you're right."

***

Mrs. Webb's first day was a baptism of fire. Not only did she have a great deal of housework to accomplish, but a delivery of furniture arrived from Monsieur Fernesse's gallery. And then there were the applications for the maids' positions to sift through.

When the cart with our new sofa and armchairs rolled up shortly after lunch, Lincoln instructed Gus to remain home with me "to assist with the lifting," while he took Seth with him to speak to Widow Drinkwater. I suspected he wanted Gus near me as an extra safety measure while strangers came and went from the house. Apparently more of our French purchases were on their way.

I didn't mind. I enjoyed Gus's company, but he had a terrible eye for decorating. "The vase would look better on the table by the window," I told him, setting it there. "And that old statue is hideous. Put it in the attic."

He pouted at the clay statue of a bulldog in his hand. "But it's unique!"

"It's still hideous. I wonder where it came from."

"Last owner of Lichfield, prob'ly. The committee bought the house and contents, lock, stock."

"Should we leave the new sofa on the right of the fireplace, where the old one was, or on the left? I can't decide." It wasn't lost on me that in a matter of months I'd gone from stealing food to survive to rearranging furniture and managing a household. Fortune had certainly smiled upon me. I would never forget it.

Gus stroked his grizzly chin. "Don't know. I ain't good at this sort of thing."

"Perhaps we'll ask Seth when he returns."

"What about Lady H?" At my wrinkled nose, he added, "P'haps not. Mrs. Webb?"

"Why not. Will you fetch her, please? I think she's in the kitchen, going through applications."

He placed the statue in a chest earmarked for the attic and went in search of the housekeeper. She entered a few minutes later, Gus at her heels carrying a tray of tea things and slices of walnut cake.

"This looks lovely," Mrs. Webb said, running her hand along the curved back of the sofa. "What marvelous pieces!"

"Monsieur Fernesse has an excellent eye," I said.

She poured tea and handed a cup to me and the other to Gus. Her mood was buoyant, yet her smile was odd and not quite genuine.

"I hope you've settled in, Mrs. Webb. I know it will take time to grow used to our ways here at Lichfield, but I hope you'll be happy."

"It's difficult to know, yet." She stood by the fireplace, her hands clasped in front of her.

I sipped. "Do you see anything in this room that you think ought to be changed?"

She arched a brow and glanced around again. "No. It's quite lovely."

"Good." I sipped again, and this time the tea seemed to taste odd. Bitter. "Is this a different brew?"

She nodded. "It's my own that I used to make for my last mistress. She found it soothing."

"I'm not sure I'm in need of soothing."

"I ain't," Gus said with a chuckle. He too sipped and pulled a face. He caught Mrs. Webb's pained frown, sighed, and took another mouthful. "It's...unique."

It was bloody awful, but I too took another sip so as not to upset Mrs. Webb's feelings, then put the cup down. Just in time too as everything went a little blurry and I felt unstable for a moment.

"There are several suitable candidates for the position of maid," Mrs. Webb said.

"Yes?" The room spun, making my head swim. I put my hand out for balance.

"Shall I make inquiries into their references?" she droned on.

I tried to nod, but it felt as if my head would roll off so I stopped. My heartbeat slowed, and the blood oozed through my veins like sludge.

"Charlie!" Gus rasped in a loud whisper. "Charlie! Something's been put in the tea."

I turned my heavy head in his direction, just in time to see him list to the side like a sinking ship. He slumped against the arm of the chair, his eyes closed. Oh God, what was happening?

"Mrs. Webb?" That surely wasn't me slurring. "Help."

I too must have fallen to the side because Mrs. Webb walked toward me at an angle. The smile on her face was now genuine. Not cruel, but satisfied. "You're coming with me."

CHAPTER 7

Gus was there, nearby.

That first thought dodged the hammer blows in my head and reached my numbed brain. The body beside me *had* to be his. Nobody else snored like that. Thank God he was alive. We both were.

I cracked open a dry eyelid and reached out a hand to his sleeping form, but couldn't move. My hands were tied behind my back. My feet were tied together too. I lay on my side on a lumpy bed, my back to Gus. We were in a room surrounded by damp brick walls and little else. There were no windows and a stone staircase led up to a door. The only light came from a torch flickering in a wall sconce. We were alone.

"Gus," I whispered. "Gus, wake up."

He murmured something under his breath then resumed snoring. I nudged him with both feet and he awoke with a jerk. "Huh? Charlie?"

"Here, behind you."

He rolled over with a groan. His eyes fluttered. "Me head's splittin' in two."

"Mine too, but I think I'm otherwise unharmed. You?"

He opened his eyes and wriggled. "A few sore spots at the back of my ankles, but nothin' bad. What happened? Where are we?"

I sat up. My head swam and everything turned foggy. It took a moment to clear, but the pounding remained. I tried to ignore it and think. "A cellar?"

Gus sat too, wincing. "I'll throttle that bloody housekeeper when I get my hands on her. I only drank that disgustin' tea so as not to upset her."

It galled me to think that Mrs. Webb had tricked me into hiring her, but not as much as it galled me to think I'd fallen for her lies. There was some comfort in the fact that Lincoln had also been fooled.

"If I spin round," Gus said, swiveling on his rear so that his back was to me again, "I can try to untie you."

"Good idea. Do it quietly. I don't want to alert Mrs. Webb that we're awake. I'm in no hurry to find out what she wants with us."

"Shoutin' for help's out of the question then."

"Agreed. I don't think any passersby would hear us anyway. We're in a cellar, and those walls look thick."

He fumbled with the ropes tying my wrists, muttering obscenities under his breath as he failed to make headway. "The devil take the bitch."

"Look on the positive side, Gus. We're not dead."

He grunted.

"That means Mrs. Webb isn't the one going around killing supernaturals, or I probably wouldn't have made it out of Lichfield alive. Nor would she have taken you."

"Why did she take me?" he asked.

"I don't know, but I hope Cook and Doyle are all right."

He grunted again and twisted around. "I can't see what I'm doin'."

"Here, let me try."

But it was hopeless. The knot was too elaborate and, without seeing it, I couldn't untie it. I let out a string of vile words that had Gus admonishing me.

"You can't talk like that now you're mistress of Lichfield Towers."

"I don't bloody care about that right now." I drew up my knees. How long had we been unconscious? Did Lincoln know I'd been abducted yet?

"You make a habit of this," Gus said.

"It's not my fault everyone wants a necromancer for their evil plans."

"Fitzroy's plans ain't evil."

I sighed. "I know. But you're right, I do get abducted an awful lot. It's no wonder the committee want to send me away and not tell anyone where I am."

"Don't think like that. You ain't goin' nowhere. Lichfield wouldn't be the same without you. *We* wouldn't be the same."

Tears welled and hovered on my eyelids. I tipped my head back until I touched his shoulder. "Thank you, Gus. I'd miss you all enormously." And I couldn't leave Lincoln. Not ever.

"He won't let 'em take you away," he said, as if he could read my thoughts. After a few moments' silence, he added, "So what'll we do now?"

"Wait for Mrs. Webb, convince her to untie us then overpower her."

He chuckled without humor. "Nothin' can go wrong with that plan, Charlie. Nothin' at all."

I got off the bed and hopped awkwardly around the room. I didn't know what I was looking for, but it felt better than sitting. After a moment, Gus joined me. He hopped to the bottom of the stairs and gazed up at the door.

"You'll hurt yourself if you fall," I warned him.

"Then I won't fall."

"You'll probably find the door is locked."

"I have to try."

It was a good plan, but I had a better one. "I could summon a spirit and then ask it to go to the mortuary, find a dead body, and rescue us. Do you remember Gordon Thackery? He helped us capture Captain Jasper."

"Aye."

"He's a nice fellow and I'm sure he'll help again."

"It might work, but what if we're a long way from a mortuary or cemetery? What if Thackery don't reco'nize where we are and gets lost on his way back?"

"He *can* read street signs."

"What if someone sees him, all decayin' and disgustin'." He pulled a face and shivered. "We don't want to frighten the public."

"He's smart enough to hide himself beneath a hat and clothing."

He glanced up at the door again. "S'pose it's worth a try. I'm still goin' up though. I'd feel a right idiot if the door was unlocked the entire time."

"Be careful."

I watched him as he hopped up on the first step, paused, then hopped onto the second. It would take a while for him to reach the top, but at least he was doing something. I couldn't sit idly by either.

"Gordon Moreland Thackery, I summon you here. Gordon Thackery, it's Charlie Holloway. Please come. I need you."

The white cloud slipped through a crack in the brickwork and swept across the room. I didn't flinch as it washed through me and came to a stop near the bed. The familiar face of Thackery broke into a grin.

"Miss Charlie! I never thought we'd meet again." Even in spirit form, the ravaging signs of the opium that had taken his life were evident. While his eyes were clear, they were sunken into his skull along with his cheeks. He looked much older than mid-twenties, the age he'd been at his death, but his cheerfulness made up for it.

"We're in a spot of difficulty." I turned so he could see my bound hands.

"Having another adventure, eh?"

"Gus and I were kidnapped."

He glanced at Gus, who'd paused in his laborious progress up the stairs when I began talking. Gordon nodded but Gus couldn't see, and he jumped up to the next step.

"I can't untie you." Gordon held up his ghostly hands.

"We were hoping you'd find yourself a fresh corpse and come back and rescue us."

His brows arched. "A fresh corpse?"

"I know it's gruesome, but we're desperate."

"So I see. I'm happy to help." He glanced around the room. "Where are we?"

"I don't know. We were brought here while unconscious. The walls must be thick, or we're deep underground, because I can't hear a thing."

He circled me then drifted up to the ceiling. "I'll get you out. When I do, I want a full account of all the adventure I missed out on."

"I promise. Now please hurry."

He disappeared and I blew out a breath. I felt more at ease now that Gordon had been enlisted. Although I'd never known him during his lifetime, I trusted him.

He'd not only proven very capable in the past, but also loyal and rather sweet. I liked him.

A key tumbled in the lock and Gus and I glanced at each other. The door opened and Mrs. Webb appeared like a black raven about to swoop. A few steps down and too far away to tackle her, Gus groaned. He slumped against the wall.

"An admirable attempt at escape, but it wouldn't have worked." She held up her lantern, illuminating that pale, ethereal face. She looked as ghostly as Gordon. "The door was locked and it's too thick to break down, even if you had a run at it. Return to the bed, Gus. You too, Miss Holloway."

I considered defying her, but decided against it. Escape was now a matter of biding time until Gordon returned. If we protested in any way, she might hurt us, and then we wouldn't be in any shape to get out.

"Do as she says," I told Gus.

He scooted down the steps on his rear end and hopped back to the bed. We both sat down. Mrs. Webb stood at the bottom of the staircase, well out of reach.

"I trusted you," I spat. "I allowed you into our home!"

She lifted her chin. The effect was one of entitlement and poise, not of a humble housekeeper. I couldn't believe I'd been so easily fooled. "There was no other way. I would apologize, but your immorality makes me disinclined to do so."

"My what?"

"Your living arrangements are disgusting. Lichfield Towers is a den of vice. A young woman living unchaperoned with an older man in his house…it's unthinkable." Her voice had become louder and more aggressive as she spoke, and her lips pursed into a tight O.

"We're not sleeping in the same room! Mr. Fitzroy is a gentleman, and your implication that he is not shows more about how your mind works than his or mine." I lifted my gaze to the ceiling. "I can't believe I'm arguing about morals with someone who abducts people and ties them up in her cellar."

"Desperate times and all that." Mrs. Webb set the lantern down on the floor at her feet. "Besides, you're not hurt, are you?"

"The backs of Gus's feet are sore."

"Aye," Gus muttered. "Untie me and I'll show you."

"He was too heavy and I had to drag him down the steps then lift him onto the cart and drag him down here," she said.

So she had worked alone. Escaping from one person ought to be easier than two. Hppe rose in my chest. "Which cart?"

"I borrowed one from the Lichfield stables."

Gus clicked his tongue, admonishing her. "Death don't take kindly to having his belongings stolen or his fiancée kidnapped."

"You call your master Death?"

"It fits. I should warn you, the last person to abduct Charlie died, as did the men who helped him. Violently. It weren't pretty."

I wasn't sure I liked Gus spreading rumors that Lincoln had killed Jasper and his two thugs. Lincoln had assured me he hadn't done it, and I believed him. We'd never learned who had murdered the captain in the holding cell after his arrest, and we likely never would.

"What do you want, Mrs. Webb?" I asked.

"I need you to summon my husband and raise his body."

I wasn't surprised. At least it confirmed that she wasn't the killer of supernaturals. It was the silver lining on a very trying experience. "Why do you want to raise him?"

"That's none of your concern."

"It is. If I'm going to do it, I need to know certain things. That's one of them."

She stepped toward me and lifted her hand to strike my cheek. I flinched, but she didn't lash out. "I'm not a violent woman, but I am quite provoked at the moment. Don't make the situation worse for yourselves by lying."

"What makes you think I'm lying?"

"I know a lot about you, Miss Holloway. For example, I know that you can raise the dead by calling them by name. Just a name. You don't need to know anything else."

"I see that you also knew I was in need of a housekeeper. How?"

"I saw your advertisement in *The Times*."

"I don't believe you. It's too coincidental to be true, and I don't believe in coincidences." Lincoln had said the same thing to me, and it felt satisfying to spout his words at her. But if it wasn't a coincidence, that meant she *knew* to look in *The Times*. "My God," I whispered. "Who told you we were advertising for a housekeeper?"

Her jaw set hard and her dark eyes glittered.

Gus twisted to look at me. "Blimey, Charlie. Who would do that?"

"Someone who knows our situation." That narrowed it down to Doyle and the committee members. Unless Cook, Seth or Gus mentioned it in passing to someone connected with Mrs. Webb. None of us could have any inkling that posting the ad would lead to this, and our advertising for a housekeeper was no secret.

"*Who told you?*" I ground out between my clenched teeth.

"It's not important."

"It is to me."

"You're in no position to dictate terms, Miss Holloway."

I lifted one shoulder. "Then I refuse to summon your husband's spirit."

Her top lip curled. I couldn't believe I ever thought this woman suitable enough to live with us. "I was told you'd say that." She turned, picked up the lantern and strode up the stairs and out of the cellar. The lock tumbled.

"Why'd she leave?" Gus hopped off the bed again but didn't advance. There was no point. With the door locked, there was no possible escape.

"I don't know. Hopefully Gordon will return before she does."

"Don't hold your breath, Charlie. We could be in the Scottish Highlands, for all we know. If we do escape, how will we get home?"

"I doubt we're that far from London. I don't feel either hungry or thirsty, which means we couldn't have been unconscious for long. I would say we're somewhere in the city."

The lock tumbled again and the door opened. Mrs. Webb came down the stairs, the lantern in one hand and a pistol in the other. I gasped. Gus moved in front of me.

"That's very brave but rather foolish of you, Gus," she said with a smile. "It's not Miss Holloway I plan to shoot. Why would I do that when she's the one who's going to summon my husband?"

"W...what?" he spluttered.

"I'm going to shoot *you*, you big idiot. Why do you think I went to all that trouble to bring you along? I simply drugged the others, but decided to take you too, in case she refused to do as I asked. Refuse again, Miss Holloway, and I'll shoot him."

"Don't!"

She smiled. She knew she had me. "Move a little away, Gus. You wouldn't want me to miss you and get her now, would you?"

Gus hesitated then hopped to his right until he was well away from me.

"Listen to me, Mrs. Webb." My voice trembled. My heart thundered. We could no longer delay her in the hope that Gordon would return. I had no doubt that she would shoot Gus if I didn't do as she wanted. "Raising a spirit is not safe. It should only be done in extreme circumstances, and only when I can be sure nothing will go wrong."

"Nothing will go wrong. We're good people, Miss Holloway, although you probably don't believe that at this moment."

"You're quite right there."

"My husband was a little eccentric, but all brilliant men are. He helps people. Or he used to, before he died." Her face crumpled before she reigned in her emotions and schooled her features again. "I only wish to punish his killer."

"Killer?" I whispered. "He was murdered?"

She nodded and pointed the gun at Gus. He winced but otherwise went very still. "For no reason at all that I could see. It was horrible. Quite horrible." She placed a hand to her heart before returning it to the pistol again with the other. "I want him to avenge his death, Miss Holloway, and for that, I need you. Only he knows his killer's identity."

I had a very bad feeling about this. How did the widow of a murdered man come to know about necromancers and, in particular, me? "Mrs. Webb, was your husband magical?"

She tilted her head to the side. Her sad smile softened her gaze. "Yes, he is. Was. He can—could—move things just by thinking about it."

I closed my eyes against the nausea rising up my throat, the sick worry settling into my chest. If I summoned him and he entered a body, he might know how to override my control like Estelle Pearson had. But if I didn't do it, Mrs. Webb would shoot Gus.

He swore under his breath. "Don't do it, Charlie. It'll go wrong."

The woman I knew as Mrs. Webb gave an uncharacteristically inelegant snort. "The only thing that will go wrong will be me shooting you, if she doesn't do as I say."

I opened my eyes. "Your name's not Webb, is it?"

"It's Merry Drinkwater."

Drinkwater. One of the murdered supernaturals had been Reginald Drinkwater.

"Merry. Ha!" Gus must have worked it out when I did, because he didn't sound surprised.

"My husband's name is Reginald Rochester Drinkwater." She adjusted her grip on the pistol. "Summon his spirit, Miss Holloway. Now! Or I will shoot."

I swallowed. "Reginald—"

"No!" Gus shuffled toward me.

The gun went off. The shot deafened me for a second. Its echo seemed to reverberate around the walls for an age.

"Gus!" I fell to my knees beside his body.

He moved, thank God, and groaned. "I'm alive."

I glanced up at Mrs. Webb. She looked even paler, if that were possible, and her hands shook. "You almost killed him!" Blood seeped through the rent in his sleeve near his shoulder. "He has to see a doctor."

"He has to stay here." She waggled the pistol at us. "Summon my husband, Miss Holloway. Do it now, or I will shoot again."

I swallowed. Gus protested, but I shut out his voice. "Reginald Rochester Drinkwater, I summon your spirit here to this realm. Come to us."

The mist came from a different side of the room from which Gordon had arrived. It flew past us, dashing back and forth like a frightened rabbit, before regaining control and settling nearby. Reginald Drinkwater was of middling age with a slender build and intelligent eyes behind spectacles. Intelligent, cool eyes. If I didn't know he'd been shot, the gaping hole in his chest would have told me how he'd died. He smiled when he saw his wife but it quickly slipped away at the sight of the pistol. He frowned at her.

"Good afternoon, Mr. Drinkwater," I said to the spirit. "My name is Charlotte Holloway and I'm a necromancer."

"A what?"

"Necromancer. I can raise the dead."

"You summoned me?"

"I did, at your wife's request. She forced me to." I indicated Gus, now sitting up and trying to inspect his wound.

His eyes widened. "Merry?"

"She can't hear you. Only I can."

"I underestimated her." He smiled. "Didn't know she had all this in her."

He was proud? I swallowed down the bile as it threatened to rise up my throat again.

"Tell him that he must search for his body," Mrs. Drinkwater said.

"I don't need to repeat what you say. He can hear you."

"Reginald." She didn't quite look directly at him, but near enough. "Listen to me. I had you summoned so you could avenge your death. I know you must want to."

"Oh yes." His tone chilled my blood.

"You must find your body and...go into it. Then you'll be able to walk around again as a living man."

Reginald eyed me. "Is this true?"

I stood very still.

The ghost swooped at me. "Is. This. True?"

Mrs. Drinkwater pointed the gun at Gus again.

"You will be able to walk around," I said. "But you'll still be dead, not alive. The body is merely a vessel for your spirit."

As soon as he disappeared to find his body and Mrs. Drinkwater left, I'd give the order to send him back. I didn't need to be within hearing range of him.

"You're buried in Old Brompton," Merry Drinkwater went on. "It was a beautiful ceremony." She smiled sadly. "Go, Reginald. Go and find whoever it was who did this."

He lifted a hand and patted his wife's shoulder. "Good girl." She felt nothing and simply stared straight ahead.

"Mr. Drinkwater, tell me who killed you," I urged. "There are people looking into your death. I can pass on the name or description of your murderer—"

"The police are incompetent." He flew up the stairs to the door.

"Not the police." Hysteria pitched my voice high. "Others from a special organization."

He shook his head and the mist dissolved. He was gone.

I plopped onto the bed and swore.

"Language, young lady!" Mrs. Drinkwater scowled.

I managed to refrain from telling her where she could shove her hypocrisy—just. I looked down at Gus. "Are you all right?"

He nodded. "He's gone?"

"Yes. Mrs. Drinkwater, you've done a very foolish thing by telling your husband about his body. I could have seen justice served for him by giving the name of his killer to Mr. Fitzroy."

"It's not the same as doing it yourself. Not as satisfying." She set the gun down on the floor beside her lantern. "Come over here, Miss Holloway, away from Gus."

"Why?"

"Just do it!"

I hopped across the floor to her. She reached into her skirt pocket and withdrew something. It wasn't until she slapped her hand against my mouth that I realized it was a gag to keep me quiet. To stop me sending Reginald's spirit back.

I shut my mouth. I twisted and struggled, throwing my weight into her.

"Keep still!" She hit me hard across the jaw, but still I kept my mouth shut.

Gus protested and I saw that he'd made progress toward us, but not enough. He was still too far away to do anything.

She pinched my nose. It was no use now. Her grip was too tight and slowly, slowly the air leached out of me until my chest burned.

I opened my mouth to gasp in a breath and she shoved the gag inside. Before I could spit it out, she'd wrapped another cloth strip around my head, covering my mouth, to hold the gag in place. I swallowed reflexively and almost choked. I coughed violently and fell to my knees. Snot and tears streamed down my face. I couldn't control them. Couldn't catch my breath. Surely she wouldn't kill me. Not like this.

She stood back to admire her handiwork. "I know that keeping you silent will mean you can't control my husband's spirit or send him back. I could kill you, but I'm not a violent woman, nor do I have any intention of having my husband here forever. But until he exacts his revenge, you must be quiet."

This woman knew everything about my magic. But how, when her husband hadn't even known what a necromancer did?

CHAPTER 8

"Charlie! Charlie!"

I could hear Gus shuffling toward me, and then a thump and a grunt as he fell. My vision cleared a little, and I was able to breathe normally again.

Mrs. Drinkwater picked up the pistol and aimed it at Gus. "I can't have you removing her gag. Up the stairs. Now."

"I ain't goin' nowhere." Gus sat, his legs stretched out before him, doing his best to look immovable.

Mrs. Drinkwater aimed the pistol at his head. "Very well, but I no longer need you. You've outlived your usefulness. While I don't wish to kill anyone, I will do so if necessary."

I tried to encourage Gus to move, but my shout came out garbled and only made me descend into a fit of choking coughs again.

"I'm goin', I'm goin'." I wasn't sure if his grumbling assent was directed at our captor or me.

I watched him jump up the stairs, Mrs Drinkwater behind him. He managed it without falling, but he was breathing heavily by the time they reached the top.

She shut the door and locked it. I was alone.

The cloth around my head bit into my cheeks. I rubbed my shoulder against it, but it was too tight and wouldn't budge. Damn her. Damn both the Drinkwaters.

I didn't know if attempting to speak the words to send a spirit back with a gag in my mouth would work, but I tried anyway. It came out muffled and I had no way of knowing if I'd been successful.

I spent the next little while alternating between trying to remove the gag again and untying my bonds, but it was useless. All I managed to achieve was another debilitating coughing fit followed by a flood of angry tears that made me gulp and choke on the gag.

I lay on the cold flagstone floor on my side and stared at the door at the top of the stairs. Despite willing it to open, it remained firmly shut. Where was Gordon? Why hadn't he returned yet? How much time had passed?

The only comfort was the knowledge that Drinkwater was going after the man who'd killed him. If his wife could be believed, he wasn't a danger to anyone else. As soon as he had his revenge, she would let us go and I could send him back.

I sat up and scooted across the floor to the bed where I waited. And waited. My stomach growled and I needed to use the privy. The skin on my cheeks felt raw from the chafing cloth and drool seeped from the corners of my mouth. It took effort not to choke or cough reflexively.

Finally the door opened and Reginald Drinkwater stood in his body, candelabra in hand. The flickering flames picked out his bloodless face, his soulless eyes, and the gaping hole in his chest. He descended the stairs, alone. Neither Gus nor his wife was with him.

"Good evening," he said. "The deed has been done. My murderer is dead."

I arched my brows.

"He deserved it." His grim smile was made even grimmer thanks to the deathly pall of his lips.

I arched my brows higher and tried to say, "Why did he kill you?"

"I don't know his name," he said, misunderstanding my muffled words. "I'd never met him before. I only knew where to find him because he made the mistake of talking to himself after he shot me. 'Another successful job deserves an ale at The Feathers,' he'd said. The Feathers is a rough pub in Clerkenwell. I simply bought myself an ale, bided my time and waited for my murderer to enter. I lured him into the lane out the back with the promise of a job for him."

Job. He was a hired gunman? Who would hire another to kill Drinkwater?

Someone who didn't want blood on their hands.

I twisted and wiggled my numbed fingers.

"I can't release you until you promise not to send me back," he said.

No. Oh no. Why couldn't he just return to his afterlife? I shook my head.

The muscles in his face hardened. His lips pressed together. If blood flowed through his body, a vein would have bulged in his throat or temple. "I'm not going to harm anyone. I simply want to continue with my work." He paced from wall to wall of the cellar, his booted footsteps loud on the stones. "Imagine if I can achieve my objective and transfer my magic into the limbs I create? Imagine the benefits to mankind!" He stopped pacing very close to me. I swayed back, away from the stench of decay. "My magic still works, you know. Death hasn't affected it."

He frowned at me and I suddenly felt myself lifting off the bed. He was levitating me! I continued to rise and rise until my head skimmed the ceiling. I held myself very still in case movement broke his concentration. It was terrifying and yet oddly thrilling too. I wondered how long he could keep me up here, and if there were limitations with an object's weight.

With a derisive snort, he lowered me again. "Impressive, isn't it?"

Once I felt the mattress beneath me, I scooted away from him, even though I knew it would do no good. With his power, he could pick me up and slam me against the wall.

"I would very much like to untie you, but I can't without your promise that you won't send me back," he said. "Do I have it?"

Reneging on a promise didn't sit well with me, but I saw no other choice. I nodded.

"Good girl. A wise decision. As soon as I find a way to harness my magic and transfer it into the limbs, I'll return to my afterlife. But not until then."

Harness? How could something so ethereal and wild be rounded up like a flock of sheep?

He set the candelabra down on the floor and began untying my ankles. "Once my legacy has been established, I can go in peace. I will be immortalized in the scientific community, and outside it too, I hope."

Ah, yes, immortalization. The lure of it drove many madmen.

My feet and hands now released, he removed the gag. I spat out the ball of cloth from my mouth and swallowed several times and rubbed my jaw. It ached and my tongue felt twice its size, but there seemed to be no lasting damage.

"You may go," he said.

I couldn't believe it. I was actually going to walk free. Despite my stiff limbs, I hurried up the steps and flung open the door.

"Don't forget your promise!" he called after me.

"I won't," I croaked.

I found myself in the service rooms of a modest sized house. Across the corridor was the kitchen. To left and right were closed doors. Was Gus behind one? I couldn't leave without him and the house was large enough that it would take several minutes to search every room. There was no sign of Mrs. Drinkwater, however, but Mr. Drinkwater's plodding footsteps echoed on the cellar stairs. He was coming up. I had only seconds.

"Go back to your afterl—"

"Stop!" Mrs. Drinkwater stood in the kitchen doorway, the pistol aimed at me. "How did you get out?" Her gaze darted past my shoulder. "Reggie! You're back."

My stomach plunged. *Don't tell him. Please don't tell him.*

"What are you doing, Merry?" Drinkwater asked. "I let her go."

"Charlie! Charlie, is that you?" Gus's shout came from behind a closed door to my left. Thank God he was alive.

"Gus! Yes, it's me."

"Are you all right?"

"I'm quite safe." I eyed Mrs. Drinkwater, and she lowered the pistol.

"It's done then?" she asked her husband. "Your murderer is dead?"

Drinkwater came to stand beside me. "It's done. I'll be in my workshop if you need me. Goodbye, miss. Do not forget your promise."

Mrs. Drinkwater frowned. "Your workshop? Reggie...you want to stay?"

"Of course. I have much to do. The commission may have fallen through, but that is of no consequence."

Commission?

"Then..." She glanced at me. "Then why did you release her? I interrupted her casting the spell to send you back. She won't allow you to remain, you know."

Those blank, dead eyes turned to me. "You gave me your word." His grinding tone froze my blood.

I swallowed. "Mrs. Drinkwater is mistaken. I was simply...talking to myself."

She stiffened. "I'm no fool. I overheard you." To her husband, she said, "Now that you have your revenge, you ought to go back anyway. You don't want to anger anyone up there." She eyed the ceiling.

"No one will be angry, particularly when they see what I can achieve after a few more months here. My dear, I'm close to a breakthrough. I know I am."

She winced. "You weren't all that close before your death."

"I beg your pardon! How would *you* know?"

She swallowed. "Reggie, I do think you ought to go. Besides, we can't keep Miss Holloway and Gus shut up in the cellar for weeks, or months, or however long it takes for you to succeed. For one thing, the first time I remove the gag to feed her, she'll say the words to send you back. Unless she's complicit, it's hopeless, and I can assure you, she will not be complicit."

He shrugged. "Then shoot her."

I gasped and stumbled away from him, but he caught my elbow and pushed me roughly forward. "Go on. Shoot."

His wife's jaw dropped. Her eyes bulged. "I can't do that! That's murder."

"You were going to kill her friend earlier."

"I only told them that to frighten her into summoning you. I wasn't really going to go through with it."

He clicked his tongue. "Weak."

"Reggie, please. Don't ask that of me. They'll hang me for it. I missed on purpose before. I'm really quite a good shot with this thing," she said with an apologetic smile.

Well then, if she wasn't going to shoot anyone... "Return to your afterlife, Mr—"

He struck out. Long fingers circled my throat and squeezed. "Shut up!"

"Charlie!" Gus's shout was almost drowned out by the blood thudding between my ears.

I couldn't utter a sound. Not even a squeak. It felt like everything in my throat was closing under the pressure from Drinkwater's fingers. He was much stronger in death than life, and fearless too. Besides, he'd already killed once...why not again?

I thrashed at him, tried to shove him off and kick him, and when that failed, I scrabbled at his fingers, scratching and digging into his rotting flesh with my nails. I struck bone.

"Reggie! Stop!"

Drinkwater didn't stop. My lungs screamed for air. It felt like a ton of bricks pressed on my chest. Silent tears streaked from the corners of my eyes, down my cheeks.

A gunshot deafened me. Drinkwater's body jerked, and his fingers loosened.

"I'm already dead. Foolish woman," he added with a mutter that could be barely heard over Gus's shouts and bangs against the closed door.

Drinkwater's weaker grip allowed me to draw in priceless air. I wasn't far enough away to speak all the words necessary to send him back, however. I needed a few feet between us at least or he'd catch me. I gasped in a few strong breaths then smashed my fist into his face. His head snapped back. He couldn't feel pain so stomping on his toe wouldn't do anything, nor would kneeing him in the nether regions. I had to use brute force to send him off balance. Unfortunately, with my size and his superior strength, brute force wasn't something I possessed.

Nevertheless, I threw myself at him, swinging my fists to distract him with my punches. It worked. He stumbled and swayed backward. Unfortunately, he also caught me and used me as an anchor.

"Damned girl." Ignoring my fists and kicks, his fingers closed around my throat again.

"Reggie, please! You can't kill her. She's done nothing wrong!"

"You've been a good wife to bring me back, my dear. Now don't spoil it with your foolish sympathies. Think of what I can achieve! I must finish my work. The girl's life is unimportant when you consider the greater good."

She nodded numbly, like a puppet on a string. I tried to speak, to implore her help, but no sound came out of my mouth, and she simply stood there, her stunned gaze on my face as she watched me die.

Darkness crept in from the edges of my vision. I felt my life slipping away with every slowing pound of my heart. Somewhere in the recesses of my mind I heard Gus's shouts and thumps, but he seemed so far away.

Another voice joined his, high pitched and feminine. I didn't recognize it, nor could I see who'd arrived.

Suddenly Drinkwater's hands were ripped from me. I fell to my knees and clasped my throat. I sucked in sweet, sweet air. Noise surrounded me—shouts from a number of different sources, and the slap of skin against skin, and the snap of...bones?

Mrs. Drinkwater knelt near me and peered into my face. She was shaking. "If you want to live, you have to get away. Now. Your friend is gallant but she is merely a woman."

I glanced up to see a woman dressed in a crimson and peacock blue dress fighting Drinkwater. She was smaller than him and her skirts hindered her kicks, but she was nimbler and the better fighter. Her punches struck true whereas his were wild and had little effect when they connected. I didn't need to see the pock marked face to know this woman was dead. Her strength alone was indication enough.

It took a moment for my addled, air-starved brain to put all the pieces together. The dead woman must be *Gordon*.

She—he—thumped Drinkwater, over and over, with well-timed punches. There was nothing feminine about her movements, from the way she balanced herself with her feet apart, to the way she disregarded her breasts as she slammed into Drinkwater, driving him into the wall.

I got to my feet, eyeing Mrs. Drinkwater carefully, but she made no move to raise the pistol. She looked defeated, numb, and somewhat lost. The competent woman who'd presented herself at Lichfield Towers was gone.

"She's dead too?" she asked me in a small voice.

I nodded. "Release Gus." I scrambled far away from the two fighters, just as Gordon slammed into the wall.

Drinkwater hadn't touched him. Gordon hit the wall again and again, like a ragdoll thrown at full force. He was at the mercy of Drinkwater's powers. And so was I.

Drinkwater turned to me.

Just as I was at the mercy of his magic, he was at the mercy of mine.

"Return to your afterlife, Reginald Drinkwater." I spoke the words in a rush and hoped it was fast enough. "I release you."

He stumbled to his knees. His bloodless lips pulled back in a snarl. "No! No, I'm not finished!" His body slumped forward, smashing his face against the floor. The white mist drifted out and up toward the ceiling. He hovered a moment, in which he growled his fury at me, before disappearing altogether.

Gordon slumped against the wall. If he'd been alive, he would be drawing in great gasps of air, but he didn't need to breathe. He pushed his hair off his face and smiled. Most of the body's teeth were missing and those that were not were yellow.

"Charlie! Charlie!" Gus threw his arms around me in a hug so fierce I could only gurgle in response.

"Easy now," Gordon said in a husky feminine voice that I could never associate with him. "Let her up."

Gus pulled away and patted my arms. "You all right?"

"I am. You?"

He nodded.

Thank God. I looked to Mrs. Drinkwater, standing near the door of the storeroom where Gus had been imprisoned. She swiped at her tears and handed the pistol to Gus. She was as meek as a mouse.

"All's well?" Gordon asked, marveling at his long gray hair. He stroked it, pulling out a clump. The body looked quite fresh. She must have only just died.

I suddenly giggled, partly in relief and partly because he looked ridiculous in the garish dress with feminine features. "You couldn't find a man's body?"

"This was all the mortuary had."

"Isn't the cemetery nearby?" I asked Mrs. Drinkwater. "Isn't that where your husband found his body?"

"The one on Old Brompton Road is few streets away to the east," she said.

"Ah. I went west." Gordon picked up his skirts and pirouetted. "Don't suppose I can stay in this body for the rest of the night. Just to see what it's like to—"

"No!" Three shouts drowned him out.

He held up his hands. "Very well. Walk back with me to the mortuary, Miss Charlie?"

"Of course." I turned to Mrs. Drinkwater. "Your husband's spirit has returned. Do not try to raise him again."

She nodded quickly. "I won't. I don't know how, anyway."

"If I were you, I'd get out of London," Gus muttered. "Death'll be furious when he finds out what you did."

Mrs. Drinkwater's lips trembled.

"Don't frighten her," I said. "Lincoln's not vindictive. He won't harm her."

Gus merely grunted. He took my hand and steered me along the corridor. "I hate this place."

"You must remove your husband's body," I said over my shoulder to Mrs. Drinkwater. "Return him to the cemetery tonight. Rest assured, Mr. Fitzroy won't come seeking vengeance. He's above that. You have my word."

She wiped at a tear that slid from her eye and looked down at her husband's limp form. I didn't know how she would manage to move him, and I didn't care. I just wanted to see that Gordon returned the body he'd borrowed and left too. I'd had enough of lingering spirits for one day.

The dark, miserable night embraced us. I wasn't sure of the hour, but nobody was out in the misty rain. Without so much as a cloak to huddle into, I was soon wet through to my skin and as cold as ice. I couldn't wait to get back to Lichfield and sit by the hearth with a bowl of Cook's soup and Lincoln's warm touch. He must be going out of his mind with worry.

***

Seth scooped me up, only setting me down when Cook demanded he have a turn hugging me. "Thank God you're back safe," Seth muttered. "We were so worried."

"Aye." Cook frowned as he studied the bruises around my throat. "You hurt bad?"

"Not really. I'm mostly tired, and very hungry."

"You need soup."

I kissed his cheek. "You're wonderful."

Gus thrust out his hands, exposing his bloodied wrists. "What about me? I was abducted too *and* shot, and no one's givin' me soup."

Seth shrugged then enveloped his friend in a hug until Gus shoved him off, only to have Cook follow suit.

"Stop it, you lump o' lard." Gus grinned, however, and allowed Seth to inspect the wound at his shoulder.

Cook chuckled and retrieved two bowls from the cupboard. I sidled closer to the stove and its delicious heat. "Is Lincoln here?"

"He's out looking for you." Seth shook his head and sighed. "He's been in and out most of the day, hoping you'd show up again here. I'm sure he'll walk in that door soon."

A set of footsteps echoed along the corridor, but it was only Doyle. "Miss Holloway, Mr. Gus! I'm so glad to see you both again."

"Thank you, Doyle. Are you all right?"

He nodded. "Cook and I were drugged with some awful tea, but there appear to be no lingering effects."

Cook handed me a bowl. "Aside from going deaf when Fitzroy shouted at us, wanting to know what happened and getting mad when we couldn't give answers."

I drew in a deep breath as he ladled broth into my bowl. "Where is he looking?"

"That's the problem, he didn't know where to start," Seth said. "The Mrs. Webb employed by the Powell's is not the same as the housekeeper we knew as Mrs. Webb. No surprise there."

"She tricked us."

"Don't take it to heart." He put his arm around my shoulders and kissed the top of my head. "So who was she really, and why did she take you?"

"And how did you get away?" Doyle chimed in.

Gus and I briefly filled them in on some of the particulars, leaving out all the supernatural elements so as not to overwhelm Doyle. Cook swore several times, as did Seth, to a lesser extent, but Doyle was the perfect butler and merely made sour faces and horrified little gasps.

"Diabolical," he muttered.

"It is," I said. "And if this sort of thing concerns you, Doyle, then I'm afraid we'll have to let you go. Dangerous incidents happen with alarming frequency around here."

"Thank you for your frankness. I'll keep that in mind." It was not, I noticed, an answer one way or another.

I hadn't forgotten that he was under suspicion either. Mrs. Drinkwater had been helped by someone who knew we needed a housekeeper. Doyle might seem innocent and concerned, but I hadn't ruled him out.

Lincoln still hadn't returned by the time I finished my soup, so after overseeing the cleaning and dressing of Gus's wound, I retired to my rooms to freshen up. A knock at my door several minutes later sent my heart tripping over itself.

It was only Seth. "Don't look so disappointed," he said. "May I come in?"

"Do you want to know what really happened, now that we're alone?"

"Gus already told me."

"You've grown quite serious," I said. "What's wrong?"

"The committee came shortly after we discovered your disappearance."

I screwed up my nose. "Why?"

"Fitzroy sent messages to each of them demanding to know every last detail about the two supernatural deaths."

"He assumed my abduction was related to the murders?"

"He did. And in his correspondence, he mentioned your abduction, and demanded they come to Lichfield immediately for questioning."

"Were they helpful?"

"They gave no further information, and then proceeded to tell him that they were right and he was wrong, and you should be sent away."

I sat down on an armchair near the fire with a resigned sigh. "I expect that didn't go down too well."

"Fitzroy went very quiet."

"He's more dangerous when he's quiet." It meant he was shutting himself off emotionally. An unemotional Lincoln was a ruthless Lincoln.

"Charlie..." He sat opposite and rested his elbows on his knees. He bowed his head, sending his blond locks tumbling over his forehead into his eyes. "The committee will probably try to contact you now that you've returned safe and sound. Julia indicated to me that they'll try to convince you to leave of your own accord."

"How?"

"By telling you it's best for the ministry if you're not here. And best for Fitzroy too."

I slumped back and rubbed my aching temples. "They think I'm being selfish."

He looked up through the curtain of his hair.

"Do you think I'm being selfish, Seth?"

"No!"

"Should I leave? For Lincoln's sake?"

He sat up straight and squared his shoulders. "No. Definitely not. I hate to think what he'd turn into if you left. He was a cold block of ice before you arrived, but these last few weeks have seen him thaw. You've humanized him."

To hear it put like that made my heart swell, but I felt compelled to defend Lincoln. "I'm not sure I can take all the credit. I simply brought out what was already there, only deeply buried."

He shrugged. "I wanted to warn you so you can prepare yourself. Don't take what they say to heart."

I smiled and was about to thank him when Lincoln strode in.

CHAPTER 9

I barely had time to register his presence before he lifted me out of the chair and drew me into a fierce hug. He buried one hand in my hair, holding my head against his chest. The rapid, erratic beat of his heart drowned out everything else, so that I didn't hear Seth leave. When Lincoln set me down again, we were alone with the door closed.

He held me at arm's length and checked me over. His stormy gaze settled on the bruises at my throat then lifted to my face, questioning.

"It's the only injury," I told him. "And it's not too sore."

He nodded. Swallowed. I was acutely aware that he hadn't yet spoken.

His thumb stroked my jaw and he angled his head to kiss me. What began as a chaste kiss quickly turned into one of longing that told me how worried he'd been. There was no need for words between us. All the built-up fear and his immense relief poured out of him in that kiss.

I circled my arms around his neck and held him as tightly as he held me. I wanted to comfort him as much as his presence comforted me, and for several minutes we simply cherished one another's company.

And then, as if he'd doused that part of himself, he drew away and regarded me through eyes that were as black and bleak as a deep lake in winter. "What happened?"

"What has Gus already told you?" I asked.

"Nothing. I saw he was back and he said you were up here. I came immediately. Who was the woman calling herself Mrs. Webb and where did she take you? Why?"

"Mrs. Webb was in fact Mrs. Drinkwater."

A muscle in his jaw pulsed. "I didn't consider the victims. She wanted you to raise her husband?"

"So he could get revenge on his killer, although I think she simply missed him. She is somewhat dependent on her husband's good opinion of her. I think she felt lost after his death, alone."

"She forced you to raise his spirit by threatening Gus?"

I nodded.

It was some time before he spoke again, and I feared he was warring with himself about whether to tell me I should have sacrificed Gus.

"I raised Drinkwater's spirit and was then gagged so I couldn't send him back. He re-entered his body and killed his murderer before returning to the house."

He stroked his thumb across my lower lip. His steely façade slipped, revealing a flicker of raw emotion before schooling it again. "He knew his killer?"

"He'd never seen him before, but the fellow mentioned going to The Feathers to celebrate a successful commission, so Drinkwater waited for him there. He must have been a hired gunman, but he didn't divulge who he worked for before Drinkwater killed him."

Most people wouldn't have noticed the effect this news had on Lincoln, but I spotted the telltale tightening of his lips.

"His wife wanted to send him back to his afterlife again," I went on, "but he decided to stay. There was a fight, and while he was distracted, I spoke the words to return his spirit. Mrs. Drinkwater took care of his body."

"You overpowered him alone or did Gus help?"

"Gus was locked in the storeroom at the time, and I'll never have enough training to teach me to overpower a reanimated body. We had help from Gordon Thackery."

His brows shot up.

"I summoned him as soon as I woke up in the cellar. He found himself a body and returned to assist us in that guise."

He gave a firm nod. "Thackery was a good choice."

It was as much praise as I would get. It was enough.

"Lincoln, she knew so much about me. Somebody must have helped her. I suspected Doyle, since he knew we needed a housekeeper, but it couldn't have been him. He isn't aware of my necromancy. Or is he?"

"Seth wouldn't have told him."

"I hate to say this, but it must be someone on the committee."

He dragged his hand through his hair and stared at the fireplace. After a moment, he stoked the coals. Each thrust of the fire iron was more vigorous than the last until I stopped him by placing my hand over his.

"Sit with me by the fire," I said gently.

"I can't." He returned the iron to the stand. "I have to go out."

"But it's late." After midnight, according to the clock on the mantel.

"Go to bed, Charlie."

"I'd rather sit by the hearth and fall asleep in your arms."

He pecked the top of my head. "Goodnight."

"Goodnight!" I threw my hands in the air. "How is it a good night when you're going out and I'll probably have night terrors."

"I'll look in on you when I return if I hear you."

I thrust my hands on my hips. I'd been looking forward to sitting with him, being held and comforted by him, and he was heading out again! "Are you going to question the committee members?"

He turned and strode to the door. I raced past him and stood in front of it.

"Do not shut me out, Lincoln. Tell me where you're going."

"You won't approve."

He mustn't be going to see the committee members then. "Mrs. Drinkwater?"

His gaze shifted away.

"Lincoln! Don't harm her. She isn't the villain here."

"I beg to differ."

"You should speak to her to find out who helped her, granted, but do it gently, and in daylight. I'm sure she'll tell you if you ask nicely."

"I have to do this now," he ground out through a clenched jaw. "And I certainly can't be *nice*."

"You need to calm down first."

"I *need* to do this *now*." He stretched out his fingers then bunched them into fists. "Move aside."

I folded my arms. "The Drinkwaters are victims. The poor woman just lost her husband."

"She kidnapped you and held you captive for hours, and you feel sympathy for her?"

"She didn't hurt me, or Gus, and she could have." I wasn't sure when my feelings toward her changed from anger to sympathy. Perhaps when I realized she'd only tried to bring back the man she loved and had never planned to kill anyone. Perhaps I would have acted just as irrationally in her position.

He thumped his palms flat on the door, either side of my head. He leaned in, but I was under no illusion that he would kiss me. His temper was written in every hard plane of his face. "She is the reason I was sick with worry all day. I don't like worrying. It prevents me from thinking clearly, and that makes me useless." He stepped back. "Move."

I lifted my chin.

He grasped my arms, picked me up and set me down again, out of the way. He jerked the door open.

"Don't kill her!" I called after him.

"I'll do as I see fit."

I watched him stride along the corridor to the stairs and listened until I could no longer hear his light steps. He wouldn't kill her. He simply wanted answers.

If I repeated that over and over perhaps I might eventually convince myself.

***

Lincoln hadn't returned by the time I awoke in the morning. According to Doyle, his bed hadn't been slept in, although that didn't mean Lincoln hadn't returned, merely that he hadn't been to bed.

I felt too restless to sit in the parlor alone and present a show of being a lady for the butler's sake, so I ignored Doyle's disapproving frown and ate breakfast in the kitchen. Afterward, I joined Seth in the stables, only to be summoned back inside when Doyle announced we had a caller.

"Mr. Andrew Buchanan to see you, miss."

"Buchanan!" Seth and I exchanged glances. "Is he here to see me or Mr. Fitzroy?"

"You, miss."

Seth followed me inside, and we were joined by Gus and Doyle. It would seem I wasn't to be left alone, even with someone we knew. Not that I trusted Buchanan. Not in the least. I mentally added him to my list of people who may have helped Mrs. Drinkwater kidnap me, although I couldn't think why he'd do it.

"Miss Holloway." He stood with his hands behind his back and bowed upon my entry. When he straightened, I saw that he appeared fully recovered from his ordeal in Bedlam's insane asylum. The color had returned to his cheeks, and the shadows had been erased from his eyes. He gave me a lazy smile that would have melted most female hearts, but not mine. I knew him well enough to dislike him.

"Good morning, Mr. Buchanan. You're looking in fine spirits."

"Thanks to you." He cleared his throat and glanced pointedly at each of my chaperones.

"You know Seth and Gus, and you've just met our new butler, Doyle."

Doyle dutifully bowed.

Buchanan acknowledged only Seth with a curt nod. "Good to see this old place getting some staff finally. If you're in need of maids, please allow me to direct you to several I know. All good girls, I assure you."

Behind me, either Seth or Gus snorted. I, however, was intrigued with how much he knew of our domestic situation.

"Do you know someone who will make a suitable housekeeper?" I asked.

"Maids only. You'll want someone staid for a housekeeper, and I don't know any women who'd fit that description." He smirked. "None from the serving classes, anyway."

I believed him. I couldn't see him even knowing a woman like Mrs. Drinkwater, let alone collaborating with her. Helping her was of no benefit to him.

"I have something for you." Buchanan produced a small package that he'd been holding behind his back. It was tied with a red bow.

"What's this?"

"Open it and see."

I didn't take it. "Is this a gift, Mr. Buchanan?"

His smile became strained. "Yes. Hence the bow."

"I can't accept it."

"You must. I owe you."

"You don't. Besides, you've already thanked us."

"I wanted to give you something that truly showed my appreciation for your efforts. I might still be in Bedlam, if it weren't for you."

"Then perhaps you ought to give Mr. Fitzroy a gift too, as well as Seth and Gus. We all worked together to free you."

He shifted his weight and the color rose in his cheeks. He cleared his throat. "You see, the thing is, I never treated them the way I treated you. Once I realized that I ignored you upon our first meeting, I...I felt terrible. I wanted to make up for it and show you that I've turned over a new leaf."

"Have you?"

"Most assuredly." He puffed out his chest. "I'm a new man. No more gambling for me."

There was another snort from the men, and this time I was sure it was Gus. Buchanan's nostrils flared.

"I'm glad to hear it," I said quickly.

He held out the package again. "I know you're engaged to Fitzroy, but I don't think he'll mind. Please take it, Miss Holloway."

I accepted the gift, not because I wanted to appease him, but because I wanted him to stay and talk to me. At least until I managed to get some answers out of him.

I sat and asked Doyle to bring tea. Gus and Seth craned their necks to watch as I untied the ribbon and unwrapped the gift. It was a book of poems by Wordsworth. "Thank you."

"Julia said you like to read."

"I do. And it's a very handsome book." The pages were thick and edged with gold, the cover a deep red leather stamped with the title, also in gold.

He smiled that lazy, charming smile of his again. I could well believe he'd turned over a new leaf. Gone was the sneering lift of his lip, the half-closed eyes, as if he couldn't be bothered to open them fully. He sat straight and tall in the chair opposite, whereas I expected him to sprawl. He seemed so changed that I hated to tell him that, while I liked to read novels, I didn't particularly like poetry.

I set the book on the table and tried to think of something to say. I couldn't. The way he stared at me unnerved me. The book was most likely a ruse, but why this sudden interest? Was he interested in me or my necromancy?

"Forgive me for being a little flustered this morning," I said, "I've recently returned from my own ordeal."

"Oh? Nothing too awful, I hope."

I decided to tell him the truth, or some of it. If I wanted to know if he was involved, then I needed to be direct. "I was kidnapped, as it happens."

"Good lord. Were you harmed?" He did seem quite surprised; concerned, too.

"I'm all right now, thank you. Lady Harcourt didn't mention it?"

"She did not. Was this related to your ministry?"

"Most likely, but it's difficult to know for sure," I lied. "I'm surprised she didn't speak about it."

"She doesn't see fit to keep me up to date with everything in her life. I suspect she sees the ministry as something of her own. I have, after all, only just learned of its existence. I don't expect her to inform me of everything. Yet."

"You want to become more involved in ministry affairs?"

He lifted one shoulder. "Why not? It's my birthright."

"Actually, it's your older brother's birthright."

"He has no interest. I do. I find the occult business fascinating. Your magic, for example...what's it called again?"

I eyed the door to make sure Doyle hadn't returned. "Necromancy."

"Necromancy. Fascinating stuff."

This was a new development that I hadn't anticipated. Andrew Buchanan hadn't been considered for the committee position vacated upon his father's death because Lord Harcourt didn't think his second son responsible enough. Based on previous encounters, I tended to agree.

"The committee is merely an advisory body, with no real power," I told him in an attempt to discourage him. "Mr. Fitzroy is the leader and makes all the decisions."

"The committee placed him in the position of leader."

"No. An old prophecy saw to that." I waylaid further discussion on the matter by steering the conversation toward his stepmother. "How is Lady Harcourt? I ought to visit her and thank her for her concern. She called upon Mr. Fitzroy when she learned of my disappearance yesterday, you see."

"She did?" His sly smile reminded me of the Buchanan of old. "Be careful with my dear step-mama. She has sharp claws and likes to dig them into things she believes belong to her. My father found himself thoroughly hooked."

"Are you warning me because you think I have something of hers?"

He stroked his lips with the side of his finger. I hadn't forgotten that this man had been in love with Lady Harcourt before she became his stepmother, when she'd been a dancer at The Alhambra. Was that what this visit was about? His attempt to find out if Lincoln and I were in fact engaged and Buchanan was safe to pursue a dalliance with her again? That family's affairs were dirtier than a pigsty.

"I expected her to come to your fiancé for help, as it happens," he said.

"Is she in trouble?"

"She's troubled, if that's what you mean, and I've noticed that she likes to involve your fiancé in her little problems whenever possible."

"Go on," I said tightly. He clearly wanted to tattle. I was beginning to think he hadn't changed much at all.

"Someone is blackmailing her about her past."

"As a dancer?"

He nodded. "She received a letter threatening to reveal her secret."

"That's awful," I said, with utmost sincerity. Lady Harcourt had tried so hard to pull herself free from her middle class roots, and it certainly appeared as if she'd succeeded. But it had become clear to me when I visited The Alhambra that some resentment still existed from other dancers who'd not been so fortunate or ruthless. "And she has no notion of who might have penned the letter?"

"None, so she tells me, although I'm not entirely convinced. She refused to show me the letter itself."

"Then how can you be certain of the threat?"

"Because of her anxiety. Nothing but a threat of that nature would cause so much fear on her part. She's deeply worried about her past coming out in the gossip columns, you see."

"And you're worried about her becoming too anxious."

"I am."

"That's very sweet of you, Mr. Buchanan. I'm sure she appreciates the concern. Everybody needs someone trustworthy to lean on in difficult times."

His mouth twitched to the side. "Indeed."

"I'm surprised that she would even bother Mr. Fitzroy with it if you're there to help her."

"She seems to consider him highly competent. More so than me, I'm sure. Do you know if she has spoken to him about this letter?"

"He's been somewhat busy lately."

"Rescuing you from kidnappers?"

I squared my shoulders. "I rescued myself, thank you." In a way.

"She did," Gus chimed in. "And me too."

Buchanan ignored him. "I'm glad I was able to discuss this with you, Miss Holloway. While I adore my stepmother, and would do anything for her, I am aware that she has her faults, and one of those is the enjoyment she gets out of manipulating things to her benefit. I would hate for you to be unaware of Julia's machinations until too late."

I couldn't decide if he was jealous of Lincoln and worried about the two of them because he was in love with her, or if he despised her and wanted to ruin her machinations, as he called it. Perhaps both. Love and hate were two sides of the one coin, so my adopted mother used to tell me.

"Thank you," I said. "There's no need to concern yourself on that score. If Lincoln wishes to help Lady Harcourt, he will, but that is all. Just help." What else could I say? It seemed absurd to be having such a discussion with him. If Lincoln were here, he would have thrown Buchanan out.

"I'm glad I was able speak with you, Miss Holloway." He stood and assured me he had to leave when I politely protested the briefness of his stay. "Things to do and all that."

I saw him out just as Doyle arrived in the entrance hall carrying a tray laden with tea things. He sighed, turned, and left again.

Seth, Gus and I followed him to the kitchen and enjoyed tea and cake with Cook. Doyle ate too, although he refused to sit in my presence and remained standing.

"What do you think that was all about?" Seth asked.

"Don't ask me." Gus didn't bother to finish his mouthful of cake before speaking, earning him an eye-roll from Seth. "Toffs are a strange lot. I don't understand 'em."

"Amen," I muttered into my cup.

Doyle finished his tea and went in search of some silver to polish. I signaled for Seth to follow me into the scullery.

"Want me to fetch water?" he asked, picking up the pail.

"In a moment." I kept my voice low and my gaze on the door to the kitchen. "I hate to ask this, but are you sure Doyle wouldn't betray us to Mrs. Drinkwater?"

"Quite sure. Why would he?"

"Money."

"The man is exceedingly grateful for his position here. He's very proud and wants to work. He wouldn't jeopardize this opportunity for a little extra ready."

"Oh. Poor man. You're right, but I needed to ask. He knew we were looking for a housekeeper, for one thing."

"It was hardly a secret. You placed an ad in *The Times*."

"Yes, but Mrs. Drinkwater didn't know to look there until someone informed her."

"True. But Mrs. Drinkwater knew about your necromancy, and Doyle doesn't."

"You haven't told him?" At his head shake, I sighed. "Then it couldn't have been him. I'm very relieved, because he's awfully efficient. Although I don't like the way he looks at me when I want to sit in the kitchen."

"He'll get used to the way things are done at Lichfield soon enough."

"Do you think he'll get used to the strange goings on?"

"You mean the odd kidnapping here and there?" He grinned. "We'll have to tell him about the ministry eventually."

He carried the pail outside, and I assembled the dirty dishes. By the time he'd returned with the water, my thoughts had steered toward Lincoln. He mustn't have found Mrs. Drinkwater yet or he'd be back. I didn't feel as relieved about that as I thought I would. Despite my earlier misgivings, I *knew* Lincoln wouldn't harm her. He might scare her or threaten her to get answers, but that was all.

But he had to find her first.

If he'd told me what he'd learned about the Drinkwaters so far, perhaps I could have been of assistance in narrowing the search, but he'd refused to discuss the matter at all.

"Seth," I said before he could walk out of the scullery. "Tell me everything you know about the Drinkwaters."

He shrugged. "You must know more than me, since you were in their house and have met them."

"What did Lincoln learn from the police who investigated Reginald's death? Who were their friends and relatives? Do they holiday at the seaside? That sort of thing."

Another shrug. "I don't know. He doesn't tell us much." His gaze narrowed. "Why?"

I dried my hands on my apron. "Come with me, as my bodyguard. I want to—"

"No." He chopped his hand through the air. "Absolutely not. It's too dangerous for you. Besides, can you imagine what he'd do to me if something happened?"

"Nothing will happen with you there as my protector."

"Your faith in me is admirable, but misguided. We both know that. I'm not him, and even he can't stop a bullet."

No, but I knew something that could. I slopped a teacup into the tub. "Never mind."

Some twenty minutes later, when a delivery of more furniture arrived, a plan formed.

I paid the cart driver and his boy and urged them to keep my lark to themselves. I quickly changed into the boys' clothing I'd kept in my dresser and tucked my hair under the cap. Keeping my head low and my fingers touching the amber pendant around my neck, I sat beside the driver as we exited through Lichfield's gate.

Nobody tried to kill me and I couldn't see any strangers lurking nearby. I let out my pent-up breath and drew in fresh, free air.

The boy was already waiting for us around the corner, having climbed the fence at the rear of the estate. I thanked father and son, then asked them to take me to Kensington Police Station.

CHAPTER 10

Dressing as a boy made sense when it came to sneaking out of the house. It was a useless disguise for coaxing names and addresses from detective inspectors, however. The ruddy-cheeked man investigating the Drinkwater murder refused to tell me anything, even after I assured him that I worked for a scientific organization who wished to posthumously award Mr. Drinkwater a research prize.

"Tell your master I don't give away information like that to children. Or anybody! Get out of here, boy." He shooed me with a motion of his short, stubby hands and returned to his paperwork.

I didn't move. "I can pay you."

My attempted bribery earned me a glare. "Do you want to be arrested?"

I ran out of there as fast as possible. I'd been thrown into a police holding cell once before and did not want to repeat the experience.

I waited until darkness descended and the detective inspector went home for the evening. A constable remained on duty, but it would be easy enough to avoid his notice. I made my way along a lane, pocketing pebbles as I went, then scrambled over the back fence into a large courtyard.

Using Gus's principle that it was always worth trying the door to see if it was unlocked, I tested the knob. It turned but the door didn't budge. It must be bolted from the inside. There were no external locks on either of the high, narrow windows either. One of them probably led to the holding cells.

There were no crates nearby, so I had to climb up the side fence and stand on my toes to reach the roof. I was a little out of practice, but I soon learned that scrambling up structures wasn't a skill easily forgotten. The roof wasn't too steep either, which helped.

I lay flat on my front and curled my fingers around the gutter edge, just above one of the windows. I sucked in a deep breath, blew it out again, and peered through.

Three prisoners sat inside a whitewashed room, looking utterly bored in the lamplight. I quickly snapped my head back out of view before they saw me.

Inch by inch, I slithered over to the other window and repeated the exercise. I couldn't see anything in the darkness. The lack of lighting meant it was probably unoccupied. I slithered back to the section of the roof directly above the door and removed a pebble from my pocket.

I threw it as hard as I could against the door. A moment later, it opened.

"Anyone out here?" the constable called into the darkness when no one answered.

He clicked his tongue. "When I catch you, you little turds, I'll—"

My second pebble hit the back fence and my third flew over it, making a sound as it landed on the cobbles in the lane. The constable came into view. Hands on hips, he stood in the center of the courtyard and looked around.

I threw three pebbles this time. All landed on the other side of the fence.

The constable drew his truncheon from its holster and unbolted the gate. Clinging to the edge of the roof by my fingers, I swung down and through the open door, landing softly in the empty corridor. After a quick glance back outside to confirm that the constable hadn't noticed, I slipped inside the dark room and closed the door. In the moment before it shut, the light from the corridor lamp revealed a room with mop, brooms and other cleaning equipment at one end and a large cabinet with numerous small drawers on the side.

I pressed my ear to the door and listened. Someone hummed quietly but I heard no voices. The back door closed and a bolt slid home. Footsteps passed by the storeroom door without stopping. I waited another moment and, when all remained quiet, I crept out to the corridor. The detective inspector's office was two doors down, visible from the front desk where the constable sat with his feet up, his back to me.

On tiptoes, I snuck into the unlocked windowless office and silently cursed the lack of light. I fumbled in the dark until I located the lamp on the desk and lit it. The gas hissed a little but not too loudly. I checked the stack of papers and found the Drinkwater case on top.

I flicked past the gruesome photographs and the information he'd gathered from witnesses. That wasn't what I needed. Near the back, I found the name and address of Mrs. Drinkwater's sister, but no other kin. If she wasn't there, I had no notion of where to find her. Lincoln would already know this information too and would be there ahead of me. Indeed, he should have returned to Lichfield hours ago.

I flipped the pages back in place, going slower to skim read them. A name caught my eye.

Joan Brumley.

From the look of things, this detective wasn't working on the Brumley case, but he or someone else had linked the two murders. The timing and method of death must have given them a clue. I made a mental note of Brumley's details, including that of her cousin, listed as the next of kin.

I continued to flip the pages back in place, only to pause again when I spotted another familiar name. Two. *Oh my god.*

Victor Frankenstein and Captain Jasper.

They were listed with two other men under the heading Known Associates. Beside their names were the letters 'DEC'. Deceased. The detective must have found correspondence between them. I couldn't believe I hadn't made the connection earlier. All three men were scientists involved in reanimation, of sorts. Frankenstein had wanted to bring dead bodies to life using my necromancy, Jasper had wanted to bring them to life using medicine, and Drinkwater wanted to make false limbs work.

Had they shared the results of their research with one another? Had Frankenstein and Jasper known Drinkwater was magical? Was Drinkwater's death in any way related to this connection? And Brumley's too?

My mind spun with so many questions. I needed to speak with Lincoln. And yet...he must have known. He would have snuck in here in much the same way I did, and searched through these same papers. If he knew...why hadn't he told me?

Footsteps approached along the corridor. I extinguished the lamp and ducked beneath the desk. I clasped the pendant around my neck. Its warmth reassured me.

The door opened and a rectangle of light beamed across the floor. Polished shoes approached, pausing only inches from where I hid. My heart hammered so hard I felt sure he must have heard it, even over his whistling. Papers rustled for what seemed like several minutes, but was more likely only seconds. Then finally, the shoes retreated and the constable shut the door. The room fell dark, but I didn't dare move.

I waited until I was sure he wouldn't return and emerged from my hiding spot. I tiptoed to the door, opened it and checked up and down the corridor before emerging fully. The bolt on the back door wasn't as quiet as I would have liked, but nobody came after me, so it must have been quiet enough. I closed the door, sprinted across the courtyard, out the back gate and down the lane.

I didn't stop running until I reached the corner where the numerous streetlamps provided comfort and a sense of protection. It was still early and, despite the cold, people were out and about, coming home from work or making evening calls. I found a cab and paid the driver to take me back to Lichfield.

The journey gave me time to think. I had so many questions, and I knew Lincoln might know the answers to some of them. I hoped he'd returned, because I wanted to confront him about keeping information from me. Then again, if he'd come home to find me not there…

I dismissed that possibility from my mind and considered everything I knew, which was very little. Mrs. Drinkwater might be able to tell me more about her husband's association with Jasper and Frankenstein, but finding her would likely prove difficult now. If she hadn't gone into hiding, Lincoln would have returned home hours ago. I didn't think I could succeed where he'd failed.

But I didn't need Mrs. Drinkwater's help. There were other ways to get information.

***

Lincoln wasn't home, to my immense relief. Not only that, but my ruse of retiring to my room due to a headache had worked, so the others were utterly surprised to see me stroll into the kitchen wearing boy's clothes. None more so than Doyle.

He dropped the eggs he'd been about to pass to Cook. They smashed all over the floor and splattered his gleaming black shoes. "*Miss Holloway*?" His scandalized tone matched the look on his face.

"That it is, Mr. Doyle," I said in my old slum accent. "Close yer gob, now. Don't want no one finking yer a fish."

"I...I..."

"Aye, I'm dressed like a boy." I removed my cap and bowed. "What's for dinner, Cook? I'm starving."

"Leftover beef." Cook shook his head and cleared his throat. When he finally got Doyle's attention, he nodded at the mess on the floor.

Doyle crouched to pick up the bits of shell, but continued to glance up at me as if he expected me to do a jig.

Seth and Gus stood by the door, blocking my exit, their arms crossed over their chests, matching scowls on their faces. "You're lucky Fitzroy's not here," Seth said.

"I know." I smiled but that didn't wipe off their scowls. "I was quite safe. I had my pet with me." I pulled the necklace out from beneath my shirt.

"That don't make it right," Gus said, lowering his arms. "You should tell someone when you go out."

"You wouldn't have let me go."

"There's a good reason for that."

I sighed. "I can't stay in here day and night doing nothing." Not when people were keeping things from me.

"Where did you go?" Seth asked, staying by the door.

"Kensington Police Station. I wanted to find out where Mrs. Drinkwater's sister lived. I'd like to speak to her again, without Lincoln glaring daggers at her, that is."

"And did you find the sister's address?"

"The detective inspector wouldn't speak to me." There. That wasn't a lie.

I ate some bread and cheese and a slice of beef, all while my heart beat out a guilty rhythm against my ribs. I finished and washed my meal down with a glass of red wine. "Lincoln hasn't sent word?"

"None," Gus said.

"He's been gone a long time. Do you think he's all right?"

"Of course he bloody is. He's always all right."

I didn't think that was a good reason not to worry. And I *was* worried. What made it worse was that I had no idea where to begin looking for him.

"Give him until the morning," Seth said quietly. "If he's not back by then, we'll begin a search."

I gave him a flat smile. "Very well. You're probably right, and he's just busy looking for Mrs. Drinkwater." I stood. "Goodnight all. This time I really am retiring to my room."

Seth followed me out of the kitchen. "Then you won't mind if I make sure you get there, and check on you from time to time."

"Forget checkin' on her," Gus said, also following. "I'm standin' outside her door."

I let them walk with me up the stairs. It didn't matter whether they remained on guard or not, so I closed the door and thought nothing more about them.

Instead of preparing for bed, however, I sat in the armchair by the fire and loosened my hair. It reached just past my shoulders now, still much shorter than it had been before I cut it at age thirteen. One day, it would grow long again. Sometimes that day felt like a lifetime away.

I must have fallen asleep. It was still dark when I awoke, and the orange glow of the coals provided the only light. I lit a candle, wrapped a shawl around my shoulders, and slipped out of the room. Neither Gus nor Seth had remained in the corridor and the house was silent. It felt empty.

I knocked lightly on Lincoln's door, and entered when there was no answer. His sitting room and study were undisturbed and his bed made. I set the candle on the table and slipped under the covers to wait for him. With his scent enveloping me, I soon fell asleep.

I awoke alone the following morning. I quickly dressed and joined the others in the kitchen. "He didn't come home," I announced.

"What you want us to do?" Gus asked.

Cook set a plate of poached eggs and bacon in front of me. "Eat first, worry later."

"I don't feel like eating." I pushed the plate away.

"He'll be fine," Seth said.

"He was angry when he left. I'm worried that his anger will cause him to make mistakes."

"He don't make mistakes," Gus said, hacking into his bacon. "Besides, if we want to find him, where would we start lookin'?"

I sighed. I truly didn't know. They were right, and searching for Lincoln would be like looking for a needle in a haystack. But I had to try. "Let's do something different. Since we only know the Drinkwaters' London address and Mrs. Drinkwater's sister's address, we've struck a dead end. Lincoln would have already searched there, and my guess is that she won't be at either of those places. So let's speak with Joan Brumley's cousin."

"Who?" Cook asked.

"The other supernatural victim," Seth told him. "How will we find the cousin?"

"Her address was noted in the detective's files," I said.

Seth folded his arms. "You told us you didn't learn anything from the police."

"That's not precisely what I said. Anyway, I think Lincoln may have widened his investigation, having hit a dead end when it came to finding Mrs. Drinkwater."

"P'haps." Gus shoveled the rest of his eggs into his mouth then proceeded to speak before swallowing. "He might not need to be found. He might be well into the hunt and not able to come home yet."

"I am aware of that. I'm also aware that he won't want us to go looking for him—if nothing is wrong."

Seth held up a finger. "*We* will go looking for him at the Brumley cousin's house. *You* will stay here."

I suspected they'd say that. I had no intention of forcing the issue or sneaking out. They could do as I asked perfectly adequately without my presence. "I have some specific questions I'd like you to ask Miss Brumley's cousin. I'll write them down after breakfast."

Gus wiped his mouth with the back of his hand. "She don't trust us to think for ourselves, Seth."

Seth merely scowled.

After they left, I spent the morning with Doyle in the formal drawing room. It hadn't been used since Lincoln moved into Lichfield Towers, and dust covers blanketed what little furniture had been left behind by the last owner. After the previous day's delivery, Doyle had set about removing the old and arranging the new. He'd done a marvelous job. Together, we made plans and moved the new furniture again to see how it looked in other positions, only to put most of it back again.

I was sweating by the time Gus and Seth returned from visiting Joan Brumley's cousin, Edith. "Well?" I asked before they'd had a chance to remove their hats and gloves.

"Fitzroy went there late yesterday," Gus said.

I blew out a breath. So he was alive and well then, thank God. "And?"

"And he asked the same questions you wanted us to ask her. Mostly. The Drinkwater name wasn't familiar to her and she'd had no visits from anyone asking about her cousin except for the police and Fitzroy."

"So there's most likely no other link between them except they were both supernaturals. Go on. What else?"

"As far as Edith Brumley knew, her cousin didn't know she was a necromancer, as such. She knew she could speak with ghosts, of course, but she didn't have a name for her magic. She didn't consider it magical at all, or supernatural, it just *was*. Aside from Fitzroy and us, no one has mentioned the word necromancy to her, and the police didn't discuss Joan's magic at all."

"What about Frankenstein and Jasper? Had Joan ever mentioned them to Edith?"

"The names weren't familiar to her."

Damn. This wasn't going as I thought it would. "What about my final question? Had Joan associated with anyone new lately?"

They gave me matching looks of triumph. "This is the interestin' part," Gus said.

"It was an inspired question," Seth added. "It turns out that Joan had a paramour. Edith thought this highly unlikely, considering Joan had been a spinster for years and no one had shown interest in her before."

Gus circled his finger at his temple. "No surprise there."

"According to Edith, the fellow avoided meeting her although she was Joan's only family. He kept putting it off, which made Edith suspicious that he was merely a figment of her cousin's imagination. She changed her opinion when Joan became very upset after the gentleman broke off contact. One day he'd been talking to her about building a life together, and the next...nothing. He simply never showed at their prearranged meeting place, and since she had no way of contacting him, the relationship ended."

"Did Joan give Edith a description of him?"

Both men shook their heads. "You won't believe it, Charlie," Gus said. He couldn't stand still, he was so eager to tell me. "Edith Brumley keeps a diary. She looked through it for the date when Joan came to her all upset. Guess when it was."

"Just tell me!"

"The day after Frankenstein died."

I pressed a hand to my chest. "My God," I whispered. "You think *he* was her paramour?"

They both nodded. "He wanted a necromancer and she was one."

"Yes, but...he thought I was the last one. That's why he was so desperate to get me."

"What if he didn't *know* Joan was a necromancer?" Seth said. "He might have seen her articles in the history periodicals and thought she might be of interest. Remember, her articles only mentioned she spoke with spirits. There was no indication that she could place the spirits inside bodies to reanimate them. Perhaps he wasn't yet sure if she could do it."

"Perhaps *she* didn't know she could do it." I wished I'd added that question to my list to ask Edith Brumley. "He might have been trying to find out more about her magic while courting her, even while he was looking for me." As he had done with my mother. "His efforts were cut short by his untimely death. This is an extraordinary development. I wonder if Lincoln learned about the connection too."

"We asked Edith if she'd told anyone else about Joan's lover, and she said she hadn't because no one asked."

"Not even the police?"

He shook his head. "They only asked for recent connections, not ones that were months old. I suppose Edith didn't think it was relevant either, since the contact stopped some time ago."

"So what now?" Gus asked. "You goin' to summon the Brumley woman's spirit?"

I shook my head. "It's too dangerous. She was a necromancer. I can't risk her overriding my control." I blew out a shaky breath, unable to quite believe what I was about to do, and not yet sure how I felt about it. "I'm going to summon my father, Victor Frankenstein."

CHAPTER 11

"Are you certain you want to do this?" Seth asked with quiet concern.

"Frankenstein's not magical," I assured him. "So we know he can't override my control."

"That's not what I meant."

I spread my fingers over my lap and blew out a breath. I sat on the new sofa, made by Fernesse himself, in the redecorated parlor. New furniture, new clothes, new fiancé, yet I didn't feel like I'd changed all that much since Frankenstein died. Sometimes, when I remembered he was my father, I found the whole thing difficult to fathom. Despite some physical resemblances, we were very different. I hoped never to become like him. He'd used people in the most callous way to complete his life's work. He'd used people he was supposed to love.

"I'll be fine," I said. "It's time I faced him."

"Maybe we should wait for Fitzroy." Gus eyed the door as if he expected Lincoln to walk in at any moment.

"I'd rather not wait. Besides, we don't know when he'll be back." Or if he needed us to fetch him.

I angled myself toward the fire, to chase away the sudden chill, and summoned Frankenstein. His spirit seemed to come out of nowhere, from no particular direction. It streaked around the room like a crazed, scared hare, passing through objects until it finally settled.

It formed his shape on the sofa beside me. "Charlotte!" He touched the ragged wound where his eye should have been. Lincoln's knife had caused it in a killing blow.

I swallowed. Sometimes I forgot what Lincoln had done. "Good morning." It didn't feel right calling him 'father' or 'sir', so I didn't call him anything. "I need to speak with you."

He spread his hands over his lap, much as I had just done, and stared at their ethereal form. "I...I'm a ghost."

"Yes. You died a little over three months ago."

He glanced up to the ceiling, then down to the floor. "You saved me."

Had he forgotten? I hadn't saved him. I'd been instrumental in killing him.

"You won't send me back, will you?" He smiled and reached out a hand to me. I felt nothing as it went straight through. "You're my daughter...you wouldn't be so cruel as to send me back there."

It took me a moment to realize he was referring to his afterlife. It must not be the utopia he'd hoped for. I felt no sympathy for him, no concern. He'd made his bed, and now he must lie in it.

"Charlie," Seth urged. "Ask him what you need to ask."

"Where is this?" Frankenstein said before I could speak. "Where am I?"

"Lichfield Towers, in Highgate."

True to form, Lincoln strolled in at that moment. I didn't see him or hear him enter, and the first indication I had that he'd joined us was Gus's sharp gasp.

"Sir," Seth said, removing his arm.

I opened my eyes to see Lincoln standing very close to me, a deep frown furrowing his brow. He looked exhausted, disheveled and absolutely wonderful. I stood and tumbled into his arms, burying my face in his jacket at his chest. He felt warm, and the beat of his heart was both a comfort and a relief.

"I'm sorry we didn't part on good terms," I murmured.

I heard Seth and Gus leave. Lincoln's arms tightened, as if he felt more comfortable alone. He stroked my hair back and pressed his lips to my forehead in a lingering kiss.

"You have something to tell me?" he asked after a long moment.

I drew back. "That's the first thing you wish to say to me?"

"I walk in here to see my men touching you, you're in tears, and you throw yourself at me. Forgive me for being unable to think of another response."

"I am not in tears, and I did not *throw* myself." I hugged him again, fiercely. "But I am terribly relieved to see you. I've been worried."

"Why?"

"Because you've been gone since yesterday, and you were in a black mood when you left. Any woman would be worried if her fiancé disappeared for that long without word."

"You are not a typical woman, and I am not a typical fiancé."

I caressed his cheek above the rough stubble. "I wouldn't have you any other way."

He lifted my hair off my shoulders and kissed me until my toes curled and our bodies heated. Then he suddenly let me go. "I'll be back in a few minutes."

I shook my head and smiled. His abrupt changes baffled me. Gus brought in supper before Lincoln returned and asked me if I'd told him about Frankenstein yet.

"We've not had a chance to talk," I said.

"He won't like that you went to the police station without us."

I held the door open for him. "Thank you, Gus, but I won't keep things from him." Not like he'd kept things from me.

He left when Lincoln returned. His hair hung in damp waves and he smelled like the spicy soap he liked to use. I found myself drawn to his arms again, and to his lips. He tasted as good as he smelled.

Our kiss was all too brief. With a frustrated huff, he directed me to sit. "I want to know why you were upset."

I sat on the armchair by the fire. "After you tell me where you've been and whether you found Mrs. Drinkwater."

Two beats passed before he answered. "I've been to her sister's house, visited her neighbors, and checked hotels in the vicinity. I broke into her house to find out what I could about her life and movements. When that investigation proved futile, I visited the Brumley woman's kin. I believe the two victims may have known one another." He rubbed a hand over his eyes and down his face. The exhaustion etched into the lines tugged at my heart. It must gall him to have failed, but at least his exhaustion was better than his anger. "I didn't find the Drinkwater woman."

"I see. I can't pretend I'm sorry for that."

His gaze sharpened.

"Before you accuse me of not trusting you," I went on, "I want you to know that I do. You won't hurt her, but *she* doesn't know that."

He blinked slowly and looked away. "I find it remarkable that you can still think me harmless after witnessing me kill your father."

"That's different. He was a danger to us both, and to Seth and Gus. You had no choice." I cleared my throat. "Speaking of my father, I summoned his spirit tonight."

The sharp gaze returned, piercing me like an arrow. "That's why you were upset."

I sucked in air between my teeth. My reluctance to continue did not go unnoticed, if the quirk of his eyebrow was an indication. "I haven't been idle while you were away," I said. "Can I speak without risk of you interrupting?"

"Probably not."

I gave him a withering glare. "I snuck out of the house with my imp and broke into the Kensington Police Station to find out what they knew about the Drinkwater murder."

His lips pressed together in what I assumed was an effort not to interrupt.

"I learned some things, which I'm sure you already knew, since you probably have also broken in at some point."

"Are you going to admonish me for not sharing the information with you?"

"Lincoln, I thought we'd agreed to be partners in ministry business. In everything!"

"For one thing, you're my assistant, not my partner. For another, being betrothed makes you my partner in life, not in work."

"The two are inextricably linked. You said so yourself once. And anyway, you should have involved me in the investigation because I believe I've learned more about the murders than you."

"I have no doubt, since you summoned Frankenstein. You saw the connection in the detective's files?"

"And with Jasper too."

He didn't look surprised, so he must have known.

"That's only partly why I summoned his spirit. I sent Seth and Gus to talk with Edith Brumley, Joan's cousin, and they learned that Joan had a lover, but all contact between them suddenly ceased when Frankenstein died."

That brought quite a reaction. *Both* his eyebrows lifted. "He wanted to use her necromancy?"

"He wasn't sure if she could reanimate bodies, but he planned on testing her, only he died first. If he couldn't find me, he hoped he could use her instead. He was using her as he used my mother."

"And you," he said quietly.

"I think I've also found the link between Drinkwater, Jasper and Frankenstein. His spirit mentioned that he was approached by an anonymous benefactor who wanted to sponsor his work, only to retract his offer when he learned Frankenstein planned to use a necromancer. Drinkwater's spirit also mentioned a commission from someone who pulled out after learning about his magic."

"Jasper had a commission too."

"We never investigated that angle at the time because we didn't realize there was a link."

He nodded slowly, his gaze unfocused. "His benefactor was still current at the time of his death."

"Do you think that's because Jasper was using actual medicine and not magic to bring the deceased back to life?"

"It's likely, given what we know now."

It was thrilling to have discovered the link, and my heart soared to know that I'd had a key role in the discovery. But then it sank like a stone when I considered the implications. "Someone else has been involved all along, perhaps the same person who is now killing the supernaturals."

"Perhaps."

"But the killer is not the one who helped Mrs. Drinkwater kidnap me. She could have killed me but she didn't."

"She did not," he said, icy.

I waited for him to say something more, to perhaps thank me, or discuss what to do next, but he didn't speak. "You're still angry with me?" I asked. "Even after I learned all that *and* avoided being abducted or killed?"

Perhaps treating it lightly was inconsiderate of me. Shadows banked in eyes the color of molasses.

"I'm sorry," I mumbled. "But I wouldn't have had to sneak out if you shared your discoveries with me and allowed me to discuss my thoughts with you. But instead you hared off after Merry Drinkwater."

He stood and approached, but did not drop to my level. "She kidnapped you."

I stood too, but he towered over me. "That is not a valid reason! Stop excluding me and start involving me more."

"Stop placing yourself in danger and I will."

I stamped my hands on my hips. "You promised me you would try to involve me more, to allow me to be part of your team."

"I am trying!"

"Forgive me for thinking it doesn't look like it."

He sucked in air between his teeth and looked to the ceiling. After a moment, the rigidity left his jaw and the veins in his throat no longer throbbed. He fixed his gaze on mine. Although he was calmer, the shadows hadn't vanished.

"Charlie, involving you would have put you in more danger. I believed that after we first learned of the murders, and I still believe it. Even more so, now that we know of a link between Frankenstein, Jasper and the victims. I am only trying to keep you safe."

"While that sounds logical, your plan isn't working. You tried to keep me safe and yet I was kidnapped anyway."

He flinched and stepped back from me as if my words had pushed him. With a rapid blink, he turned away and strode to the door.

Hell. My mouth had run away from me again. "Lincoln, I'm sorry. I shouldn't have said that." I caught his arm and forced him to look at me. He didn't quite meet my gaze, but at least he didn't try to walk off. "It's not your fault. Mrs. Drinkwater was too well organized and too knowledgeable about us to fail."

When he still didn't look at me, I clasped his face in both my hands. Finally, his gaze met mine. "I love you, Lincoln. You frustrate me at times, but I love you regardless."

He rested his hands on my waist and with a sigh, pressed his forehead against mine. "I'll do my best to keep you informed. But please, do not leave the house unless the danger is inside."

"Considering how Mrs. Drinkwater operated, that is a distinct possibility."

He stiffened. "I know. Wear the necklace at all times now. Please."

I smiled. "Since you asked so nicely." I pulled it out from beneath my dress.

He kissed me gently then we said our goodnights.

I slept restlessly, and the following morning, as I prepared to go down for breakfast and see him again, I discovered a note that had been slipped under my door. It was in Lincoln's hand and it said he'd gone out again, to follow more leads into his search for Mrs. Drinkwater. There was no mention of where, however. I sighed, unsure if that was a deliberate omission, or simply because he didn't yet know where he would end up.

***

The morning dragged, but at least I wasn't as worried today as I had been the day before. Lincoln was safe, and ultimately that was all that mattered.

The monotony was broken up by a visitor at around eleven. A visitor I neither expected nor wanted.

"Why can't the committee leave me alone?" I muttered to Seth when I spotted the black coach through the parlor window, rumbling up the drive.

"Let's hope he's the only one coming," he said. "Any more could pose a threat."

We exchanged concerned glances. "You'd better fetch Gus."

"Wait until we return to question him."

"Question him?" I echoed.

He stopped in the doorway. "You do want to find out if he helped the Drinkwater widow, don't you?"

"Yes."

"Good. Because so do I."

I watched him stride off, wondering how I was going to get a committee member to admit involvement in my abduction.

CHAPTER 12

"Good morning, Charlie." Lord Marchbank had never smiled a greeting, and this time was no exception. Even so, his grim tone worried me. He hadn't come to deliver good news.

"Good morning, sir. Has a committee meeting been called?"

"No." Unlike General Eastbrooke and Lord Gillingham, he looked directly at me when he addressed me. Although I appreciated it, it was somewhat unnerving, with his scarred face and abrupt manner. He was a fearsome looking man. Despite the trappings of a gentleman, he wouldn't have looked out of place on a medieval battlefield.

He handed his coat, hat and gloves to Doyle. "I wanted to speak to you without the rest of the committee present. Have you recovered from your ordeal?"

"Yes, thank you."

He gaze flicked to Doyle, Seth and Gus. "May we speak alone, Charlie?"

"Tea, please, Doyle." I did not dismiss Seth and Gus, and nor would I. "I'd like them to remain with me," I said once Doyle had disappeared.

His brows drew together. "You don't trust me?"

"Someone who knows where to find supernaturals is killing them, and I am a supernatural. You have access to the ministry files. So no, sir, I do not trust you completely."

Some of the brashness left his eyes, replaced by a flicker of uncertainty. My boldness had taken him by surprise. Perhaps he wasn't used to it. "I hardly think you can draw that conclusion from just two deaths."

"Added to which, someone also helped Mrs. Drinkwater kidnap me. Someone who knew we were looking for a housekeeper but also knew about my necromancy. That limits the pool of suspects considerably."

"I say again, you're accusing me?"

"I'm keeping an open mind."

He grunted. "Good for you." He indicated I should walk ahead of him.

I led the way into the parlor. Marchbank took in the new furniture and decorations with an air of polite indifference. Of all the committee members, he seemed the most removed from his surroundings, as if he weren't a part of them but was merely on the fringes, observing and listening. It was much like that now, as he sat on the armchair furthest from me. It wasn't until much later that I wondered if that were a deliberate choice to ease my mind.

"You've been busy," he said, indicating the new furniture.

"Quite."

Seth and Gus didn't sit. One stood by the door and the other near me, their arms crossed, identical frosty expressions on their faces. Neither took their gaze off Marchbank.

"Tell me, Charlie, why do you think I would help Mrs. Drinkwater abduct you?"

It was a question that had puzzled me ever since I concluded that someone had assisted her. Who had the most to gain? In Marchbank's case, I could only think of one reason. "You want me gone from here. Having me abducted shows Lincoln that I'm vulnerable and a target for those who want to use my necromancy."

"True, but your prior abduction proved that. Another wasn't necessary. All this one achieved was to draw Fitzroy's ire. If you hadn't returned, he would still be looking for you and he wouldn't have given up until he found you, dead or alive."

I swallowed.

"There's no point removing you from Lichfield if it only serves to keep him busy *away* from ministry business. I want him focused on his work, Charlie, not distracted from it."

If what he said was true—and I'd not yet thought it through enough to make that decision—then that meant no one from the committee had helped Mrs. Drinkwater. They all wanted the same thing—Lincoln's attention on the ministry, not me.

Or did they? Had my abduction served some other purpose for the committee that I'd not yet fathomed?

"I suppose that leads nicely to the reason for your visit," I said. "Me distracting Lincoln, and you wanting me gone, one way or another."

He stroked the white scar slicing through his short gray beard. "You're very forward."

"Being demure is not in my nature. I'm sorry if that offends you, but I am what I am."

"Many people would be offended. I'm not one of them."

I gave a nod of appreciation. Neither of us spoke as Doyle entered with the tea. We waited as he served and watched as he left, shutting the door behind him.

I picked up my teacup. "In the spirit of being forward, sir, I think it's time you told me why you're here. I doubt it's to check on my health."

"You're wrong there. Or partly, at least. I did want to ask how you are. You may not believe this, but I like you, Charlie. You're spirited, clever, and have a quality about you that other girls your age lack. If you were my daughter, I would be proud."

His unexpected praise made me blush and, to my horror, turned my vision misty. I studied my tea until the moment passed. It wouldn't do to lower my guard around this man. "If you like me, why are you here to convince me to leave?"

He set down his teacup without taking a sip. "I thought it might be better to talk to you without the other committee members present. They tend to bring a certain amount of unnecessary drama to a discussion of this nature, and I think you're someone who appreciates reason and logic."

"Thank you," I said, once again surprised. Was that part of his plan—stun me with his kindness and trick me into agreeing to something while my guard was down? "Don't waste your breath, my lord. I'm not leaving."

"Hear me out."

I stood. "No."

He picked up his teacup and sipped slowly. Several moments ticked by. With a sigh, I sat again. I could storm out and leave him alone, but I wouldn't put it past him to remain all day and night.

"There is a school up north, near my country seat in Yorkshire."

I spluttered a humorless laugh. "I'm too old for school."

"It's not a regular kind of school. It's more of a finishing school for young ladies."

"I'm not a lady, and I don't need finishing." Whatever that was.

"You could pass as a lady if you were finished properly—as long as your past was kept quiet. Being finished will help you after your school year ends."

"It's nice of you to consider my long-term future," I said with sickly sweetness. "And here I assumed you wanted me to stay at the school until the end of my days."

"Not unless you choose to stay on as a teacher. But I think you could do something else, if you wanted to. Something more."

"More?"

"After your lady's education is complete, I thought you might like to leave for the continent."

"The continent!"

"France, Italy, or any of a number of countries. Perhaps even America or the Antipodes. The world is your oyster, as they say." He held up a hand when I began to protest. "Hear me out. It would be the chance for a new life for you, a new beginning where no one knows you. No one will come after you because of your necromancy."

"If it's kept a secret, that is."

"I assumed that you would want it that way, considering all that has happened since people discovered it."

I sat back in the chair, disregarding my bustle. I shook my head at him in disbelief. "You don't know me at all. I have no wish to have a new life. I like this one. It has my friends in it, and my fiancé."

Beside me, Seth touched my shoulder. "I don't think it's an offer, Charlie. Not one he expects you to refuse."

Marchbank sipped again, seemingly oblivious to my glare. "Vickers is correct."

I set my cup down with a clatter. "I thought you were the decent one, sir, but I see you are just like them and against me too."

"No," he said with bland indifference. "I am the only one who doesn't want to exile you to a remote island in the middle of nowhere without a hope of escape."

My stomach plunged. Although I knew they wanted to do that to me, and perhaps worse, the thought never ceased to make me feel ill. Sometimes it felt like a thin veil separated my desire for freedom from their desire to hide me, and it would only take a puff of wind to blow that veil away.

"At least with my plan you can have a good life," he went on. "A far better one than you had when you lived on the streets too."

"But not better than this one."

"Are you quite certain of that?"

"Yes! And what of my engagement to Lincoln? I won't leave him. I can't." This last came out on a choke.

Marchbank's unruffled gaze settled on me. "You say you love him, but I don't believe you."

"What!"

"You have placed him in a difficult position. He feels obligated to marry you because he has feelings for you. That's not love, that's manipulation."

"It's not an *obligation*," I snapped.

"It is, for him. He's not the sort of gentleman who will have a dalliance with a young woman then discard her."

It was very close to what Lincoln himself had said. That I wasn't the sort of girl to keep as a mistress, and that he *must* marry me. I picked up my teacup again and held it tightly. I tilted my chin. "I can't leave him. We belong together."

"Are you sure he feels the same way?"

"Yes."

"He's a man who has been alone his entire life. I'm sure I don't need to lay it all out before you, Charlie. You know he's never had a proper family."

"What are you getting at?"

"He might be infatuated with you now, and seduced by the idea of having a wife and family, but once the novelty wears off, he will return to himself."

"He *is* being himself, now, with me." It was frustrating that I felt compelled to defend Lincoln and my own reasoning. I thought I didn't care about Marchbank's opinion, or that of any of the committee members. It seemed I was wrong. "I've brought out a different side to him. A better side." I sounded so arrogant, yet I *had* to believe it, otherwise that meant Marchbank was right. And if he was right, then I should leave Lincoln for his own good.

"Old habits are hard to break. People don't change overnight," he went on.

There was certainly some truth in that. Lincoln struggled to involve me fully in ministry business, despite our numerous discussions about it. Even in the note he'd left this morning, he'd told me he was going out, but not where.

But he would learn and change. He simply needed time to adjust, and I could give him that. I must remember not to push him so much in future and allow him to adapt to being in a relationship at his own speed.

"I see you're giving some serious thought to what I'm telling you," Marchbank said.

"I'm not leaving him. That's final. Gus, please see Lord Marchbank out."

"Gladly," Gus growled.

Marchbank held up his hands in surrender. "I've said my piece. Thank you for listening." He gave me a brief bow and left. Gus followed him out.

I didn't let out my breath until I heard his coach roll away. "Am I being foolish, Seth? Selfish, even?"

"Neither." He sat on the sofa beside me and patted my hand. "Fitzroy needs you, Charlie. I'm convinced of it. Don't listen to Marchbank or anyone else. Do what *you* think is right."

That was the problem—what if staying turned out to be the wrong thing to do?

***

"No," Gus said with a scowl that rivaled Lincoln's best. "You're not going anywhere, Charlie, and that's final."

"She be doing the right thing," Cook told him before I could speak. "She's got to show 'em she ain't a burden."

"Thank you, Cook." I smiled at him. He responded by chopping through a carrot and handing a chunk to me. "Gus, I have to do this. Everyone thinks I'm a hindrance. I need to show them I'm an asset, that I can be useful." I nibbled the carrot. "If I don't do this now, it'll just get harder and harder."

"But now's when people are tryin' to kill your kind. I'm just sayin' to wait until the killer is caught."

"And Holloway," Seth chimed in from where he stood leaning against the doorframe. It was the first he'd spoken since I mentioned wanting to go out to search for Mrs. Drinkwater.

"Are you against the idea too?" I asked.

He held up his hands. "Just pointing out the dangers."

"Thank you, I don't need them pointed out. I'm well aware of what can go wrong."

"I don't like it," Gus muttered, sounding resigned. Perhaps he knew that I would do it, with or without his consent. He picked up the other end of the carrot and pointed it at Cook. "You shouldn't encourage her."

Cook gave him a rude hand gesture then snatched the carrot back.

"Let me put it this way," I told them all. "Me leaving Lichfield will achieve two things. One, I can search for Merry Drinkwater."

"Fitzroy's already doing that," Seth said, folding his arms and looking every bit determined to stop me.

"Using different methods to Lincoln. Methods that may be more effective, in this case. And two, I'll draw out those who are trying to kill me. Or reform me, in Holloway's case."

Gus and Seth spoke over one another until I could no longer differentiate between their protests. I let them finish before adding the final detail.

"You will both come with me, and I'll have my imp, too."

Gus stamped his knuckles on the table. "We ain't relying on a cat to save you!"

"It ain't a cat." Cook shook his head. "And it be better at saving her than you."

Gus bristled. "Shut your mouth, Moon Face."

Cook merely snorted and scooped up the slices of carrot in his big hands and plopped them into a pot. "You can do better than that."

Seth pushed off from the doorframe. "What will you do if we say no?"

"Take the imp and go anyway," I said.

"I thought as much." He slapped Gus on the shoulder. "Better get our coats."

Gus threw his hands in the air. "You're as mad as her!" He followed Seth out of the kitchen, arguing with him all the way. "If she dies, I'm tellin' Death it's all your fault."

Doyle entered, wearing white gloves and holding a polishing cloth. "May I get you something, miss?"

"No, thank you." I had a note to write. If Lincoln returned while I was out, I needed to allay his fears. A note might not be enough, but it was better than silence. Hopefully.

I could no longer sit at Lichfield waiting for Lincoln to succeed. I could no longer pretend that I was safe here. Not only was I a sitting duck, I was reinforcing the committee's belief that I was useless and a hindrance to Lincoln. If I wanted to be neither of those, then I had to *do* something. I only hoped he agreed with my point of view...eventually.

***

Merry Drinkwater's sister lived with her husband in Acton, in a modern red brick house with a small front garden behind an iron picket fence. Seth stepped out of the coach and held his hand out for me, the way a well-bred gentleman would for his sister.

"I still don't see why *I* couldn't be your brother," Gus muttered from the coachman's seat.

"Because someone needs to be the servant," Seth said.

"But why me? Why not you?"

Seth tugged on his cuff and beamed to show off his perfect teeth. "Do I look like a servant to you?"

Gus narrowed his eyes. "After I get a few good punches in, you will."

"See! That's what I mean. Charlie's brother wouldn't threaten violence to get his way."

"You're a pompous prig."

"And you're an idiot." Seth offered me his arm. "Come, sis, before the help gets ideas above his station. And before you're seen by any murderers."

"You shouldn't tease him," I said as he opened the gate for me.

"Do you honestly think he would have done a serviceable job as your brother?"

"Perhaps."

He snorted. "Only if he pretended to be a mute." He struck the door with the knocker.

It was opened by a housemaid.

"Good afternoon," Seth said, turning on his most charming smile.

The maid bobbed a curtsy, dipping her head but not quite hiding her blush. It never ceased to amaze me how quickly women fell under his spell. "Good afternoon, sir."

"My name is Seth Guilford and this is my sister, Charlotte. Is Mrs. Southey at home? We'd like to speak to her about her sister."

"I'll see." She opened the door wider to allow us into the entrance hall then disappeared into an adjoining room. She emerged a moment later. "Mrs. Southey is available to see you now."

She took our coats and hats and led the way into what turned out to be a modest sized parlor with floral wallpaper, sofa and curtains. There were flowers everywhere, as if spring had bloomed early and vigorously all over the furnishings. A younger but plainer version of Mrs. Drinkwater greeted us with an inquisitive raise of her brows.

"You're friends of my sister's?" she asked, once again taking a seat.

"Acquaintances," I said. Seth and I had decided that I would do most of the talking to put her at ease. He would only speak if that wasn't working and his charms were required instead. "In fact, we're looking for her. She doesn't appear to be at home. Do you know where we can find her?"

"I'm afraid not, but do you know, you're the second person to ask that question in two days?"

"Indeed?"

"A fellow came by yesterday. Rather wild looking man, and not at all friendly. I didn't let him in."

Lincoln. "Perhaps he was a policeman who wanted to update Mrs. Drinkwater on the investigation into poor Mr. Drinkwater's death."

"If he was, he ought to have declared himself. Not that it would have mattered. I didn't know where to find Merry, and I still don't. She told me she needed to spend a few days in peace, but wouldn't tell me where." A small crease connected her brows. "I do hope she's all right."

I exchanged a worried glance with Seth.

"What is it?" Mrs. Southey touched the high ruffled collar at her throat. "Is she in danger?" She gasped. "Do you think Reggie's murderer is after her now? My lord, I just thought of something. What if that man who came yesterday is the murderer? I knew he was no good from the moment I set eyes on him. Too dark, too...foreign looking. Those eyes." She affected a shiver.

I clenched my teeth and forced out a sympathetic, "There, there. Don't fret. That's why my brother and I are here, to warn her. You see, my brother is a scientist and friend to Mr. Drinkwater."

"Was," Seth chimed in with a sad smile. "We were colleagues, working in a similar area. We shared our research from time to time. After Drinkwater's death, my rooms were ransacked but nothing was taken."

Mrs. Southey gasped again. "What were they looking for?"

"Research papers. We're both working on something highly sensitive."

"False limbs?"

"I can't confirm or deny that, I'm afraid. I wouldn't want to endanger your life too."

Good lord. If I rolled my eyes any more they'd do complete loops in the sockets.

"It's my belief he was killed for them," Seth went on, "but the killers didn't find what they wanted, so they came looking in my study, only to leave empty handed. I believe they think your sister may have hidden her husband's papers instead—to keep them safe."

"Surely she would have said something to me."

"Perhaps, perhaps not. She might decide that you're safer not knowing."

Her fingers fluttered at her trembling lips. "It explains why she didn't tell me where she was going."

I nodded. This was going rather well. "The police have been informed, of course, but I'm afraid Detective Inspector Tench doesn't agree with our theory. He's unwilling to commit resources to protect her."

Using the detective's name seemed to have the desired effect. Mrs. Southey nodded eagerly along with everything I said. "He did strike me as a rather lazy fellow. Fat people often are."

It was fortunate that she didn't know about my necromancy or my background living on the streets. She seemed to be prejudiced against anyone who wasn't like her.

"We've decided to warn your sister ourselves," Seth told her. "We've known her a long time, and she'll trust us."

She chewed on her lip and blinked at him. He smiled warmly back, but it didn't have the usual effect. She squinted at him. "She never mentioned you to me before. I thought Reggie worked alone."

"He did, usually, but he brought me on board for his latest experiments. If I had *my* papers here, I would gladly prove it you. Unfortunately they're all the way back in my study in Mayfair."

"Mayfair!"

"My home," he added with wide-eyed innocence.

Her back straightened, reminding me of her sister with her erect posture. While not as poised as Merry, Mrs. Southey had a neat, precise way of moving that both sisters possessed. "Where in Mayfair?"

Seth waved his hand. "It's just an old pile of bricks, really, but it's been in the family for years."

I half expected him to drag out the family title of Vickers, but he merely smiled at her again. This time it worked. Mrs. Southey blushed and touched her hair.

"Mrs. Southey, it's imperative you help us find Merry," he said, turning serious. "You can't allow that foreigner to get to her first."

I glared at him but he ignored me.

Mrs. Southey swallowed heavily. "You're right. I didn't trust him from the moment I laid eyes on him. I ought to tell the detective."

"We'll do it, won't we, Charlotte?"

"We're on our way to Kensington now—if you tell us where to find her, that is. We'll hand over everything we know to Tench immediately. It's the right thing to do."

"Oh, I don't know where she is," she said.

"Perhaps not, but you know her better than anyone. There must be someone she trusts enough to visit for a few days."

"She has few close friends left. Reggie wasn't the most sociable man." The pinched lips and sour tone told me what she thought of her brother-in-law more than her words did.

"What about friends from before she married?"

Her cheeks flushed. She looked away. "She hasn't remained in touch with them."

"Are you sure?"

"Yes," she snapped.

"Mrs. Southey," Seth said gently. "Your sister's life might be in danger if he finds her before us. You must help us so we can inform the police. They can't protect her if they don't know where she is."

"It's just that...she would be so ashamed if any of her set knew." She bit her lip and glanced at me through lowered lashes. "Particularly someone as lovely as you, Miss Guilford."

Lovely? Me? "We'll keep her secret safe," I assured her. "I'm no gossip."

"Very true," Seth said. "She knows a thing or two about me that she's never told. The soul of discretion is dear Charlotte."

"This is quite a scandal, though." She nibbled her lip again. "But if the murderer finds her..."

"We'll see that he doesn't," Seth said, moving to sit beside her. He tucked her hand between both of his, winning a wide-eyed blink from her. "Trust us, Mrs. Southey. We only have your sister's interests at heart. She won't come to any harm if we find her first."

He was laying it on rather thick, but she seemed to be warming to the idea with every passing moment. She stopped biting her lip and sighed.

"You're right. Well then." She blew out a breath. "There was a particular friend from before she married. A woman by the name of Redding. Miss Letitia Redding."

Redding! I knew that name.

"And where will we find Miss Redding?" Seth asked.

The Alhambra.

"A theater known as The Alhambra." Mrs. Southey touched her hair again and didn't meet our gazes. "My sister used to dance there when she was younger, as did Miss Redding."

And Lady Harcourt.

CHAPTER 13

"It was Lady Harcourt," I announced to Seth in the coach. "She *must* be the one who helped Mrs. Drinkwater."

"Yes," he said simply. He looked troubled by the prospect, but I was in no mood to offer excuses or alternative theories. I was too angry. How *could* she? I knew she blamed me for keeping Lincoln from her, but I didn't think she hated me enough to have me kidnapped.

"I can't believe I didn't realize earlier," I said. "Mrs. Drinkwater had a certain way of walking, like Lady H. She would *glide* into the room, like a dancer. And her poise..." I shook my head, annoyed I'd not made the connection between the two. "We must hurry."

"Gus is driving as fast as he can. Anyway, there's no cause for alarm."

"Of course there is. Lady Harcourt must be worried that Lincoln will find Merry Drinkwater and she'll tell him about her involvement."

"You think she'll silence Merry? Charlie! She's no murderess."

"Are you very certain of that?"

"Yes!"

I drummed my fingers on the leather seat. "You may be right."

"I know I am. She may not be the kindest soul, but she's not violent. Besides, she has no reason to harm Merry Drinkwater. She knows we won't inform the police. Killing her achieves nothing. Fitzroy will be furious, but her relationship with him is well and truly over, thanks to your engagement. She can't have any hopes of renewing it now."

"I agree with you there. She isn't foolish enough to think having me abducted would make Lincoln love her."

He pinched the bridge of his nose and shook his head. "So what possible motive could Julia have had for helping her?"

"If we don't get an answer from Merry herself, we'll confront Lady H with what we know."

Gus stopped the coach directly outside The Alhambra. Seth got out first and opened the umbrella. The rain wasn't heavy but it provided cover from passersby. I flipped the hood of my coat up as I stepped onto the pavement. Now that we were in the heart of the city once again, it paid to be careful. No one had tried to harm me since leaving Lichfield, but that didn't mean I could let my guard down. I touched the amber pendant nestled against my chest. It was a comfort knowing the imp slept inside, awaiting my command.

We entered through the side door to the promenade, the undercover walkway that surrounded the theater itself. Seth folded up the umbrella and took in the stained carpet, the cobwebs and peeling paintwork.

"It looks so different in the daytime. So..." He shook his head.

"Gaudy? Unseemly?"

"I was going to say out dated, like a faded beauty trying to relive her youth with too much rouge. The low lighting of the evenings hide her age. This place is quite magical when the lamps are lit and the dancers come out, all dressed up in their feathers and finery. At least, it used to be."

"You sound sentimental. I thought you didn't come here much."

"So where do we find this Miss Redding?" he asked, ignoring me.

"Backstage." I led the way along the promenade but stopped at the top of the steps leading to the backstage corridor. I kept my voice low. "Try not to flirt with her."

He grinned. "Are you jealous?"

I rolled my eyes. "No, it's just that I think she's had some disappointment in her life. Unless you plan on a permanent arrangement with her rather than a single night, don't allow her hopes to rise."

"I'll try, but what you often call flirting is my usual charming character. I can't help it if ladies find me interesting when I'm not even trying."

"You said all of that with a serious face, too."

He gave me a blank look.

I headed down the steps into a corridor where Jonathon Golightly, the theater's stage manager, kept his office. I steeled myself for an unpleasant meeting with him and his assistant, Miss Redding. The last time I'd seen him, he'd invited me in, thinking I was related to a potential investor, only to ask me to leave when he learned that I wasn't.

Miss Redding, on the other hand, had been most helpful. A dancer once herself, she'd told me how Lady Harcourt, known then as Miss D.D., had performed at

The Al before her marriage to Lord Harcourt. Andrew Buchanan, her stepson, had also been infatuated with her at the time. Money must have been paid to Mr. Golightly, or threats made to keep the connection quiet, but Miss Redding either wasn't part of that financial arrangement or she was jealous of Lady Harcourt's good fortune. She'd imparted her gossip a little too easily, and her waspishness had left a bitter aftertaste.

The triangular connection between Lady Harcourt, Miss Redding and Merry Drinkwater was a curious one. If Miss Redding disliked Lady H but was friends with Merry, shouldn't the relationship between Lady H and Merry also be strained? Why would she help someone she disliked to kidnap me?

Mr. Golightly's office door was closed and the corridor empty. We slipped into the small kitchen and waited, without speaking, for several minutes until finally we heard voices, one male, the other female. Seth raised his brows at me, asking if I recognized them. I nodded.

"Tea," demanded Mr. Golightly. "And one of those little orange cakes."

"There aren't any left," Miss Redding said.

Golightly's mumbled response didn't reach me. A moment later, Miss Redding entered the kitchen. She let out a small squeal of surprise before I placed a finger to my lips to shush her. I listened for footsteps, but Golightly didn't come to investigate.

"You!" Miss Redding's wide eyes inspected me as if she were expecting to find me changed from our last meeting. "I thought I'd never see you again."

"Oh?" I said, rather stupidly. I hadn't yet decided how to approach her on the topic of Mrs. Drinkwater. It might be time to tell the truth, or part of it. Hopefully it wouldn't have the opposite effect of silencing her.

"Good afternoon." Seth had been standing by the door so that she'd sailed right past him upon entering.

At the sound of his voice, she spun and gasped loudly. "Who are you?" Her hand came up to her blonde curls and twirled them as a shy little girl would. It was perhaps a habit born from years of being self-conscious about the pockmark scars on her face. Although she'd not shown such shyness with me, Seth was quite a different matter. The man was beautiful, and if one admired beautiful men, it was easy to feel inadequate in his shadow.

It would seem I was immune to his appeal. "This is my dear friend, Seth," I said. "Seth, this is Miss Redding."

She held out her hand to him. He took it and kissed it then smiled up at her. She blushed to the tips of ears. If he was trying not to flirt, he was doing a terrible job.

"Your...friend?" she said to me.

Perhaps I should have introduced him as my brother. "Yes."

"What about your fiancé?"

"How do you know about him?"

"You told me."

Oh. Of course. She meant Andrew Buchanan, not Lincoln. After all my questions about Lord Harcourt's family last time, she'd assumed Buchanan and I were engaged. I'd not corrected her. "Seth is actually a friend of Andrew's," I said, hoping Seth would play along. "Andrew couldn't escort me here today, so Seth offered."

"You didn't require an escort last time."

"Andrew has become more and more jealous of late. Silly fellow."

"Then it's surprising that he wanted *this* fellow to escort you."

Seth shot me a grin from behind her back, but quickly schooled it when she turned to him. "Andrew trusts me implicitly," he said.

"He does," I agreed, "because of your...affliction." I glanced pointedly at his groin.

Miss Redding flushed scarlet and toyed with her curls again. Seth looked like he wanted to strangle me.

"Actually, Seth is the reason we came. He's a friend to Reginald Drinkwater. Or should I say, he was. That's why we're here, because you know the Drinkwaters too."

"Yes, I do," Miss Redding said. "Poor Merry. She misses him terribly."

She spoke about her as if she'd seen her recently. Good. We were on the right path.

"How do you know Mr. Drinkwater?" Miss Redding asked.

Seth told her the same story he'd told Mrs. Southey.

"You don't look like a scientist," she said when he finished.

Seth opened his mouth to speak, but I got in first. "Don't let his pretty appearance fool you. He's actually quite intelligent."

"You're too kind, Charlotte," he said through a hard smile.

"So you see, we're worried about Mrs. Drinkwater," I said. "After Seth told me all about Mr. Drinkwater's tragic death, I promised to look in on his widow. Later, after Seth's rooms were ransacked, he insisted we warn her and so we went to visit again, but she wasn't at home or at her sister's. She's particularly vulnerable right now, and I don't think she's aware that she may be targeted next. I hoped *you* knew where to find her so we could inform her."

"How did you know we were friends?"

"She told me she danced here with you in her youth. You and Miss D.D."

Her mouth twisted to the side as she studied me. Miss Redding was an astute woman, and not as trusting as Mrs. Southey. Convincing her would be a real test of our acting skills. "It's very unlikely she would have told anyone about her past."

She did not deny that Mrs. Drinkwater and Lady Harcourt had danced together. That was something.

I took both her hands in mine and squeezed. "You're right to be skeptical at a time like this. Mrs. Drinkwater must be protected. But I assure you, she did tell me herself. How else would I know about your friendship if she hadn't?"

Her mouth twitched right then left as she thought. "I suppose so. Thank you for stopping by to warn me. I'll pass the message on to her."

"We'd rather do it ourselves," Seth said. "To check on her wellbeing, you see."

"I'm not sure she wishes to see anybody right now."

"She'll see us," I assured her. I squeezed her hands again. "I also want to pass on the regards of Andrew's stepmother."

"Julia Templeton?"

"Lady Harcourt," Seth corrected.

"Why would she send her regards?"

"She's concerned for her friend too, and wishes to offer shelter, if necessary," I said. "We're to pass the message on to Mrs. Drinkwater in person."

Miss Redding snorted. "Is this a joke?"

"Why would it be?"

"Because the high and mighty Lady Harcourt wouldn't even look at either Merry or me if she passed us in the street, let alone speak with us. She certainly wouldn't offer shelter."

"Of course she would," Seth protested, quite sincerely.

I agreed with Miss Redding. Lady Harcourt had been desperate enough to become a dancer to stave off poverty, and she must be desperate now to save her reputation and keep her scandalous background a secret. If her society friends found out, her life in London would be over. She would have to move out of the city to avoid the stigma. The darling of London's social scene wouldn't want that.

"No, sir, she would not offer us a single thing." Miss Redding pulled her hands free of mine and crossed her arms. Her shyness had completely vanished, replaced by the cold steel I'd glimpsed on our first meeting. "Julia Templeton is a manipulative, ruthless cat who'll do anything to hold onto the position she gained through her marriage. Acknowledging those of us who knew her when she danced at The Al would mean admitting to that past. You must understand, a woman like her doesn't even want to remind herself. So I'm afraid I don't believe she ever said such a thing to you and I'm baffled as to why you would mention her at all."

"I can assure you, Lady Harcourt did offer to help Mrs. Drinkwater." Just not offer to shelter her, but to assist in my kidnapping. "There must be a reason," I said, for Seth's benefit.

His face brightened. He stood straighter, taller. "Someone wrote Lady Harcourt a letter, threatening to go to the weeklies with details about her past. Was that you, by any chance?"

"No!" Miss Redding pulled a face. "I would never do such a thing."

"Thank you." He leaned forward and kissed her cheek. "You've been a marvelous help. Come on, Charlie. It's time to go."

He took my hand and pulled me out of the kitchen, barely giving me enough time to toss out a "Thank you," and "Goodbye, " to the very flushed Miss Redding. She looked quite stunned, but I wasn't sure if that was due to our sudden departure or Seth's kiss.

We raced past Mr. Golightly's office so quickly that he didn't even see us, up the steps and out to the promenade.

"Slow down," I said as I stumbled.

He stopped to allow me to regain my balance. "She *blackmailed* her," he said. "Merry Drinkwater blackmailed Julia into telling her everything about you, and about Lichfield needing a housekeeper *et cetera*."

"I suppose." I shook my head. "But she would have had to know about my necromancy in the first place—and Lady Harcourt's connection to me. How? Who told her?"

"I don't know. We'll ask Merry Drinkwater."

"How can we do that if we can't find her?"

"I think Miss Redding does know where her friend is, but won't say. We'll follow her home at the end of the day. It's likely we'll find Merry there."

He opened the door for me, almost knocking over a woman who was about to enter The Al. She looked up and gasped.

"Mrs. Drinkwater!" I went to grab her hand but she ran off.

Seth ran after her. "Gus! Stop her!"

But Gus must have been half asleep. He tilted his hat back as he sat up from his slumped position on the coachman's seat. "What?" He saw the woman run past and Seth follow. "Blimey!" He too jumped down. "Charlie, watch the horse."

"I'm not sure it requires both of you," I called after them.

But he didn't listen to me. He followed after Seth who'd slowed down when several gentlemen eyed him with suspicion. The horse stood quietly, but I reached for the bridle anyway.

A gloved hand caught mine and something pressed into my back.

"Do as I say. I have a gun." Holloway! Oh God. He wasn't dead then.

Pity. "What do you want?" I kept my voice low, level, so as not to startle him. If I moved suddenly, he might fire.

"I want to save you, my girl."

"I'm not your girl, and I don't need saving."

"Of course you do. Look at you, cavorting with men." He spat out the words as if they tasted vile. Despite the strength of his conviction, he was suffering from illness. His grip felt weaker and his hand shook. I could feel the heat of his fever through our clothing, and his breath stank. "The devil is in you, *Whore*."

It was pointless arguing with him. He wouldn't listen. His mind was closed, and perhaps touched by the fever, madness, or both.

There were few passersby, and none seemed to notice my peril. I didn't scream or plead for help. Holloway was just mad enough to kill me there on the street. I wanted to glance back to see if Seth and Gus had seen, but I didn't dare.

He shoved me. "Up."

"You want me to drive?"

"We're going somewhere safe. Somewhere far away so I can exorcise the beast from you without disturbance."

I plopped down on the seat and grabbed the reins. He stretched his arm around my shoulders and placed the barrel of the small pistol at my throat. My coat collar hid it, but no one was looking anyway.

"I don't know how to drive," I said lamely.

"Flick the reins."

I did and the horse moved off. Another coachman shouted abuse when he had to pull up quickly to avoid a collision. When he saw that a woman drove, he shook his head. "You should be in the home! Leave the drivin' to them who can manage!"

The horse followed the traffic at a steady pace. I spotted Gus rounding the corner. He didn't see me and I didn't shout out. He would soon notice the coach gone. I felt some sympathy for him and Seth. They would go into a panic when they found me gone.

But I wouldn't try to fight Holloway, nor would I summon my imp. Not yet. I had the perfect opportunity to ask him who'd helped him escape from prison, and I wasn't going to waste it.

I only hoped he wouldn't try to kill me first.

CHAPTER 14

"Who helped you escape from jail?" It was the third time I'd asked, and Holloway no longer bothered to answer. The first time, he denied having help, and the second time he said it was none of my business.

Once we'd left behind the busy streets of central London, driving had become easier. The first half an hour or so had taken all of my concentration to control the horse. Holloway had offered little assistance, only telling me to go faster when the horse slowed.

"I've never driven before," I snapped at him when he once again told me the pace was too slow.

"Don't lie to me. I know your whoremaster taught you to ride."

"First of all, he is not my whoremaster. Or anyone's, for that matter. Secondly, yes he taught me to ride, but not drive." Although I had picked up a little of the technique by watching him and the others. "Where are we going?"

"Be quiet," he growled. "I taught you to speak only when you're spoken to."

"Along with a number of other foolish things. 'Novels will corrupt your delicate mind,' is a particular favorite of mine."

He grabbed my jaw and forced me to look at him. His thumb dug into my skin, mashing my teeth against the inside of my cheek. "Stop it," he hissed.

I jerked away, only to drive the barrel of the small pistol into my neck. I sucked in air as it bit into my skin. "You're hurting me."

"Good. The devil only responds to pain."

He let me go and I remained quiet. I didn't want to risk his ire. He might want to save me, but if I became difficult or a burden, I didn't know what he'd do. His eyes were bright with the fever, his lips pale and his skin glossy. The hand that held the gun at my throat shook. Despite his illness, he seemed alert. He tensed whenever I moved, and that cold metal gun barrel continued to press against me. I couldn't have touched the pendant at my chest even if I'd wanted to.

We headed north and east through London until the houses became smaller and then gave way to industry altogether. High factory walls lined the road on both sides. Enormous chimneys spewed smoke into the already gloomy sky. We passed an ironworks, a rubber works, dye factory and even a piano maker, with a showroom attached. The air in London was never clean, but here it was thick with the odors and sooty smoke of manufacturing. I could feel it on my face, settling into my skin. The few people out on the street in the miserable weather kept their heads bowed and took no notice of us.

I'd never been to this part of the city but I'd taken careful note of our route, and I felt confident I could make my way out again. That's if we stopped soon. I began to worry that Holloway wanted me to drive forever when he finally directed me to enter a lane. It was home to more workshops and factories, but on a much smaller scale, each one jammed up against its neighbor to stake its claim on the street.

"Pull over here." He pointed to a low, brown-brick building squashed between an upholsterer and a French polishing workshop. "Tie the horse to the bollard near the trough."

"What if someone tries to steal him or the coach?"

He didn't answer me. He took the reins and got down first. I followed slowly, not taking my eyes off him. Once on the ground, I touched the pendant at my chest. I could say the words and the imp would save me, but then I wouldn't get answers.

I needed those answers. Who hated me enough to release Holloway from jail and set him upon me? Was this Lady Harcourt's doing too? Or was it someone outside the committee altogether? Either way, finding out would go a long way to proving my worth to them.

Holloway fished out a key from his inside jacket pocket and tossed it to me. "Unlock the door and get inside."

My hands trembled but I managed the task. There was enough light streaming through the high arched windows to see that the factory was mostly empty. An enormous kiln occupied the center of the vast space, its bricks blackened at the mouth. The thick chimney could easily fit two of me, side by side. Broken crates and barrels formed a pile in the corner, and a white powder spewed from torn sacks. Newspapers littered the floor, along with pieces of pottery, some of them jagged and sharp. I took note of all the potential weapons within reach.

It was colder in the cavernous factory than outside, and I wasn't the only one feeling it. Holloway waggled the gun at me. "Light a fire."

"Do you have matches?"

He jerked his chin at the window where a box of matches sat on the sill. I retrieved the box and gathered some newspapers, placing them in the kiln. Holloway dragged over a bag of coal. He was puffing by the time he reached me and sweat dripped from his brow. He wiped it off with the back of his hand and shivered.

"Hurry up." He hunched into his coat. Whoever had assisted him to escape had given him clothing for winter. He couldn't have retrieved them from home; it would be the first place the police would look for him.

It made me wonder if his neighbors and parishioners would protect him or alert the police if he had gone to them. Probably not. His reputation would be ruined now. How ironic that I was the cause.

I finished making the fire and knelt on the flagstone floor to soak up the warmth. Slowly, slowly, my fingers thawed, and I could once again feel my face.

"You like that, don't you, Devil Child? You're used to the flames of hell."

I didn't respond. Nothing I could say would convince him that I wasn't possessed by the devil.

He wiped his brow on the back of his sleeve. His breathing hadn't returned to normal after his exertion. If anything, he looked paler, his skin slicker. He'd lost weight since his arrest. The bones in his face were more prominent, his cheeks and chin sharper. Prison hadn't been good for him.

Perhaps I should have felt sorry for him, but I couldn't muster any sympathy. I felt nothing for him, not even fear. I'd seen what my imp could do. It might be time to summon it, if I could be sure I could do so before Holloway fired the gun.

He lowered it to his lap as if it had become too heavy. He wiped his brow again. No, not his brow, his eyes. They were wet. From crying or from the fever? "You were such a good little girl. Such a dear little thing." He shook his head and his lips trembled. He *was* crying.

A lump filled my throat. I swallowed it down. I would *not* feel sympathy for this man, for the life I could have had if he'd never thrown me out. That was the past and I refused to dwell upon it.

"How?" He spoke so quietly I almost didn't hear him. "How did the devil get in? I don't understand, Lord." He searched the ceiling, but the rafters remained quiet, still. "Why did you forsake my daughter? What did I do to deserve this?"

Slowly, slowly, so as not to alert him, I raised my hand to the amber. It throbbed in time to my heartbeat.

"Guide me in this time of need. Help me expel the demons inside her."

"Who released you from prison?" I demanded again, one last time. "Was it Lady Harcourt?"

His muddy eyes didn't quite focus on me. He swayed too, but the gun remained steady.

If I wanted answers, I needed to change questioning tactics. "I had a wonderful childhood. It was filled with everything a little girl needs—dolls, toys, pretty ribbons and an education." Albeit one confined by Holloway's strict beliefs. "And parents who loved me."

He wiped the beads of sweat off his forehead. "We tried so hard to bring you up a good Christian girl." He shook his head, as if he couldn't believe all that effort had been wasted.

"You and Mama were my entire world."

"And you were ours. We never told anyone you were adopted. It seemed unnecessary, when we loved you as much as any parent loved their child." He looked as if he would start crying again. "And yet this is how our efforts are repaid."

"It's not your fault," I told him. "Or mine. I was born this way. You weren't to know."

His gaze sharpened. "Yes! Yes, you're right. It's not our fault. We did everything we could. We loved you...but our love could never be enough because of what you truly are. A de—"

"Don't say it." The pendant throbbed harder, as if the imp were begging me to release it.

He eyed me for a long moment, as if trying to see the demon he thought lurked inside me. I stared back, unblinking, willing him to see the little girl he'd once called his own. Wanting him to call me 'daughter' again, if only because it meant there might be a chance that I could walk free without hurting him. It was impossible to tell from his fever-ravaged face whether I was getting through.

"I wish Mama was alive."

"Do not call her that," he snarled. "She is not your Mama. She never was." He pushed himself to his feet and stumbled forward. For one heart-stopping moment I thought he might fire the gun accidentally. He seemed hardly in control of his own movements as he swayed back and forth. Spittle frothed on his lower lip and sweat dripped from his brow. "She was my beautiful, loving wife." He began to shake and cry, the tears and sweat pouring down his face. "And now she is dead."

"I miss her," I hazarded.

"*You* miss her!" He clutched the gun in both hands and aimed it at my forehead. "She is not yours to miss!"

"I...I only meant—"

"Quiet!" He began to circle me slowly, not lowering the gun. I followed his progress, my fingers twitching around the pendant. "I thank the lord every day that he took her so she can't see what you became, you disgusting creature. You filthy, grotesque abomination! If she had learned what lived inside you she would have been appalled. She would have cast out the devil immediately. She was strong, where I have been weak. I should have destroyed it—destroyed you—the moment I saw what you truly are. But I—I couldn't. Sending you away was all I could manage."

"I was thirteen!"

"I was too sentimental." He bared his teeth, now yellow and rotting in his gums from lack of care in jail. "I should have cut your throat."

"You almost did. You're mad."

"You're wrong. They're all wrong. Only one understands."

"Who?" I blurted out.

His eyes burned with the fever, not quite focusing on me anymore. "He can see the devil too. He knows you for what you truly are, and he wants you gone from this Earth, back to Hell, where you belong."

He. So it wasn't Lady Harcourt. "How did you get out of jail? They thought you were dead."

"He gave me a foul concoction that slows the heart to almost nothing. Once the effects wore off, I woke up in another room, alone. It was easy for him to get me out of there. No one was watching."

"He wants you to kill me?"

"He showed me that I have been weak, that I should have killed you years ago. He gave me this chance to make amends, to conquer the evil you've brought here. I won't waste it." His fingers flexed around the pistol handle. Squeezed the trigger.

"Imp!"

I rolled to the side as the gunshot rang out. My shoulder and hip smacked into the floor despite putting out both hands to save myself.

"Imp, I release you!"

Nothing happened.

I felt at my chest for the pendant, but it was gone. No, no, no! I couldn't summon the imp without touching it. It must have come off when I fell. Where had it gone?

He aimed the gun again. I scurried across the floor, kicking the barrel toward him as I did so. He dodged it, stumbling to one knee, and the barrel rolled past and into the fire. I got to my feet and ran behind the kiln.

"Come back, Devil," he snarled. "You cannot escape."

He was right. I had to pass him to get to the door, or expose myself to reach one of the windows. Where was my pendant? Why had I waited so long to summon the imp?

Because I wanted answers. I wanted to convince him that I was still his daughter. My foolish delay had almost got me killed; it might yet. Without the imp, I had to get free on my own. If Holloway didn't have a gun, it might have been possible to overpower him, but even in his fevered state, he could still shoot.

"Come back here." His snarl came from closer than I expected. He was rounding the kiln to my left, so I moved to my right.

I continued around the large oven, back to where he'd been standing when he fired. A beam of late afternoon sun glinted off the pendant lying on the floor a few feet away. Too far. He would see me if I tried to retrieve it.

I needed a distraction.

A piece of wood from a broken barrel cracked as the fire caught it. The end stuck out, unburned, just near my feet. I picked it up and threw it as hard as I could into the pile of barrels and crates. It didn't quite reach, but skidded across the floor, spitting off sparks and sweeping up pages of newspaper in its path.

Holloway gasped. "Are you trying to frighten me, Devil?"

I pounced on the pendant. It flared to life in my gloved hand. "I release you, Imp. Come out now."

Yellow light burst from the pendant. I shut my eyes against the brightness but didn't let go of the necklace.

"What are you doing?" Holloway shouted. "Cease your devil's magic!"

I opened my eyes again and peered down at the creature at my feet, its long pink tongue lolling out of its mouth. It panted and looked up at me, waiting for instruction.

"Go," I told it. "Save me from that man."

It sat on its haunches and tilted its head to the side.

"Go, imp!" I pointed in the direction of the kiln.

Its gaze followed my hand, still holding the pendant, but when I returned it to my side, the imp once again merely peered up at me like a dog waiting for its mistress to throw a stick.

Flames flared in the corner of the factory, licking at the barrels and crates. They'd caught alight quickly thanks to the newspaper, and the fire was in danger of spreading to the sacks filled with powder. It would run out of fuel soon and burn itself out without spreading.

Holloway might even now be heading to me. I had to direct the imp to stop him somehow. If only I could be sure it wouldn't kill him.

"What have you done?" Holloway's high-pitched cry came from the other side of the kiln. "This entire place will go up!"

I was about to tell him it was just a small fire when an explosion boomed. Glass shattered. Wood splintered. I fell to the floor and covered my head as another explosion ripped through the warehouse, sending shards of wood flying about. It felt as if the building itself shook.

Holloway shouted obscenities over the roar of the fire that now engulfed all the barrels and crates and danced along the beams above. "The powder is explosive!" he shouted. "We're both going to die, you stupid girl!"

Something pulled at my sleeve and for a moment I thought it was Holloway, but it was the imp, urging me to get out.

I glanced toward the kiln, only to see that one side of it had collapsed, the bricks strewn around the base. The chimney bowed, in danger of falling. I scrambled further away from it, drawing the imp with me.

Yet another explosion shook the factory. I pulled the imp against my chest, protecting it, momentarily forgetting it was supposed to protect me. I glanced up just in time to see the chimney shudder then crumple in on itself. Dust mushroomed up to the ceiling and blocked out light from the windows and flames. The almighty crash drowned out the roar of the fire, but only for a moment.

The imp and I huddled on the floor. No sound came from the other side of the chimney rubble, only the roar of the fire. It had taken hold of most of the warehouse now, filling it with black billowing smoke that smelled bitter and stung my eyes. That powder had been noxious as well as flammable.

Someone shouted from the doorway: "Anyone inside?"

Holloway didn't answer.

I opened my mouth to shout back but only managed a splutter. Smoke clogged my throat and chest. I coughed and coughed until my body hurt. I tried to breathe, but the hot, smoky air only made me cough harder.

The imp's claw grasped my collar and lifted it over my nose and mouth. I gasped in a breath. It wasn't pure air but it was enough, for now.

The imp tugged my sleeve again, trying to pull me toward the door. I pocketed the pendant and headed the other way. On hands and knees, I crawled around the pile of bricks that had formed the chimney. I couldn't see anyone through the smoky haze.

I searched the rubble, pushing aside debris. Another coughing fit overtook me, but I didn't stop. The imp kept tugging and tugging, whimpering like a puppy. But I couldn't leave yet. I had to know.

I tossed bricks aside, revealing a booted foot and a trouser leg. The rest of him was buried beneath the rubble. I shook his foot, but there was no response.

"Holloway!" The word felt like a shard of glass in my throat, and was barely audible. I shook his foot again.

He didn't respond. Didn't move. He was gone.

The imp pulled harder on my sleeve. Then its head jerked back suddenly, as if it had heard a noise on the roof. I glanced up, just in time to see the flames eat through one of the rafters. With an agonised groan, the massive black beam fell straight for me.

CHAPTER 15

I dived to the side, covering my face, but I knew it wouldn't be fast enough or far enough to save myself from the falling timber.

Yet the wooden beam didn't hit me. I looked up to see it land harmlessly on the pile of bricks a few feet away. The imp, now the size of a horse, stood on its hind legs. I hardly had time to consider what had happened when a creak and another monstrous groan from above signaled the imminent collapse of the ceiling. I scrambled to my feet. The imp grabbed my hand and pulled me after it. It was strong, and I couldn't have resisted even if I'd wanted to.

More beams fell. Roof tiles crashed onto the rubble. I ducked whenever a beam came close, but it wasn't necessary. The imp batted them away as if they were merely twigs, flinging them around the room. Without it, I would have been crushed.

It hauled me toward the open door. I stumbled through, coughing uncontrollably, and barreled into a man.

"Steady, miss. Blimey! Didn't know anyone was in there."

Hissing. I could hear steam hissing over the crack and growl of the fire. Shouting too. Everyone seemed to be shouting at me. Through my damp, stinging eyes I could make out a lot of men running about. Where had they all come from? I tried to speak to them, but my throat felt like it was on fire. Breathing hurt, too. I couldn't get enough air into my lungs. And that infernal hissing! It wouldn't stop. When my eyes cleared a little, I could see that it belonged to the brass pump on the fire engine. The people were firemen and they were dragging a large hose up to the burning factory.

Windows popped. Glass shattered. Someone pushed me down and out of the way. When I looked up again, smoke spewed from the broken windows, and the firemen were trying to put out the flames licking the frames.

"Anyone else in there?" the man who'd caught me asked.

I shook my head. "Dead," I managed.

He patted my shoulder. "Least you got out alive, eh? You and your...cat. Lucky. Very lucky. Whole place is about to fall."

Something tickled my cheek. I wiped it and my sleeve came away damp. My tears surprised me. I'd not thought I would shed them for Holloway. Perhaps it was only the smoke making my eyes water.

More men arrived, running past me. Local factory hands perhaps, come to help the firemen to stop the fire spreading. There was no sign of my horse or coach.

The imp, however, sat on its haunches at my side, panting, its tongue out. Nobody paid it any notice. "Come," I said.

No one tried to stop me as I headed away from the fire. They were all too busy. My chest still felt as if something were crushing it, but I managed to reach the end of the lane before another coughing fit overtook me.

I placed my hand to the wall to regain my strength and my breath. The imp watched, waiting. It mewled once then lay down, its chin on its paws. The poor thing must be tired after repeatedly saving me.

I glanced around, but nobody was near. "Back into your amber, imp. Go to sleep now. Return."

I shut my sore eyes against the blinding light. When I opened them again, the imp was gone. I checked my pocket. The pendant was still there, thank God. It felt warm.

I stumbled out of the lane and around the corner. I wanted to get away before someone stopped me and asked questions. I just wanted to go home.

I began to walk. Without a reticule, I couldn't pay for a hansom back to Lichfield. Then I saw the coach, and the horse still with it, tied to a bollard. Someone must have led it away from the fire. I couldn't believe my good fortune.

I gathered up the reins and, with effort, climbed up to the driver's seat. Unsure exactly where I was, or how to get to Highgate, I returned the way we'd come, back into the city until I recognized a familiar street. From there, it didn't take long before I reached the gates of Lichfield Towers.

Home.

I couldn't wait to get inside and collapse on the sofa with a cup of hot chocolate and Lincoln's arms embracing me.

The horse knew its way to the stables and coach house, so I didn't have to do anything except hold the reins. I was still some distance down the drive, however, when the front door burst open and Gus, Seth and Cook hurtled out. Doyle brought up the rear.

"Bloody hell," Gus growled, snatching the bridle. His prominent brow crashed together. "What'd you take off for?"

"Holloway forced me," I rasped.

"Holloway?" He looked to Seth, but Seth was watching me with a frown. "Where'd he take you?"

"To a factory on the edge of the city. It was set alight and I escaped."

"That be why you're covered in ash and soot," Cook said, hands on hips. "We be worried about you."

"Aye," Gus muttered. "Very. You're a sight for sore eyes, let me tell you. Where's Holloway now?"

"Dead."

Seth expelled a breath. "Are you all right?"

I nodded. I felt numb now that the danger had passed. Perhaps later, when I thought about it during a quiet moment, I would feel something. But not yet.

"That's that, then." Gus patted the horse's nose. "Go inside, Charlie. I'll see to the coach and horse."

"And I'll make you something warm." Cook headed back into the house, and Doyle followed him like an automaton. I don't think he'd blinked once as he'd stared at me through wide eyes. I must be a sorry sight.

"Hot chocolate," I called after Cook, although I was not sure if he heard. My roughened voice held little strength.

Seth helped me down and we didn't speak as he gripped my elbow and steered me inside. Doyle removed my coat, pinching it between thumb and finger. It was filthy. I plucked off my gloves, only to see that the tips were worn through and the palms scratched up from when I searched for Holloway's body beneath the bricks.

"Throw them out," I said to Doyle. "They're ruined."

"Of course, miss. And I'll see to your coat. Er..." He glanced at my head. "Your hat?"

I touched my hair. It no longer seemed to be contained by pins and tumbled to my shoulders. "I must have lost it." It had probably burned by now, along with Holloway.

Seth directed me to the sofa in the parlor. "Sit. Rest."

"I'm all right."

"You don't look it. Are you sure you're not hurt?"

"I'm sure. Just a little shaken and very dirty." My dress was mostly clean, thanks to being covered by the long coat, but the hem was filthy and when I wiped my face, my hand came away black.

"Lincoln isn't back?" I asked.

"No, but he sent you a message to say that he would be home before nightfall."

"That's considerate of him." I wished he were home, although I was rather glad that he wouldn't see me in such a state. I needed to wash up before nightfall and think of the best way to tell him of my...adventure.

Seth added more coal to the fire then came to sit beside me. He dragged his hand through his hair and slouched back into the sofa, regarding me. He looked unhappy.

"Are *you* all right?" I asked him.

"I'm just glad you're back. We all are. To say we were worried is putting it mildly. We didn't know if you'd left of your own accord or been taken."

"Holloway waited until you and Gus were out of sight then forced me to drive off."

"Gus should have stayed with you."

"It's not his fault."

He grunted. "Why did you wait so long to escape? Why not do it then and there?"

"He had a gun."

"You had the imp."

"I didn't want to use it until I had answers. Besides, I've discovered that it only saves me when my life is in direct danger. It wouldn't attack Holloway while he held the gun or threatened me, but based on previous experience, would stop the bullet if he fired." I fished the pendant out of my pocket. The tiny creature in the amber slept soundly, exhausted after its ordeal. "It saved me from the fire."

"Did Holloway start it?"

"I did. It was an accident. I didn't know the powder in the sacks was explosive."

"Bloody hell, Charlie." He stroked the amber in my palm.

"I know."

Doyle came in carrying a tray with a jug of water and a cup. He poured and handed me the cup. "Your throat will appreciate it."

He was right. I drank the contents in a single gulp. "Thank you, Doyle. All these happenings must seem odd to you."

"I've seen many odd things in my time." He eyed Seth sideways.

I was grateful for his professional manner. Despite his calm exterior, recent events must have rattled him too, but I wasn't ready to tell him everything. It would be necessary to do so soon, however.

"Doyle, if you would be so kind as to run me a bath," I said.

He left as Cook arrived with a cup of chocolate and Gus not much later. "Horse is jittery," he said. "You did well to control him."

The three men stood or sat around me, not speaking. It was as if they were waiting for something, but I didn't know what. Tears? Hysterics? They ought to know me better than that. I gave them a fuller account of what had happened, merely to break the silence. They listened without interrupting.

"I hope the fire doesn't spread to the other factories," I finished.

"I'm sure the firemen will have it under control by now." Seth glanced at Gus.

Gus cleared his throat and folded his arms. He didn't meet my gaze.

"What is it?" I asked. "What's happened?"

"We found Mrs. Drinkwater."

"Bloody hell! Why didn't you tell me earlier?"

"We wanted you to recover first."

"I am recovered."

"You ain't," Cook said. "You be shaky and filthy."

Seth and Gus nodded in agreement.

I rounded on Seth. "Where is Mrs. Drinkwater now?"

"The tower room."

"You locked her in?"

"Of course. We don't want her to escape."

"She's afraid of Fitzroy," Gus said. "Hardly blame her for that, but we can't let her go until he speaks to her."

"I'll speak with her first." I stood and marched to the door.

They didn't try to stop me as I suspected they would, but they did follow me. "What has she said to you so far?"

"Nothing," Seth said. "She says she'll speak only to you."

"Is that so?"

"She's afraid of us too."

"Can't think why," Gus chimed in. "We're the nice ones."

"You look frightening," Seth told him.

"Do not! Charlie, do I frighten you?"

"Not at all." I didn't tell him that his scars and craggy face had given me nightmares when I first met him.

"Are you sure you don't want to talk to her *after* your bath?" Seth asked.

"I don't want to waste another moment. I think it's best that I talk to her before Lincoln, in case she closes up when he confronts her. If he's still furious about the kidnapping, he might scare her into silence."

"Precisely what we were thinking," Seth said.

He pulled the key out of his pocket when we reached the top of the tower, the highest level in the house. He unlocked the door and went in first.

"Charlie's back," he announced.

"So I saw," said Mrs. Drinkwater, sitting on a chair by the window. The room was cold, the fire had gone out.

I asked Seth to re-light it. Mrs. Drinkwater took in my disheveled appearance before smoothing her hands over her lap.

"I hope my men didn't harm you," I said.

She rubbed her right wrist. "They weren't particularly gentle."

"Please accept our apologies," Seth said from the fireplace.

Gus snorted. "I ain't apologizin'. She deserved that, and more, for what she did to Charlie and me."

"You were unharmed," Mrs. Drinkwater protested.

"You shot me!"

"I minor wound. If I'd wanted to hurt you, I could have."

"We were locked in your cellar!" he went on.

"And now I'm locked in here. Shall we call it even?"

He grunted again. "*We* were tied up."

I interrupted before he could suggest someone fetch rope. "Mrs. Drinkwater, I'm sorry for keeping you here, but you must understand, we need answers and we can't risk your escape."

She glanced past me to the door. Gus closed it and stood in front of it, arms crossed.

"And after I give you answers? What will you do with me then?"

"Set you free. We have no reason to detain you indefinitely. Or harm you," I added in case she wasn't sure.

"Does Mr. Fitzroy agree?"

"He's not here. He's out looking for you, as it happens. But I'm sure he'll see there's no sense in keeping you here. He only wants answers too."

"Not revenge?"

"You have my word that he won't harm you, Mrs. Drinkwater. He's not a cruel man, merely...upset at what happened. He has calmed down somewhat."

She twisted her hands together in her lap but it didn't hide their trembling. "I must congratulate you on connecting me to The Alhambra. How did you know?"

"Your sister was forthcoming with the information once she realized your life may be in danger if you weren't warned."

She shot to her feet. "Danger! From someone other than Mr. Fitzroy?"

I refrained from rolling my eyes and telling her *again* that she was in no danger from Lincoln. "We think the person who helped you may want to...silence you."

She plopped down onto the chair, her hand to her chest. "No, I don't believe she would. She had ample opportunity after I approached her that first time."

"Do you mean Lady Harcourt?" Seth asked, coming to stand beside me.

She nodded.

"You've known her a long time," I said. "From the days you danced together."

"My sister told you that too? I'm sure she took delight in imparting the details."

Seth sat on the edge of the bed with a heavy sigh. "Damn, damn and hell."

I felt a little sorry for him at hearing the confirmation of Lady Harcourt's guilt, but not too much. He'd had blinkers on where she was concerned, and it was past time they came off. "You said *you* approached *her*," I prompted Mrs. Drinkwater. "Do you mean to say that the abduction wasn't her idea?"

"It was mine. I wanted my husband back..." She touched her nose and her eyes misted. "I wanted Reggie back, and I knew she was familiar with the occult. I asked her to assist me."

"Asked?" Seth snapped. "Or blackmailed."

She looked down at the rug.

I sat on the bed beside Seth, tired and a little overwhelmed. "Mrs. Drinkwater, perhaps if you tell us everything from the beginning. Leave nothing out. We need to get to the bottom of this. I need to know who I can and can't trust."

"I wouldn't trust Julia," she spat. "That woman would sell her own mother if it meant she could bury her past."

I placed my hand over Seth's when he bristled. Thankfully he got the message and kept quiet.

"I admit that I enlisted Julia in my scheme," she said. "I knew her from our time together at The Al, but we'd lost touch. She wanted nothing to do with any of us after her marriage to Lord Harcourt." She sighed. "I suppose it's understandable, but honestly, it was the way she went about it. She was such a hoity-toity miss, always putting on airs, even when she was simple Miss Templeton, the schoolmaster's daughter."

Her mouth twisted into a sneer as she spoke, reminding me very much of Miss Redding. Both women disliked Lady Harcourt intensely.

"You threatened to go to the newspapers if she didn't help you," Seth said.

"I did write a letter to her implying such a thing, yes, but I would never have carried it out."

"That is irrelevant!"

She lifted her chin. "I beg to differ. One cannot be accused of something that one didn't do. Besides, she deserved to be a little shaken and reminded of her past. Someone like that shouldn't be allowed to lord it over the rest of us. She's just as common as we are."

"How did you know about her connection to me and my necromancy?" I asked before Seth could get into an argument with her.

"I didn't. Not specifically, anyway. I knew she had an interest in magic, you see, because she approached us years ago and asked Reggie questions about his work. She must have read about his research in one of the science journals and suspected he was using magic. When she knocked on our door, I was so surprised to see her, as was she to see me." She smiled, but it was bitter, cold. "You ought to have seen her face. It went as white as a sheet. I thought she was there to see me, but she told me she wanted to ask Reggie some questions. She asked him about his skill, made some notes, then went on her way again without so much as an explanation as to why she needed to know.

"So when I decided I wanted to see Reggie again, after his death, I thought of her and her interest in magic. If anyone could speak with spirits, or know someone who could, it would be her. She denied it at first and claimed she couldn't help. I was so angry! I went home and, after thinking about it some more, wrote the letter telling her to meet me or I'd tell everyone about her past at The Al. So you see, if she ever wanted to kill me to silence me, it would have been then."

She was right. Lady Harcourt wouldn't kill her. She wasn't a murderess. "So she agreed to help after that?"

She nodded. "I only wanted to speak to Reggie's spirit to find out if he knew who had killed him, but she suggested something better. She told me all about you and what you can do."

Lady Harcourt hadn't needed to do that. She could have simply told Mrs. Drinkwater that I could speak with spirits. She didn't need to mention the full extent of my necromancy at all. I glanced at Seth.

He looked away and dragged his hand through his hair. Behind us, Gus swore under his breath.

"Who formed the plan to kidnap her?" Seth asked.

"I did, after Julia said Miss Holloway wouldn't agree to raise anyone. She was a little reluctant about the idea, but gave in once I renewed my threats. It was her suggestion that I apply for the position of housekeeper to gain your trust and access to the house and your person." She fixed her unsympathetic gaze on me. "As I said at the time, I'm sorry for the abduction, but it was necessary. I missed Reggie terribly, and he needed to exact his revenge or his spirit could never rest."

"You don't know that," I said. "What you did...I'm still rather speechless about the whole thing."

"I'm not." Gus marched up to Merry Drinkwater and leaned down so that his face was level with hers. She gave a little squeak, leaned back, and screwed up her nose. "You're a mean-spirited, selfish, connivin', cowardly bitch, and I hope Death makes you pay for what you did when he gets here."

Mrs. Drinkwater flinched. She leaned so far back in the chair she was in danger of tipping over.

"Gus," I said quietly.

"What?" he growled.

"You forgot hypocritical." Everyone looked at me. "She told me that our living arrangements here were amoral," I elaborated, "when she herself had been a dancer at The Al, of all places."

Her face flushed. "I just danced. Nothing more. Not like Julia."

"And I am just living here. Nothing more."

Gus marched back to the door where he once more stood guard, arms crossed over his chest. The scowl remained on his face, making him look fiercer than ever.

"Gus is still very upset," I told Mrs. Drinkwater. "As am I."

She looked down at the knotted fingers in her lap. "So what are you going to do with me?"

"That depends on how much more information you can give us."

"I've told you everything! Julia was the one who helped me. Ask her if you don't believe me."

"We will. But before we can let you go, we need to know about the person who almost commissioned your husband's work."

She lifted one shoulder. "I know nothing about him."

"Nothing? What is it a man, for example?"

"I...I suppose, although I never met him. Reggie did say 'he,' so I presume he was male. Oh, I don't know! What does it matter anyway? The commission ended some time ago. It never really began."

"Why not?"

"The fellow learned that Reggie used his magic to make the limbs work. He never kept it a secret from those who asked, though few did. Most people don't know anything about magic, you see, but this man must have. Reggie wrote back and never heard from him again."

"Did your husband mention anything about him?"

She frowned. "I recall now. He knew nothing about the fellow because the letter bore only a signature, and an illegible one at that. No letterhead or printed name."

An illegible signature with no monogrammed letterhead...it reminded me of the letters the orphanages had received some weeks back, asking after me. Could this be the same person? It was almost unthinkable that there could be a connection. Yet someone wanted to know about supernaturals, perhaps to kill them, and I was a supernatural.

I suppressed a shiver. "Did your husband keep the letter?"

"He threw it out when nothing came of the arrangement."

I sighed. We were no closer to knowing an identity than before.

"Of course, Reggie probably wouldn't have taken the fellow as his patron anyway, even if magic hadn't been an issue."

"Why?"

"He wanted Reggie to extend his work and reanimate bodies. Like you do, Miss Holloway."

I stared at her. Then I stared at Seth. He nodded. It *must* be the same man who'd approached Frankenstein and who went on to commission Jasper's work. He wanted to bring the dead back to life, but through scientific means, not magic. For what purpose? And why not with magic?

"Mrs. Drinkwater, do you have any notion as to why your husband was killed?" I asked.

She twisted her hands into her skirt. "None whatsoever. I suppose we'll never know now." She looked close to tears. Seth handed her a handkerchief and she dabbed at her eyes.

"Could it be to silence him?" I asked no one in particular. "Perhaps Drinkwater knew the man's name, or something that could identify him."

"Or perhaps he just wanted him dead because he was a supernatural," Seth said with a shrug.

"The Brumley woman too," Gus added. "Don't forget her."

Mrs. Drinkwater whimpered. "This is horrible. So, so horrible. I just want my Reggie back. How am I to go on without him? He was my whole life."

"There, there," I said, absently. "Perhaps move in with your sister for a while." To Gus and Seth, I said, "We should find out more about the hired gunman who shot Mr. Drinkwater and Miss Brumley. Who was he in recent contact with, for example? Perhaps he left clues as to who paid him."

The door opened, thumping Gus in the back. "Oi!" He swallowed his protest as Lincoln stormed in, still wearing his coat and gloves.

His gaze flicked from me to Mrs. Drinkwater and back again. His face remained passive but a pulse throbbed in his jaw. "Charlie," he said quietly, ominously, "why are you covered in soot?"

CHAPTER 16

"We should talk privately," I said with a telling glance at Mrs. Drinkwater.

Lincoln inclined his head and stood aside. I walked out ahead of the men and waited until Seth had locked the door again. Then I threw my arms around Lincoln.

"I'm so glad to see you!" He felt so good, so solid and warm, although he looked every bit the wild gypsy with his hair hanging loose and his jaw roughened with dark stubble.

His arms circled me all too briefly before gently holding me at arm's length. "My rooms," he said. "All of you."

Gus's audible gulp set my nerves on edge. Lincoln was in a terrible mood, but I had to believe that was because he'd seen that I'd been in danger. Once he realized I was all right, he would calm down.

He closed the door behind us and directed me to sit in the wingback chair in his sitting room. I did, only to find the men preferred to remain standing. Seth and

Gus stood near the door, as if they hoped to escape quickly if necessary.

Lincoln stripped off his gloves, jacket and tie, throwing them onto another armchair.

"We found Mrs. Drinkwater," I said in a lame attempt to fill the taut silence. "As you saw."

"You left the house to find her."

"She was at The Alhambra. Her friend, Miss Redding, hid her there. They danced together years ago, along with Lady Harcourt."

He didn't blink or show any sign of surprise. Perhaps he knew, or suspected. "How did you learn of the connection?"

"From Mrs. Southey, Mrs. Drinkwater's sister."

A slight tightening around his mouth was the only indication that this piece of information intrigued him. "I visited her and wasn't told that. What threats did you make?"

"No threats. We simply told her that her sister could be in danger if we didn't warn her. Don't blame yourself, Lincoln. Women tend to trust other women more readily. She may have my found presence reassuring."

"Don't make excuses."

"Pardon?"

His fingers dug into the leather back of the chair. "I failed at something that should have been easy."

I went to him and rested my hand on his arm. The muscles beneath his shirt jumped. "It's hardly a failure. We simply have different methods, and my method was more effective this time. Next time, yours will be."

He placed his hand over mine. Then he plucked it off. "You promised me you wouldn't leave the house."

"I decided to make an exception. It was necessary—"

"It was not!"

I swallowed. "I had Seth and Gus with me, and the imp." I pulled the necklace out of my pocket. "Don't make an issue out of this. I was successful and unharmed. It's pointless to worry now."

"Explain your appearance." He folded his arms and waited expectantly for me to tell him.

Gus and Seth glanced at one another. I decided to remove them from the line of fire.

"If you wouldn't mind giving us some privacy," I told them.

"No," Lincoln said. "They stay."

"Why?"

He strode to his desk where he proceeded to rifle through his papers. After a moment, he put them down again, having achieved nothing. It was as if he was trying to get away from me. As if he didn't want to be alone with me.

I fingered the sleeve of his jacket but stopped again when I saw how dirty my hands were. "Holloway's dead."

His head jerked round. His lips parted. He took a step toward me, then stopped and put his hands behind his back. "How?"

"I killed him, in a way."

"It weren't your fault," Gus said.

"He's right," Seth added. "If he hadn't taken you, he'd still be alive."

"Will somebody tell me what happened," Lincoln ground out.

"We spotted Mrs. Drinkwater as we were leaving The Alhambra," I said. "Seth and Gus pursued her—"

"Leaving you alone." His razor sharp glare tore shreds off his men. Both turned a shade paler.

"Holloway had a gun and threatened to kill me if I didn't go with him."

"A gun?" Lincoln dragged a hand through his hair, down the back of his neck. "What about the imp?"

I explained to him how it would only save me if I was in direct danger.

"You could have summoned it anyway so that it was ready," he said.

"In full public view?"

A beat passed, two, in which his eyes went from icy to cool, to shadowed. "You wanted to ask Holloway questions, didn't you? That's why you went with him."

I bristled. I'd expected this inquisition, but had hoped he would temper it with a show of affection. There was nothing affectionate in his barked questions and the taut planes of his face. "We needed answers," I said.

"And what did you learn?"

"That a man helped him escape. A man who doesn't like magic or supernaturals. I think this man wanted Holloway to kill me, that's why he helped him escape. I also think it's the same man who commissioned Captain Jasper's work, and almost commissioned Reginald Drinkwater, Miss Brumley and Frankenstein, killing both Drinkwater and Brumley when he learned they were supernaturals. Paying someone else to kill them, I should say. We must look at the hired assassin more closely. He could be the key to finding out the identity of the villain behind it all."

"I learned his name and address from the Kensington Police Station yesterday. There was nothing in his house to identify anyone who might have hired him. I checked thoroughly. He also has no family and few friends. There's a possibility some of my other contacts may have heard who he was working for, but I haven't questioned them all yet. I will continue tonight."

"Oh."

He arched his brows.

"I was hoping you would stay in tonight and we could..." I glanced at Seth and Gus. They looked as uncomfortable as I felt. "Talk."

"I need to go out, Charlie. This must be resolved." Lincoln dragged both hands through his hair this time then pinched the bridge of his nose.

I clasped both his arms. "If you two wouldn't mind leaving us for a moment," I said over my shoulder.

"Stay," Lincoln barked, pulling away. "You haven't explained the soot."

I sighed and retreated back to the armchair. I wouldn't beg for his attention. Not in front of the others. "Holloway took me to a factory. I started a small fire to distract him from killing me. Unfortunately the small fire became a larger one when some powder exploded and the rafters caught alight. The chimney fell on Holloway, killing him. I escaped."

"With the help of the imp?"

I nodded.

His hands curled into fists at his sides. He drew in a deep breath and let it out slowly. "Gus is right. His death is not your fault."

I rubbed my arms, to chase away the chill, and studied the floor so he couldn't see the tears puddle in my eyes.

Another deep breath from Lincoln drew my attention back to him. He quickly looked away. "Take a warm bath. Afterward, if you're feeling up to it, you can summon Holloway's spirit and question him about the man who helped him escape."

"If he didn't tell me in the factory, he won't tell me now. He thinks that man is the only one who will remove the demon from me, and telling me who it is could ruin everything. He knows you'll hunt him down. I think we'll have more chance with the hired killer."

He shook his head. "It's likely he received anonymous instructions. It's how the man operated with the scientists."

I suddenly felt utterly drained. Instead of getting closer to learning who was killing the supernaturals, we seemed to be treading water. At least we knew about Lady Harcourt's involvement in my kidnapping now.

Lincoln strode past me to the door. Gus and Seth leapt aside to get out of his way.

"Where are you going?" I asked, hating the tired plea in my voice.

"To speak with Mrs. Drinkwater."

"We've told you everything she said. Lady Harcourt helped her."

He paused with one hand on the door handle and eyed me from beneath half-closed lids. He looked as exhausted as I felt. I ached to be with him, hold him and be held by him, but in his present mood there was no chance of that. It had not been the happy reunion I'd hoped for.

"Go and have your bath, Charlie. Doyle will bring up supper for you."

He might as well have ordered me to go to bed. His brusque, impersonal response certainly drove home the point that he didn't want to be with me. I had to hope that it was a result of his fury over my leaving the house and perhaps his disappointment in himself for not finding Mrs. Drinkwater first.

But a niggling doubt told me something else was wrong. Something that I couldn't quite put my finger on. Later, when I finally got him alone, I would find out what it was.

***

I didn't wake up until mid-morning. Despite my determination to confront Lincoln, I'd fallen asleep after eating supper in my rooms. I quickly dressed and hurried to his rooms, but he wasn't there.

Downstairs, I searched the library and parlor before going to the kitchen. Cook and Doyle were there alone. Doyle stood upon seeing me, and Cook glanced up from the pot he was stirring on the stove. Both glanced anxiously past me to the door. I turned, expecting to see Lincoln, but there was no one there.

"Good morning, miss," Doyle said. "May we prepare you something for breakfast?"

"Just an egg will do fine. Where is everyone?"

"Out," Cook said. "Feeling better?"

"Yes, thank you. Out where?"

"Seth and Gus be in the stables."

"And Mr. Fitzroy?"

"Riding."

"Riding where?"

Cook and Doyle busied themselves with their tasks. Something was definitely up.

"Where is he?" I pressed.

"Riding around the estate, I believe," Doyle said.

"That doesn't sound like something he would do."

"I overheard him tell Gus that he wanted to be nearby."

"Oh. To keep an eye on me, I suppose, to insure I don't leave again." I sat at the table and sighed. "It does seem odd that he would go riding for no particular reason, though." He rarely rode for pleasure or exercise. If he wanted to stay nearby but felt restless, why not simply exercise in his rooms like he usually did, or offer to take me through a training session?

The silence thickened as I ate my boiled egg, and I got the impression they weren't telling me everything. Instead of asking them, I went out to the stables. Gus and Seth greeted me with as much nervousness as

Doyle and Cook had. Neither could hold my gaze for long.

"You should go back inside," Gus said as he cleaned out the empty stall. The stall belonged to my horse but she was nowhere to be seen. "It's freezin' out here."

I checked the next stall along for Lincoln's horse. It was also empty. "Who's riding Rosie?"

Seth dusted off his hands. "Now don't get upset."

"Ah. It must be Lady Harcourt if that's your first response."

"Idiot," Gus muttered.

"She sent a message early this morning," Seth told me. "She wanted to speak with Fitzroy but he refused to leave the estate."

"Because of me?"

He nodded.

So he hadn't gone out to question his contacts about the killer, yet he hadn't come to me either.

"He sent word back to her, summoning her here instead," Seth went on.

"I'm sure that went down well. I doubt Lady Harcourt is used to being summoned anywhere these days."

"She came wearing a riding habit. She didn't want to talk in the house."

"Don't know why," Gus said, joining us. "We don't listen in on private conversations."

"Speak for yourself," I told him.

The corner of his mouth lifted but the smile was half hearted. "They've been gone a while now."

I eyed the stable entrance. Was Lincoln giving her short shrift over helping Mrs. Drinkwater? Or was she needling her way back into his good graces with her charms and excuses? I wouldn't put it past her to have a credible answer prepared.

"Is there something I can do in here?" I asked.

"Why?" Seth hedged.

"Because if I'm going to wait, I might as well be useful."

"I don't think that's a good idea. Go back inside where it's warm. We'll tell Fitzroy you were looking for him when he returns."

"The cold doesn't bother me. I won't even notice it once I start working."

"Charlie, stop being difficult! I'm trying to get you out of the way so you won't come face to face with Julia. The air was tense enough when she arrived, and by the look on her face, she felt awful for what she'd done. Don't make this even more difficult for her."

I snatched the broom out from beneath Gus's arm. Since he'd been leaning on it, he almost tumbled over. "I don't bloody care how difficult it is for her," I snapped at Seth. "She can bloody well face me, whether she likes it or not."

His lips pressed together. "You are being deliberately obstreperous." He marched toward the back of the stables, opened a stall door and disappeared inside.

"What's obstrep, obstrop...what's that word mean?" Gus whispered.

"Interesting?" I said with a shrug.

He chuckled.

Seth exited the stall again, leading a horse behind him. He moved it into one of the clean stalls and shut the door. He pointed to the newly emptied one. "Go on then. You want to help, you can help in there. You know where the mops and pails are. Get to work."

I peeked through the stall door. It was filthy. I pressed my hand to my nose but it didn't block out the smell of dung. "What have you been feeding him?"

"No time for talking," Seth tossed over his shoulder as he walked away with a cocky step. "There's work to do."

I signaled a rude hand gesture behind his back, coaxing another laugh from Gus.

Some fifteen minutes later, the clip clop of horses' hooves in the courtyard signaled the return of Lincoln and Lady Harcourt. Now that my temper had cooled and the time had come to face them, I wasn't sure what to say. Perhaps if I'd spent some time with Lincoln alone I would have felt more at ease. Something was bothering him, and that bothered me. I was as anxious about seeing him as I was at seeing her.

"Pleasant ride?" I heard Seth ask.

"Not entirely unpleasant." Lady Harcourt sounded like she was in a good mood. If she'd sounded upset, perhaps I would have remained hidden and allowed her to leave without confronting her, but it was that cheerfulness that brought my temper bubbling to the surface all over again.

I pushed open the stall door. Lady Harcourt's jaw dropped and Lincoln's hardened. She eyed me up and down, wrinkling her nose ever so slightly.

"Good morning," I said tightly.

"Good morning, Charlie," Lady Harcourt said, dismounting. "I'm glad you're here. I wanted to speak with you."

Seth and Gus made a hasty retreat, taking the horses with them, but Lincoln remained unmoved. He didn't seem surprised to see me or worried about the pending discussion. He showed no emotion whatsoever. Typical.

"If you've come to apologize for helping Mrs. Drinkwater, then don't," I told Lady Harcourt. "What you did...it's unforgiveable."

"I don't want your forgiveness," she said, oh-so-calmly.

"You ought to."

She tugged on the edge of her neat dove-gray riding jacket and glared down the length of her nose. "I came to explain to Lincoln—"

"To Lincoln! I think I deserve some sort of explanation and apology more so than anyone, except Gus."

"Calm down," she said through her teeth. "Your hysteria only makes you more childish."

Lincoln caught my hand, trapping it to my side before I could strike her. His gaze locked with mine, and I got the feeling he was willing me to walk away, to leave the issue alone.

But I couldn't. I snatched my hand out of his.

"Julia was just leaving," he said.

"Not until I hear the explanation she gave you," I said.

She smoothed her hand over her hips. "It's private."

"If it's about you dancing at The Al, I already know. We all do."

She shot a glance toward the stall door where Seth was seeing to Rosie.

"So is that the explanation you want to give?" I asked. "You were protecting your secret?"

She inclined her head in a nod.

"Do you hear yourself?" I asked her. "Do you hear how pathetic your excuse sounds, or do you think you're entirely justified in your actions because your secret remains safe?"

"You're being immature," she snapped. "Not to mention unreasonable."

"Unreasonable! You had me kidnapped!"

"I did not *have* you kidnapped. Merry forced me to tell her all about you, then *she* decided to abduct you. It was nothing to do with me."

"That's not what she told us. Yes, she blackmailed you, but you needn't have told her about my necromancy or about our advertisement for a housekeeper. You chose to do so."

"She's lying. I've already explained as much to Lincoln. I don't need to go over it again. The issue is laid to rest."

"I don't think she's the one who's lying."

She arched a slender brow. "You're calling *me* a liar?"

I arched my brow back at her.

"Merry is a desperate, pathetic woman," she said. "It's she you should be blaming, not me."

"Do you honestly believe the nonsense you're spouting?"

"Besides, she didn't harm you, and she had no intention of harming you. She assured me of that from the outset. This argument is all quite obsolete since you were released unhurt, as she promised."

I threw my hands in the air. "You two are more alike than you think. Neither of you is prepared to take responsibility for your own actions. It's always someone else's fault, or there's a good reason. I beg to differ. You are both to blame. You are both horrid, selfish and weak."

Her nostrils flared. Her body went rigid. "You're quite the little wasp when you get going."

"This little wasp would like to say goodbye now." I stood there, waiting for her to leave. She did not. "Please leave immediately. You're no longer welcome here unless it's on ministry business. Good day, madam."

"It's not your house to banish me from. It's Lincoln's."

"We're engaged to be married and I live here. It's more my house than yours." God, I sounded pathetic, whiny. I hated that she'd reduced me to this, but I couldn't help myself.

A short laugh burst from her throat. "Do you see now, Lincoln?"

"See what?" I asked, glancing at him.

He caught Lady Harcourt's elbow. From the way she winced, his grip must have been firm. "I think it's best that you go, Julia."

"I do have to be elsewhere, as it happens." Her nose was so high it was a miracle it didn't graze the beams.

Lincoln walked her out, leaving me standing there with my boots covered in muck and a mop in hand. My heart pounded harder than a thousand drums. The blood coursed through my veins, making me feel a little light-headed. While it felt good to express my anger, I was now more frustrated than ever. She hadn't been apologetic at all.

"I can't believe it," Seth said from behind me. He and Gus had come out of the stalls and both stared after her. "She didn't care."

Gus slapped him on the shoulder. "That's the woman you been protectin'. She ain't worth it."

"I haven't been protecting her, I've been..." Seth shrugged and shook his head. "She didn't think what she'd done was wrong. Not even a little. I can't believe it."

"You did good, Charlie." Gus patted my shoulder. "You told her a thing or two."

I shook my head. "None of it made a difference. I might as well have been shouting down a well."

Gus headed back into the stall and I left the stables to return to the house. Seth caught up to me in the courtyard. "Charlie, I want to apologize. You were right and I was wrong. She's a selfish shrew with only her own interests at heart. I want nothing more to do with her. She can keep her own bed warm at night from now on. Or get her stepson to do it."

I stopped and gawped at him.

"Don't look so surprised. It wasn't every night."

"I...I suspected, but wasn't sure. Will you be all right?"

"Of course. There was no affection between us, not on either side. We both needed a little release from time to time, that's all."

He made it sound like sneezing, a necessary function but quite ordinary. I threw my arms around him and hugged him. "Thank you, Seth. I do hope you find a replacement."

He laughed. "I already have a luscious redhead lined up."

I punched him lightly on the arm. "I hope she takes you by surprise and sweeps you off your feet."

He pulled a face. "No, thank you. I like my feet firmly on the ground. I'll leave the sweeping to him." He nodded at the side of the house where Lincoln was striding toward us.

I waited for him and Seth headed back to the stables. "You should be inside," Lincoln said to me. No kiss, no banter, no discussion about Lady Harcourt. It wasn't what I expected, and certainly not what I wanted.

"I am going inside," I growled. "I only came out here to see where you were. Not that I ought to have bothered. You were quite well occupied."

"She came to explain. She explained. There's nothing more to it."

"There is! She should be removed from the committee, for one thing."

"She can't be removed. She inherited the position."

"Then...she should be told what a horrible person she is. She should be made to see that her actions were despicable."

"She has been told. You did that admirably. Whether that will affect her, I don't know."

"That's another point." I poked him in the chest. "You didn't support me."

He caught my finger before I poked him again, held it a moment, then let it go. "I already said my piece to Julia on the ride. She knows I'm furious with her."

"Well. Good. I'm glad you told her, but that's somewhat irrelevant. A show of support just now would have been as much for my benefit as hers. *I* need to know you are on my side."

His eyes narrowed. "I see."

I waited for more, but none came. "You see? Is that it?"

"I suspected you needed to get your anger off your chest. You seemed to know what you wanted to say and I saw no reason to interrupt. I didn't realize you would assume my silence meant I didn't support you."

"Oh."

"I do support everything you said to her, Charlie. I told her as much just now."

"What did she say to that?"

"That if I can't see that she's innocent, we can no longer be friends."

It sounded like something one five year-old said to another after a fight over the last remaining slice of pie. And she called me the immature one. "What else did she say?"

His gaze slid to the ground at our feet. "She pointed out that you have an uncontrollable temper."

I huffed out a harsh laugh. "I suppose she told you that you were mad for wanting to marry such a hoyden."

"Something of that nature."

"Did you tell her that my temper only comes out when I'm very upset, like when someone kidnaps me, for example?"

"I told her that you're quite tame most of the time."

"Tame! I am not a horse, Lincoln!"

That telltale muscle in his jaw jumped again. "I see you're still upset."

I punched him in the arm, much harder than I'd punched Seth, and stormed off. He could have caught my hand but he didn't. I heard him following at a distance and turned. Stopped. He stopped too, out of reach. His gaze didn't meet mine. Something was still wrong.

"Lincoln, what is it? What aren't you telling me?"

He opened his mouth to speak, closed it again, then said, "I wish to be undisturbed for the rest of the day."

I blinked at him, hot tears burning my eyes. "Why?"

"I need to think."

"About?"

"About what to do next."

"Why can't we think together? We can discuss some ideas. We've worked well together in the past. Perhaps I should try summoning Holloway after all. Or the hired killer."

"I prefer to think alone." He moved past me and opened the door to the house. "Mrs. Drinkwater was released this morning. She was of no further use."

"I see," I said quietly, hardly listening.

He signaled for me to walk ahead, but he soon peeled away when we reached the kitchen. He headed up the corridor without a backward glance, his strides long and purposeful.

I watched him go, my heart like a lump of lead in my chest, my head woolly. I wanted to go after him, force him to tell me what was wrong.

Because *something* was the matter. He hadn't been so cool toward me in a long time. I couldn't blame Lady Harcourt either—he'd been distant last night too. I had put it down to him being worried and angry that I'd investigated without him, but now I wasn't so sure. He would have told me if that were the case, and I doubted his anger would have lasted this long.

Something else troubled him. Something that required him to close himself off from me for the rest of the day and night and not come out, despite my pleas.

"We'll talk in the morning," was all he said through the door when I asked him to join us for dinner. "Go to bed, Charlie. You need to be well rested."

CHAPTER 17

You need to be well rested.

Lincoln's words clanged in my head like an alarm. What did I need to be rested for? Summoning the spirits of Holloway and the hired killer? That was absurd. He was being patronizing and overbearing. I would tell him as much in the morning after we'd both had a chance to calm down.

I had a restless night and awoke soon after dawn to a light knock on my door. Throwing a wrap around my shoulders, I opened it to see Lincoln standing there looking even worse than he had the day before. His hair fell in tangles to his shoulders, his jaw needed shaving, and spidery red lines criss-crossed his eyes.

"What is it? What's wrong?" I reached for him, but he put his hands up, staying me. Dread settled in my gut like lump of ice.

He reached down near the wall and that's when I noticed the traveling trunk. He picked it up and barged into my sitting room, heading straight for the bedroom.

"Pack your things. Wear warm clothes and the amber necklace. You have an hour."

I stared at him, but when he didn't offer more information, I rushed up to him and pulled his arm. "Where are we going?"

"I'll explain after you've packed."

"No, you'll explain now or I won't pack. Where are we going?"

He flipped open the trunk lid. "To a school for young ladies in the north. It's—"

"A school! You're sending me away?" My heart crashed. My insides twisted. This couldn't be happening.

He opened the top drawer of my dresser. "It's for the best."

"Lincoln! I understand that you're upset and angry over my leaving the house yesterday, but there's no need for this. You're overreacting."

"I've thought about it all night and decided it's the best way. The only way. You have to leave."

Breathing suddenly became as difficult as it had in the fire. I couldn't get enough air into my lungs, no matter how many gulps I took. Lincoln transferred some of my clothes into the trunk, refolding and placing them with methodical precision. His entire attention seemed focused on his task. He didn't even spare me a glance.

This was all wrong. He didn't mean to do this, not really. Once I got through to him he would change his mind. I caught his face and forced him to look at me. But while he lifted his chin, his gaze didn't meet mine.

"Look at me," I snapped.

He did then pulled out of my grasp, but that brief moment had been long enough for me to see that the light in his eyes had gone out. The hard man I'd first encountered when I came to Lichfield had returned, the steely mask firmly in place. It was going to take more than a few words to get through to him.

"Is this because you're worried about me?" I asked.

He didn't answer.

"Lincoln, sending me away isn't going to keep me safe. If anything, I'll be more exposed alone."

"Nobody at the school will know that you're a necromancer, and no one here will know where you've gone. Besides, it's not entirely about keeping you safe. It's also about allowing me to focus again."

"Focus?"

"I should never have set aside my doubts."

"What doubts?"

"Your influence concerned me from the beginning, but I convinced myself that nothing would change. I was wrong. Everything changed. I changed. By keeping you here, I've been selfish. I haven't been thinking of you or the ministry."

"Don't lump my wellbeing in with the ministry's. And it's not selfish to want the one you love to be near you. That's human."

He paused at the dresser, his back to me. His shoulders slumped forward, but then he straightened again and continued transferring my clothes to the trunk. "You're better off away from me. You can't deny there have been many dangers."

"I think I should be the one to worry about my welfare. I should decide where I want to be, not you."

"This is my house. You are under my protection. I decide." His words echoed those of Lady Harcourt's the day before. She'd also reminded me in no uncertain terms that the house was his.

"You're being draconian."

"I'm thinking clearly for the first time in months."

"Then stop and think about what you're doing, Lincoln."

"I have thought about it. I've thought of nothing else."

"Don't make a hasty decision—"

"There is nothing hasty about it. Ever since returning from Paris, I've become more and more aware that I can't do my job properly with you here. I am the leader of the ministry. The position is not one I can set aside, and it's not one I can give only half of myself to. I need to focus on it entirely."

"That is absurd. Is this because you failed to find Mrs. Drinkwater? I already told you, that wasn't a failure—"

"This is not about that single incident!" He slammed the drawer shut, rattling the mirror, and jerked open the next one. "That was the final straw. It proved to me that I needed to focus more."

"It proved to *me* that we work better as a team than apart."

He said nothing but continued to pack for me. He stopped placing the clothes carefully in the trunk, and thrust them into it instead without a care for the delicate fabrics.

I swallowed, but the lump in my throat remained. "So...this is a permanent arrangement? You don't want me back at all?" My voice sounded small, pathetic, but I couldn't be strong anymore. My life was crumbling away before my eyes and I felt utterly powerless to stop it.

He continued to pack without answering.

My legs felt too weak to hold me. I sat heavily on the bed. "Our engagement..."

"It's best that we end it. You're young. You'll recover."

The tears slipped down my cheeks, my chin and dripped onto my lap. Recover? He thought this was just a passing infatuation for me? "No, Lincoln. I won't. Will you?"

His fingers scrunched into my chemise before he released it into the trunk. It lay in a crumpled heap. "Doyle will help you finish packing. You should dress and eat some breakfast. The journey will be a long one."

He strode out of the bedroom. I ran after him and once again caught his arm to stop him. He shook me off.

"I'll answer any questions about the school," he said. "But don't ask me again to change my mind."

I scoffed through my tears. "I'm too old for school."

"This is a school for young ladies, not children."

"Like a finishing school?"

"Of sorts."

"You've been talking to Lord Marchbank. He also mentioned sending me to a school all the way up in the north. It's the same one, isn't it? I might know nothing about being a lady, but I do know that finishing schools are usually in London or in cities on the continent."

"You'll be safe there—and busy. At the end of a year, you'll have more opportunities than you do now. The headmistress has assured me a position will be found for you in France or Italy as a governess or companion, preferably to an English family. Or you can stay on at the school as a teacher. The choice will be yours."

"Some bloody choice." I stared at him, trying to take it in. It all seemed too unreal, like a nightmare I would wake up from. "You and Marchbank have been making plans even though I told him I wasn't going."

"Marchbank mentioned the school to me months ago, but not since. I haven't discussed this with him recently. I haven't told him, or anyone, that you're going. This decision was mine alone."

"But you must have been planning it for a long time if you've already corresponded with the headmistress."

"I looked into it after you first came here but decided against it at the time. The headmistress assured me there would be a position for you if I change my mind."

"Lincoln, stop this." My voice was barely above a whisper. It was all I could manage through my tears.

He turned away and continued to the door. "You won't be without a home, and it's likely you'll make good friends there."

"*This* is my home! I have friends *here*!"

"You need to meet young women your own age."

I thrust my hands on my hips. "I won't go."

"A year at the school will present you with opportunities you wouldn't have had otherwise. It'll be good for you."

"I'll decide what's good for me. And I meet people perfectly well here."

"Not the right sort."

"The right sort?" I echoed. "You mean people like Lady Harcourt?"

His hand rested on the doorknob. He paused, his back to me. "You can't stay here. You'll be safe at the school."

"I'm not going to a damned school! I'd rather move back in with Stringer's gang and stay in London."

His knuckles turned white around the doorknob. "If you run away from Lichfield, I might not be able to find you again. At least if you're there..." He jerked open the door and walked out, closing it behind him.

I crumpled to the floor and drew my knees to my chest. This wasn't happening. He was hurt and worried, and that was making him do foolish things. He wouldn't go through with it, surely. He loved me, and he knew I loved him. He must know, deep down, that sending me away would destroy us both. I had to find a way to remind him of that. I had to get through to him.

I don't know how long I sat there. I only picked myself up off the floor when there was another knock at the door. My heart in my throat, I opened it, only to see Doyle standing there with a tray.

"Your breakfast, miss."

I took the tray and thanked him.

He cleared his throat. "I've been instructed to assist you with your packing and selecting a suitable outfit for traveling."

It seemed petty to not let him into the bedroom. The poor man was only doing as his master requested. It was Lincoln I needed to talk to, not Doyle.

I nibbled at the bacon, but didn't touch the egg. I wasn't hungry. Pulling my wrap around my shoulders, I joined Doyle in my bedroom. The trunk was full and a dark green woolen dress and underthings had been laid out on the bed.

"Forgive me," he muttered, coloring slightly. "A maid ought to have done this, but..." He trailed off.

"It's quite all right, Doyle. It wasn't fair of him to ask this of you. You may go."

He bowed and went to walk off.

"What did he say to you about all this?" I asked.

"Only that you were going away, miss. He didn't say where or for how long."

"Has he told the others?"

"Not that I am aware, miss. He gave me my orders in private."

After he left, I dressed quickly. I didn't close the trunk, but left it there. It wasn't going anywhere.

I went in search of Lincoln and found him in the kitchen with Seth, Gus and Cook. By the stunned looks on their faces, he'd just given them the news. The three of them turned wide-eyed stares to me, mouths ajar.

"We need to talk," I told Lincoln with a firm lift of my chin.

"There's no more to say. Further discussion will only make this more difficult." He pushed past me. "You have ten minutes."

I tried to grasp him, but he was too quick. I picked up my skirts to run after him, but Seth beat me to it. His footsteps echoed along the corridor up ahead.

"You can't do this!" I heard him shout. I didn't hear Lincoln's quieter response. "No! It's not! Think about—"

Lincoln must have cut him off, but once again his words were too low to reach me.

I raced up to them, Gus and Cook on my heels. Lincoln saw me, turned, and strode off. "Coward!" I snapped.

He didn't stop. I heard the front door open and close.

"Bloody hell," Gus muttered. "Has he lost his mind?"

Seth's eyes flashed with cold fury. I'd never seen him so angry before. "What has he told you?" he asked.

"That I'm going to a school in the north for a year. Afterward, I can travel to the continent and find work as a governess or—" I choked and couldn't finish.

Seth drew me into a hug. "He'll come to his senses soon enough."

"In ten minutes?"

"You need to talk to him."

"I've tried. He's not listening."

"Try again." He grabbed my hand. "Come on."

The four of us headed outside, but Lincoln was nowhere in sight. I leaned against the side of the house and folded my hands over my stomach. I felt sick. If I couldn't find him to talk to him, how could I change his mind?

"Don't worry," Seth said, returning after searching around the perimeter of the house. He breathed heavily, but I didn't think it was entirely from exertion.

"We'll speak with him after you're gone if it comes to that."

"She ain't goin' nowhere," Gus growled.

"Aye, she be stayin' here with us," Cook said.

"She can't," Seth told him. "He made it clear that wasn't an option."

"Then we'll find her somewhere to stay nearby."

"She can live with my aunt," Gus said, nodding eagerly. "She'll like the company."

Seth stroked his chin. "It's a good idea. Perhaps we can find her employment."

"Doing what?" Cook shrugged his massive round shoulders. "She ain't got the right education for a governess or nurse, and I ain't letting her work in no factory."

"Domestic service?"

Cook snorted. "That be beneath her and you know it."

"At least it's a start!"

I rested my head against the cool, gray stones of the house. "I can't believe this is happening."

Seth put his arm around me and kissed the top of my head. "It'll be all right. He just needs to calm down. He'll change his mind soon enough."

I no longer felt as confident. Lincoln was a stubborn man, and very adept at burying his emotions. But I had to hold out hope. After all, he did want me to go to the school so he'd know where to find me. If nothing else, I had to believe that he would fetch me one day. Perhaps even tomorrow, after he'd calmed down.

The rumble of wheels on gravel had all of us turning.

"It better not be someone from the committee," Gus said, squinting at the approaching coach.

"It be a hansom," Cook said.

"Not a hansom," Seth said. "Looks like a growler."

The two-horse coach pulled up at the front steps and Lincoln climbed out of the cabin. He paused when he saw me, then approached, his hands at his back. His eyes, half hooded beneath heavy lids, were blacker than London's bleakest night sky.

"It's time," he said stiffly. "Fetch your coat and gloves." He went to walk off, but I stepped in front of him.

I grasped his shoulders. "Stop it, Lincoln. Stop this at once. It's wrong and you know it."

He prised my fingers off and let my hands go. "No, Charlie. It was wrong of me to allow you to stay and let it get to this point. I should have sent you away months ago."

My tears, never far from the surface, welled again. "Don't say that," I whispered. "Don't pretend there's nothing between us."

"I know you feel hurt right now, but it will pass. You'll thank me one—"

"Thank you!" I stepped toward him but he stepped back. I drew in a shuddery breath and took strength from Seth's encouraging nod. "I love you, Lincoln, and sending me away won't stop me loving you. A year in the north won't stop me loving you, nor will a lifetime on the continent."

"Enough! You're only making it harder."

"If it's hard, then don't do it!"

He strode off toward the front steps and Gus pushed me after him. Gathering the shreds of my remaining strength, I picked up my skirts and raced up the steps. Once again I blocked his path.

He regarded me levelly, coolly, as if there'd never been heated kisses between us, or plans made to spend a lifetime together. It was like those first few days after my arrival at Lichfield all over again.

"This is Lady Harcourt's doing, isn't it?" I snapped. "She said something to you yesterday that made you doubt our relationship."

"It has nothing to do with her."

"She wants you for herself, Lincoln. You know that. That is behind everything she says and does."

"This has nothing to do with her," he repeated. "It's entirely my decision." He picked me up and deposited me out of the way.

When his hands left my waist, I went to slap him. He caught my wrist. We stood like that, so close that he must have been able to hear my heart thundering. It sounded deafening to me.

"Please, Lincoln," I whispered as my tears spilled. "Don't do this." I had promised myself that I wouldn't beg, but I was desperate now. Dignity be damned.

The muscles in his face slackened. He blinked rapidly and his lips parted ever so slightly. For that one brief moment I thought he had come to his senses. I caught a glimpse of his true self through the tiny crack in his mask.

Then his mouth shut and every muscle tensed. He let me go and marched into the house.

Seth ran after him, Gus at his heels, but after a few angry shouts that garnered no response from Lincoln, they returned. Cook drew me into a hug. He smelled of oranges. Another hand rested on my shoulder.

Nobody spoke.

Doyle came out with my trunk and passed it up to the coachman who secured it to the roof. He bowed to me, unsmiling. "Safe journey, miss. I'll keep the place in order until your return."

I opened my mouth to thank him, but no words came out. I offered him a smile, but it was weak and unconvincing.

I hugged Seth, Gus and Cook in turn. Cook surprised me by wiping his damp eyes. I patted his arm; the only comfort I was capable of providing.

"No need for that," Gus said. "She'll be back soon enough. He'll miss her too much." He kissed my cheek and drew me into another hug.

He only let me go when Seth elbowed him. "Gus is right, for once," he muttered into my hair. "Your exile won't last long."

"We'll bloody see that it don't," Gus added.

Fine, misty rain began to fall. It was the sort of rain that could last all week at this time of year and dampen the hardiest of spirits. It seemed appropriate for my departure from the place I called home. Five years ago it had also been raining when I was banished from the only home I'd known, and now it was raining again as I was banished from a different one. It was too cruel.

Seth helped me up the coach steps, folded them away, and shut the door. I tried not to cry as I peered out the window, but I couldn't turn off the tears. They streamed uncontrollably. My heart felt like it was disintegrating beneath the deluge. Soon the hole where it had been would be filled up with my tears until they overflowed.

The coach turned and drove off. I spun on the seat and waved out the rear window. My three friends and Doyle waved back.

I don't know what made me glance up to the tower room. A flutter of the curtain? Shadowy movement? I was glad that I did. It provided me with my last glimpse of Lincoln, standing in the window. He was too far away for me to see his expression, but it gave me hope, something to cling to. It meant he wasn't as indifferent to my departure as he seemed.

I pressed my palm to the coach window in a final plea, but he was already gone.

THE END

LOOK OUT FOR

Ashes To Ashes

The fifth MINISTRY OF CURIOSITIES novel.

After banishing Charlie, Lincoln finds that Lichfield Towers offers no sanctuary. With reminders of her at every turn, and employees threatening to mutiny, he must try to find the murderer who is killing supernaturals on his own. Another victim leads to further leads, but is Lincoln too distracted to work efficiently? And will he regret his decision to send Charlie away?

To be notified when C.J. has a new release, sign up to her newsletter via her website: www.cjarcher.com

ABOUT THE AUTHOR

C.J. Archer has loved history and books for as long as she can remember and feels fortunate that she found a way to combine the two. She has at various times worked as a librarian, IT support person and technical writer but in her heart has always been a fiction writer. Her first historical fantasy series, THE EMILY CHAMBERS SPIRIT MEDIUM TRILOGY, has sold over 45,000 copies and garnered rave reviews. C.J. spent her early childhood in the dramatic beauty of outback Queensland, Australia, but now lives in suburban Melbourne with her husband, two children and a mischievous black & white cat named Coco.

She loves to hear from readers. You can contact her in one of these ways:
Website: www.cjarcher.com
Email: cj@cjarcher.com
Facebook: www.facebook.com/CJArcherAuthorPage
Twitter: @cj_archer

Printed in Great Britain
by Amazon

ISBN 978-1-334-61335-7
PIBN 10750713

This book is a reproduction of an important historical work. Forgotten Books uses state-of-the-art technology to digitally reconstruct the work, preserving the original format whilst repairing imperfections present in the aged copy. In rare cases, an imperfection in the original, such as a blemish or missing page, may be replicated in our edition. We do, however, repair the vast majority of imperfections successfully; any imperfections that remain are intentionally left to preserve the state of such historical works.

1 MONTH OF
FREE
READING

at

www.ForgottenBooks.com

By purchasing this book you are eligible for one month membership to ForgottenBooks.com, giving you unlimited access to our entire collection of over 700,000 titles via our web site and mobile apps.

To claim your free month visit:

www.forgottenbooks.com/free750713

English
Français
Deutsche
Italiano
Español
Português

www.forgottenbooks.com

Mythology Photography **Fiction**
Fishing Christianity **Art** Cooking
Essays Buddhism Freemasonry
Medicine **Biology** Music **Ancient**
Egypt Evolution Carpentry Physics
Dance Geology **Mathematics** Fitness
Shakespeare **Folklore** Yoga Marketing
Confidence Immortality Biographies
Poetry **Psychology** Witchcraft
Electronics Chemistry History **Law**
Accounting **Philosophy** Anthropology
Alchemy Drama Quantum Mechanics
Atheism Sexual Health **Ancient History**
Entrepreneurship Languages Sport
Paleontology Needlework Islam
Metaphysics Investment Archaeology
Parenting Statistics Criminology
Motivational

Das Leben Juvenals

von

Professor Dr. Julius Dürr.

Wissenschaftliche Beilage zum Programm des Kgl. Gymnasiums
in Ulm.

Wagnersche Buchdruckerei in Ulm.
1888.

1888. Programm Nr. 561.

Druckfehler

S. 12 b. Z. 2 v. u. lies: *Mélanges Graux*
S. 22 b. Z. 5 v. o.: *militiae*
S. 23 b. Z. 19 v. o.: „pro suis" (R ü h l: *in* (?) *recitata*"
und „*prorsus*").
Z. 20 v. o : Handschriften (R ü h l : „*suas* (?)
competenti");
Kleinere orthographische Versehen bitte ich zu entschuldigen.

Die Feststellung der Lebensgeschichte des Juvenalis ist ein vielbehandeltes Problem[1]), die Ergebnisse der zahlreichen Untersuchungen sind aber noch immer sogar in den Hauptpunkten sehr unsicher und widersprechend [2]). Wenn ich trotz dieses wenig günstigen Prognostikons hier die Resultate einer erneuten Prüfung der Frage ·rlege, so geschieht dies, weil ich dieselbe teils durch Beibringung neuen handschriftlichen Materials [3]), teils durch vollständigere und richtigere Verwertung des schon bekannten nicht unwesentlich glaube fördern zu können. Freilich auf manche Fragen können wir keine oder keine sichere Antwort geben, in vielen Fällen müssen wir uns mit Vermutung und Wahrscheinlichkeit begnügen; wo ich in diesem Sinne im folgenden eine Lösung versuche, thue ich es in dem Bewusstsein und mit ausdrücklicher Hervorhebung der hypothetischen Natur derselben, aber in der Absicht, das vorhandene Material wenigstens soweit als möglich auszunützen. Der erste Abschnitt der nachfolgenden Untersuchung beschäftigt sich nach einer kurzen Übersicht über die Quellen überhaupt mit einer genaueren Erörterung der Frage nach Ursprung und Glaubwürdigkeit der alten *vitae*, der zweite Abschnitt versucht dann eine kritische Feststellung der Lebensgeschichte des Dichters.

Die neuere Litteratur über den Gegenstand habe ich, soweit sie mir bekannt und zugänglich geworden ist, benützt, aber eine fortlaufende kritische (zustimmende oder ablehnende) Auseinandersetzung mit den Ansichten der Früheren unterlassen, teils mit Rücksicht auf die dieser Abhandlung gesetzten räumlichen Schranken, teils deshalb, weil die Entscheidung in den einzelnen Punkten meist abhängt von der prinzipiellen Stellung zu den *vitae*, die ich meinerseits im ersten Kapitel zusammenhängend dargelegt und begründet habe.

---

[1]) Über den Stand der Frage und die Litteratur bis zum Jahr 1880 ist sorgfältig berichtet bei Teuffel-Schwabe Röm. Litter.gesch. [4] § 331. Von neueren Arbeiten sind mir zugänglich geworden: Friedländer, Chronologie des Lebens und der Satiren Juvenals (Sittengesch, 3[5], 458 ff. 1881). D. Naguiewski *de Juv. vita observationes*. Dorpat 1883. Vahlen, Juvenal und Paris (Sitzungsberichte d. Berl. Akad. 1883. 8. 1175 ff.). Rittweger, die Verbannung Juvenals und die Abfassungszeit seiner 7. Satire. (Gymn.progr. von Bochum 1886.). Die Abhandlungen von Stampini *(de Juv. vita dissertatio* Turin 1881; *de J. v. controversia* 1883*)*, Seehaus *(de Juv. vita*, Diss. Halle 1887), Nettleship *(Life und Poems of Juvenal* in *Journal of Philology* 1887. 8. 41 ff.), Pearson (Einleitung zu *Thirteen Satires of Juv. by Pearson and Strong* 1887) kenne ich nur aus der Litteratur.

[2]) Juvenals Geburt setzen an: ca. 46—48 n.Chr.: Teuffel (R.L. G [3].), Synnerberg, Naguiewski, Pearson; Mitte der fünfziger Jahre: Ribbeck, Weidner, Rittweger, Stampini; ca. 60: Teuffel-Schwabe (R.L. G[4]); in das J. 67: Friedländer. Seinen Tod setzen alle je ungefähr 80 Jahre später. Seine Verbannung verlegen unter Domitian: Friedländer, Naguiewski; unter Traian: Synnerberg, Rittweger; unter Hadrian: Teuffel, Ribbeck, Weidner, Stampini, Pearson; als Verbannungsort betrachten Britannien: Teuffel und Rittweger, die anderen Ägypten; Rückkehr aus der Verbannung nehmen an: Friedländer, Rittweger. Die Verbannung überhaupt bezweifelt Nettleship, bestreitet Vahlen.

[3]) Ich habe auf einer als Stipendiat des kaiserlich deutschen archäologischen Instituts in Rom im J. 1882,3 unternommenen wissenschaftlichen Reise nach Italien eine Reihe italienischer Bibliotheken (Rom, Neapel, Florenz), für meine Zwecke durchforscht. Was ich an neuem Material gefunden habe, lege ich hier vor.

1

I. Übersicht der Quellen. Kritik der Vitae.

Des Dichters eigene Angaben über sein Leben beschränken sich auf einige direkte Andeutungen und auf die indirekt aus seinen Satiren, namentlich den chronologischen Indicien zu erschliessenden Thatsachen.

Dazu kommen dann vereinzelte Erwähnungen bei seinem Zeitgenossen und Freund Martialis und bei späteren Schriftstellern [4]).

Als zeitgenössisches und authentisches Denkmal wichtig und für die öffentliche Laufbahn des Dichters ergebnisreich ist die von ihm selbst in seiner Heimat Aquinum gesetzte Weihinschrift [5]). Der in dem heutigen Roccasecca im Gebiet des alten Aquinum gefundene Stein mit dem Original derselben ist leider verloren, die nicht mehr vollständig leserliche Inschrift ist uns nur in Abschriften erhalten. Aber an der Echtheit der Inschrift und der Glaubwürdigkeit und annähernden Genauigkeit der Abschriften zweifeln unsere berufensten Epigraphiker nicht. Dass dieselbe auf unseren Dichter zu beziehen ist, beweisen der Name des Dedikanten, soweit derselbe erhalten ist, der Fundort der Inschrift, der Name der geehrten, von dem Dichter selbst in bedeutsamem Zusammenhang erwähnten [6]) Gottheit und die in der Inschrift enthaltene ungefähre Zeitbestimmung (flamen divi Vespasiani).

Die Trümmer der gelehrten Beschäftigung des Altertums mit den Lebensverhältnissen des Dichters liegen uns in den zahlreichen vitae vor, welche sich in Handschriften der Satiren finden und zwar am Anfang oder Ende, von derselben oder von späterer Hand geschrieben, zusammen mit Scholien oder selbständig, gewöhnlich je eine allein, doch oft auch mehrere neben-

einander. Hinsichtlich ihrer handschriftlichen Überlieferung scheint die für uns älteste die zu sein, die sich in der besten Juvenal-Handschrift, dem Codex Pithoeanus (saec. IX), allerdings erst von späterer Hand beigeschrieben, findet; die jüngsten und meisten gehören der Zeit der Renaissance an. Aber auch diese unterscheiden sich durch ihren ganzen Ton von den erst in der Humanistenzeit selbst entstandenen Arbeiten dadurch, dass jene einfach erzählen, diese kritisch räsonnieren. Diese lezteren, aus „humanistischen Kollegienheften" stammenden vitae kommen für uns natürlich nur in soweit in Betracht, als sie etwa altes, uns anderweitig nicht bekanntes Material verwertet haben. Bei einer solchen vita unter den mir handschriftlich oder aus den alten Drucken bekannt gewordenen ist dies in der That, wie unten in Beilage D nachgewiesen ist, der Fall.

Ich gebe zunächst einen Überblick über diese alten vitae, und zwar gleich in der durch ihr verwandtschaftliches Verhältnis bedingten Gruppierung. Der Text der meist schon in O. Jahns grösserer Juvenalausgabe gedruckten vitae ist unten in der Beilage A gegeben. Der Umstand, dass in vielen Handschriften mehrere vitae einfach äusserlich aneinander gereiht sind, zusammen mit einer Vergleichung der vitae selbst zeigt, dass die Schreiber derselben im allgemeinen eine absichtliche, bewusste neue Darstellung vermieden haben, schliesst aber die Annahme von untergeordneten Erweiterungen der einen vita aus der anderen oder durch eigene Zuthaten des Schreibers nicht aus.

Bekanntlich sind zu den Satiren Juvenals

---

[4]) Martial. 7, 24. 91; 12, 18. Sidon. Apoll. carm. 9, 266 ff., Joh. Malalas p. 262. Dind. (excerpiert von Suidas v. Ἰουβενάλιος) vgl. auch Ammian. Marcell. 28,4 und Rutil. Namat. 1,603 ff.

[5]) C.I.L. X, 5382 (= Mommsen I.R.N. 4312; darnach bei Orelli-Henzen 5599.) vgl. dazu die Anmerk. von

Mommsen. In der dritten Auflage von Teuffels Litt.gesch. richtig abgedruckt, ist die Inschrift in der vierten durch falsche Interpunktion leider verunstaltet (,,Delmatarum II, vir quinquennalis" statt „Delmatarum, II vir quinquennalis).

[6]) 3,319.

zwei Klassen von Scholien [7]) erhalten; die eine, bessere, von G. Valla fälschlich dem Probus zugeschrieben, geht in ihrem Kern ins 4. Jahrhundert, vielleicht noch weiter zurück [8]); die andere, die in einigen Handschriften selbst als Verfasser einen Cornutus bezeichnet, ist ein Werk der Karolingerzeit. Dass beide Kommentare von Haus aus einen Lebensabriss des Dichters enthielten, ist an sich wahrscheinlich, und der uns vorliegende Bestand bestätigt dies. I a. (= Jahn I). Dem sogenannten Probuskommentar scheint die *vita*, oder vielmehr richtiger: die Quelle der *vita* [9]) anzugehören, die jedenfalls in Vallas Handschrift mit diesem vereinigt war, in dem *Codex Pithoeanus* allerdings erst später als die mit dem Text der Satiren gleichzeitigen [10]) Scholien nachgetragen ist und sich sonst in sehr zahlreichen Handschriften selbständig findet. Das ursprüngliche Fehlen derselben im *Pithoeanus* scheint mir kein entscheidender Gegengrund gegen jene Annahme zu sein: wie die *vita* wiederholt für sich abgeschrieben wurde, so mögen wohl auch einmal die Scholien ohne die *vita* abgeschrieben worden sein. Dass die *vita* in der St. Galler Handschrift der Scholien (*saec. IX*) fehlt, erklärt sich wahrscheinlich daraus, dass diese aus aus dem *Pithoeanus* vor der Zufügung der *vita* abgeschrieben ist [11]). Übrigens ist diese Frage für uns von keiner weiteren Bedeutung. b. (= Jahn II). Im wesentlichen dieselbe *vita*, nur in erweiterter Gestalt, ist die des *codex Vossianus*. Was diese mehr hat, als die obengenannte, ist, wie sich nachher ergeben wird, teils interpoliert, teils wohl eher einseitig

aus der gemeinschaftlichen Quelle beider übernommen. II a. (= Rühl Nr. 3). Dem Cornutus-Kommentar gehört die *vita* an, die erst in neuerer Zeit durch Rühl [12]) aus einem *codex Harleianus (saec. XV.)* bekannt gemacht worden ist, aber auch in einer Reihe anderer, bis jetzt nicht beachteter Handschriften sich findet. Es ist dieselbe *vita*, die aus einem *codex Divaei* Lipsius im Auszug giebt. Sie bildet in den Handschriften meist einen Abschnitt der sehr weitschweifig nach einem bestimmten Schema angelegten Einleitung jenes Kommentars [13]).

Aus verschiedenen Stücken desselben Cornutus-Kommentars mit einigen eigenen Zuthaten der Schreiber zusammengestoppelt sind folgende *vitae*:

b. (= Jahn VII) die zuerst von Jahn nach einer Abschrift Mommsens aus *cod. Vatic.* 2810 veröffentlichte, auch in anderen Handschriften erhaltene;

c. eine noch ungedruckte *vita* des *codex Regin.* 1828 *(bibl. Vatic.)*. Zuthat des Verfassers aus *vita* I ist wohl die Bemerkung über Juvenals Abstammung von einem Freigelassenen;

d. eine gleichfalls noch ungedruckte *vita* des *cod. Barber.* IX, 3, und zwar unter den mehreren in dieser Handschrift aufeinanderfolgenden die an dritter Stelle stehende.

III. Nicht einen eigenen Typus repräsentieren die folgenden, unter einander und einerseits mit I, andererseits mit II verwandten *vitae*:

a. eine zuerst von Cramer [14]) aus einer

derungen durch Verkürzung, Verwirrung und Interpolation erlitten haben.

[7]) Für das Folgende vgl. Teuffel R.L.G.⁴ § 331,7. Ausser den dort erwähnten Schriften (**Jahn** *Prolegg. ad. Persium;* **Matthias** *de scholiis in Juvenalem)* vgl. noch G. **Schönaich** *Quaestiones Juvenalianae* Diss. Halle 1883. (S. 1 ff.: *de scholiorum genere deteriore)* und **Stephan** *de Pithoeanis in Juvenalem scholiis* Diss. Bonn 1882.

[8]) Borghesi *oeuvres* 5,515. Matthias a. O. S. 259 ff.

[9]) Wie die Scholien (vgl. Matthias a. O. S. 264 ff.), wird auch die zugehörige *vita* im Lauf der Zeit Verän-

[10]) Vgl. Stephan a. O. S. 5.

[11]) Jahn *prolegg. ad Pers.* p. 156; Matthias a. O. S. 257. Schönaich a. O. S. 5.

[12]) Jahrb. f. Philolog. 109, (1874) S. 863.

[13]) Das Nähere darüber vgl. unten in Beilage C, woraus sich dann auch die Begründung für das hier Folgende ergiebt.

[14]) In seiner Ausgabe der Scholien 1823.

Wiener Handschrift veröffentlichte, auch in mehreren anderen Handschriften erhaltene.

b. (= Jahn III). Dieselbe *vita* nur in erweiterter Gestalt ist die aus einem *codex Vossianus* von Henninius und darnach von Jahn herausgegebene. Von dem, was sie mehr hat, als die eben erwähnte, ist die Notiz über Juvenals Rückkehr aus der Verbannung nach Rom und seine Sehnsucht nach Martial gewiss willkürliche Interpolation, vielleicht im Anschluss an I b., die andere über Juvenals Alter bei seinem Tod dagegen wird wohl eher auf die gemeinschaftliche Quelle von III a und III b zurückzuführen sein.

Ähnlich ist das Verhältnis zwischen

c. der zuerst von Pinzger[15]) aus einer Breslauer Handschrift herausgegebenen, auch in mehreren anderen Handschriften vorhandenen *vita* und

d. der *vita*, welche von Crenius[16]) aus handschriftlichen Nachträgen des Petrus Scriverius zu dessen gedrucktem Exemplar der Pithouschen Ausgabe Juvenals von 1585 veröffentlicht wurde.

Die umfänglichere Gestalt bietet die erstere (c); welche aber das relativ Ursprünglichere bietet, die vorauszusetzende gemeinschaftliche Quelle genauer wiedergiebt, ist schwer zu sagen, da wir die handschriftliche Grundlage für die Nachträge des Scriverius nicht mehr kennen. Wahrscheinlich ist mir, dass die alberne Bemerkung über Juvenals Sehnsucht nach den Schauspielen Roms als Ursache seines Todes Interpolation in c ist, das übrige, was c mehr hat als d, aus der gemeinschaftlichen Quelle stammt und von d weggelassen ist. Sicher ist dies der Fall hinsichtlich der bei d fehlenden, in allen anderen *vitae* vorhandenen, Angabe über Juvenals Tod „aus Lebensüberdruss".

Die Verwandtschaft beider Paare (ab, cd)

unter einander ist auf gemeinschaftliche Quelle zurückzuführen; über das Verhältniss dieser letzteren zu I und II wird unten zu sprechen sein.

IV (= Jahn V. VI.) In Inhalt und Form wieder ein eigener Typus ist die *vita*, die, in mehreren Handschriften erhalten, von Jahn aus bestimmten Gründen in zwiefacher Gestalt herausgegeben ist. Abgesehen von ganz unwesentlichen sprachlichen Verschiedenheiten stimmen aber sämtliche Handschriften wörtlich überein bis auf einen Punkt. In den einen nämlich wird der Kaiser, welcher den Pantomimen Paris begünstigt und Juvenal verbannt, an erster Stelle bloss als *imperator*, an zweiter als *tyrannus* bezeichnet; in den anderen wird beidemal Traianus genannt. Indes ist diese Variante doch gewiss auf eine willkürliche vermeintliche Textemendation in der einen oder anderen Klasse, wahrscheinlich in der zweiten, nicht aber auf eine zwiespältige sachliche Überlieferung zurückzuführen. Wir dürfen also Jahns zwei *vitae* als eine einzige betrachten.

V. (= Jahn IV.) Ebenso steht die von Ruperti aus einem *codex Kulenkampii* herausgegebene *vita* in Form und Inhalt den anderen relativ selbständig gegenüber.

VI. Schliesslich ist noch ein Wort zu sagen über die hiehergehörigen Scholien.

a) die Scholien zu 1,1 (abgesehen von dem ersten Satz mit seinem auf Rechnung eines Interpolators kommenden Unsinn) und zu 4,38 stammen aus derselben Quelle wie *vita* I und haben aus dieser die Angabe über den Ort der Verbannung Juvenals genauer erhalten. In dem Scholion zu 7,92 ist wohl nur durch Interpolation Nero an Stelle des vermutlich vorher genannten Domitian getreten.

b) Die von Th. Öhler aus einer Londoner Handschrift ganz vereinzelt ohne Zusammenhang citierte Randbemerkung zu 7,93[17]), wie

---

[15]) Archiv f. Philol. 14 (1835) S. 267 f.
[16]) *Animadrers. philol. et hist.* 1704. P. XIII. c. 1. p. 1. 12.

[17]) Erwähnt bei K. F. Hermann *de Juv. sat. VII temporibus.* Göttingen 1843.

ich vermute, überhaupt nicht eigentlich ein antikes. Scholion, sondern eine eigene Notiz des Schreibers oder Besitzers der Handschrift ist nichts als ein Auszug aus *vita* IV (und zwar der zweiten Handschriftenklasse).

Man hat bisher meist diese *vitae* als ebensoviele selbständige Zeugen behandelt und dementsprechend teils nach allgemeiner Schätzung der Zuverlässigkeit der einzelnen, teils durch Abwägung ihrer Angaben im einzelnen Fall die Wahrheit zu ermitteln gesucht. Freilich konnte man nicht bloss auf diesem Weg bei dem Mangel bestimmter äusserer oder innerer Kriterien für den relativen Wert der einzelnen *vitae* und bei ihren gegenseitigen Widersprüchen ein bestimmtes Resultat nicht gewinnen, sondern es wurde auch dadurch im allgemeinen das Urteil über ihre Glaubwürdigkeit ein mehr oder minder ungünstiges.

In der obigen Uebersicht hat sich nun zunächst schon von sozusagen textkritischem Gesichtspunkt aus die Vielheit der *vitae* auf eine kleinere Anzahl von Gruppen reduciert, die je für sich einen gewissen Typus repräsentieren. Wir dürfen aber auf Grund einer kritischen Prüfung des gegenseitigen Verhältnisses der *vitae* hinsichtlich ihres Inhaltes noch einen Schritt weiter gehen. Eine genauere Erwägung einerseits ihrer Übereinstimmungen, andererseits ihrer Widersprüche führt zu der auch schon von anderer Seite ausgesprochenen [18]), aber, soviel ich sehe, nirgends konsequent durchgeführten Annahme, dass die uns erhaltenen *vitae* mehr oder minder verkürzte, vielfach durch Missverständnisse und Interpolationen entstellte Auszüge aus einer einzigen, ihrerseits auf guter alter Überlieferung beruhenden Darstellung von Juvenals Leben sind.

Dass allen auf uns gekommenen *vitae* eine

[18]) Synnerberg *de temporibus vitae Juv. constituendis* S. 9. Ribbeck in der *Einleitung* seiner Ausgabe S. XII. Naguiewski a. O. S. 2.

Quelle zu Grund liegt, beweisen zunächst Art und Umfang der wörtlichen und sachlichen Übereinstimmungen, die sich nicht als Entlehnungen der einen *vita* aus der anderen erklären, weil sonst als eigentlicher, ursprünglicher Inhalt der betreffenden *vita* fast nichts mehr übrig bleibt. Im einzelnen ist dies unten in der Anmerkung [19]) nachgewiesen. Sodann

---

[19]) „*Ad mediam fere aetatem declamavit*" (I a b); „*ad mediam fere aetatem satirice declamavit*" (II a); *prima aetate siluit, ad mediam fere aetatem declamavit*" (III a b); „*prima aetate tacuit, media vero declamavit*" (III c d); „*licet ad dimidiam aetatem tacuisset, satiras scribere statuit*" (II d); „*declamavit*" (V).

Juvenals Verbannung erfolgt: „*per honorem militiae*" (I a b); „*sub obtentu militiae*" (II b c, III a b c d); „*sub obtentu honoris*" (II a); „*sub praetextu honoris*" (IV); „*sub specie honoris*" (V, Sch. 4,38).

Juvenal stirbt: „*angore ac taedio*" (I a, II a b c, III c) „*senio et taedio*" (I b); „*tristitia et angore*" (III a b); „*animo consternatus ex mentis aegritudine*" (IV); „*longo senio confectus*" (V).

Die direkte oder indirekte Veranlassung bilden nach allen *vitae* die Verse 7, 90—92.

Juvenal wird gesandt: „*ad praefecturam cohorti s*" (I a b); „*princeps unius cohortis*" (III c); „*cum cohorte militum*" (III d); „*cum exercitu*" (II b c); „*ad cohortis curam*" (Sch. 4, 38); „*imperator fecit eum praefectum militum*" (IV); *militibus praefecit* (II a);

„*in extremam Aegypti partem*" (I a b); „*in extremas partes Aegypti*" (II a); „*ad ultimas partes Aegypti*" (III c); „*ad civitatem ultimam Aegypti Hoasin*" (Sch. 1,1); „*ad Aegyptum*" (II b c, III d); „*exularit in Aegypto*" (V) „*quamquam octogenarius*" (I a b); „*cum octogenarius esset* (III c).

Vgl. ferner: „*libertini locupletis incertum filius an alumnus*" (I a b; II c vgl. oben); „*ordinis ut fertur libertinorum*" (V).

„*paucorum versuum satira non absurde composita*" (I a b); „*quosdam versus non absurde composuit*" (II a); „*erat in deliciis aulae histrio*" (I a b); „*apud aulam imperatoris in deliciis sese habentem*" (II a); „*in deliciis apud imperatorem habebatur*" (IV);

„*multi fautorum eius provehebantur*" (I a b); „*qui fautores multos habebat*" (III c d);

„*quasi tempora praesentia figura notasset*" (I a b); „*quasi imperatoris tempora notasset*" (III a b); „*imperator sentiens sua tempora denotari*" (II a); „*quod sua tempora notasset*" (II b); „*cum notasset tempora*" (II c);

2

spricht für jene Annahme auch das oben bezeichnete Verhältnis der Gruppe III zu I und II; es ist an sich wahrscheinlicher, dass die Quelle der unter III aufgeführten *vitae* parallel mit I und II aus einer Urquelle abstammt, als dass sie eine Kompilation aus I und II ist.

Der vorauszusetzende ursprüngliche Bestand der Biographie hat dann unter den Händen der Schreiber und Interpreten, wie schon nach Analogie der Textgeschichte der Scholien [20]) wahrscheinlich ist, ausser zufälligen Verunstaltungen durch Schreibfehler, in zwei entgegengesetzten Richtungen eingreifende Veränderungen erfahren, bis er endlich in die uns vorliegenden Gestalten kam. Einerseits wurde er durch successives Excerpieren stufenweise verkürzt, dabei aber auch unvermeidlich der Zusammenhang durch Zusammenrücken ursprünglich untereinander beziehungsloser Nachrichten, durch Auslassung wesentlicher Mittelglieder vielfach ungenau wiedergegeben und verwirrt [21]); andererseits aber wurden diese immer dürftiger werdenden Auszüge von den Schreibern und Scholiasten wieder durch eigene Interpolationen ausgeschmückt Diese Interpolationen sind zum Teil ungeschickte Erweiterungen des eigentlich Thatsächlichen, meist aber alberne

---

„*ut mores illius temporis demonstrando posset notare*" (Sch. 1,1);

„*vitia carpi sui temporis*" (IV); „*omnium carpsit vitia*" (II b d); „*tempora graviter carpsit*" (Sch. 1,1);

„*nulla alia occasione reperta struendae mortis in Juvenalem*" (IV cod. Bodl.); „*hoc modo poëtae mortis instruendae opportunitatem invenit*" (IV cod. Omnib.); „*qualiter Juvenalem deprimeret apud se excogitavit, sed cum tantae auctoritatis virum publice punire non auderet*" (II a); „*cum non auderet eum imperator publice damnare*" (III c); „*publice (!) ob imperatore damnatus*" (III d); „*hic accusatus damnatus est*" (II b).

[20]) Vgl Matthias a. O. S. 264 ff.

[21]) Ein einleuchtendes Beispiel dafür ist die Verrückung der Zeitbestimmung „*temporibus Neronis Claudii*"; I b, III a b geben sie richtig als Zeitbestimmung für Juvenals Geburt, in III cd steht sie irrtümlich bei der Nachricht von seinen deklamatorischen Übungen.

Motivierungen und Erklärungen. Sie sind teils, wie es scheint, ganz willkürlich ersonnen, teils aus dem übrigen Zusammenhang in Verbindung mit anderweitig bekannten Nachrichten und den Anhaltspunkten in Juvenals eigenen Gedichten herausgeklügelt. Als Interpolationen charakterisieren sich solche Angaben teils durch den albernen Inhalt, teils durch den auf der Hand liegenden Anschluss an anderweitig uns bekannte Nachrichten, teils durch ihren gegenseitigen Widerspruch. Scheidet man diese, unten in der Anmerkung [22]) im einzelnen be-

---

[22]) Juvenals Verbannung wird folgendermassen motiviert: „*id genus supplicii placuit, ut levi atque ioculari delicto par esset*" (I a b); „*ut, si aliquo modo periret, sub specie dilectionis animi malignitas compleretur*" (II a); „*ut ibi Juvenalis interficeretur*" (IV);

Juvenal stirbt: „*cum Martialem suum non videret*" (III a vgl. Mart. 12,18); „*cum careret consuetis spectaculis et ludis, quae Romae fiebant*" (III c).

Aus sat. 7,86 ff. ist einfältig herausgeklügelt die Angabe in I a b, dass die Spottverse sich auch gegen den Dichter Statius gerichtet hätten, sodann in I a die Bezeichnung des Statius, in I b des Paris als „*semestribus militiolis tumentem*"; ferner in II a die Angabe: „*Paris iste pantomimus irrecitata emebat et suum titulum apponebat*"; in II b: „*hic pantomimus delator erat pessimus et per hoc gratiam obtinuerat principis cum factione*"; infolge davon wird dann in II b das ganze Verfahren zu einem förmlichen Prozess gestempelt im Widerspruch mit dem Vorhergehenden.

Um die irrtümliche Annahme, dass Juvenals Verbannung durch Domitian erfolgt sei, mit der aus den Gedichten ersichtlichen Thatsache, dass er unter Traian in Rom lebte, in Einklang zu bringen, erfindet I b III a die Angabe von seiner Rückkehr nach Rom, während andererseits V der glaubwürdig überlieferten Nachricht zu lieb, dass Juvenal unter Antoninus Pius in der Verbannung gestorben sei, von dem ihrer Angabe nach unter Domitian verbannten Dichter sagt: „*nec inde a noris principibus revocatus est*".

Ganz wie ein willkürliches Autoschediasma sieht die Angabe in I b aus: „*properantem spiritum cum tussi exspuit*"; sicher ist ein solches die Nachricht von Domitians Apotheose in I b und die Angabe des Vornamens Marcus in V.

Interpolationen sind ferner: „*satirice declamarit*" (II a); „*declamarit non mediocri fama*" (V); die versprochenen Interpolationen, die sich leicht ohne Störung des Zusammenhangs beseitigen lassen, aus, so bleibt nur ein mit dem ganzen Zusammenhang der Erzählung enger verflochtener Punkt übrig, über welchen Widerspruch unter den einzelnen *vitae* herrscht, nämlich die Verbannung Juvenals. Aber gerade hier lässt sich, wie in der Darstellung der Lebensgeschichte des Dichters im einzelnen genauer nachgewiesen werden wird, einleuchtend darthun, dass die Widersprüche auf dem oben bezeichneten Weg, durch wiederholte Excerpierung und Interpolierung des ursprünglichen Berichts entstanden sind.

Von der Erwägung ausgehend, dass die Gelehrten der Renaissance, die natürlich die erhaltenen *vitae* zur Grundlage ihrer Darstellungen des Lebens des Juvenalis gemacht haben, möglicherweise Handschriften und damit *vitae* benützt haben, die für uns verloren oder noch nicht wieder entdeckt sind, habe ich die handschriftlichen und gedruckten Kommentare jener Zeit, soweit sie mir zugänglich waren, daraufhin durchgemustert. In der That habe ich nun in einer dem 15. Jahrhundert angehörigen Handschrift der Barberinischen Bibliothek in Rom eine *vita* gefunden, die bisher unbekannte und, wie unten in Beilage D nachzuweisen versucht ist, auf guter Überlieferung beruhende Nachrichten bietet. Natürlich werden wir dann auch diese Angaben als Fragmente der von uns angenommenen antiken Urbiographie betrachten.

In gewissem Sinn zur Bestätigung der vorgetragenen Ansicht von der Herkunft und Entstehung der uns erhaltenen *vitae* und zugleich um den vorauszusetzenden ursprünglichen Bestand der Überlieferung zu veranschaulichen, habe ich den auch schon von anderer Seite [23]) gemachten Versuch einer Rekonstruktion der

ursprünglichen Gestalt der Biographie aus den uns vorliegenden Trümmern unternommen. Eine solche Rekonstruktion muss einerseits einen Zusammenhang der Nachrichten herstellen, wie ihn die Sache selbst und andere Zeugnisse als den wahrscheinlichsten erweisen, andererseits der Forderung genügen, dass daraus auf einfache Weise unter Annahme von Veränderungen durch Excerpierung und Interpolierung sich diejenigen Darstellungen ableiten lassen, welche die uns erhaltenen *vitae* bieten. Die von diesen Gesichtspunkten aus rekonstruierte Urbiographie ist in Beilage B zum Vergleiche mit den erhaltenen *vitae* gegeben. Die Erörterung und Rechtfertigung des einzelnen bleibt der kritischen Darstellung der Lebensgeschichte Juvenals vorbehalten.

Über Person und Zeit des Biographen lässt sich nichts Bestimmtes sagen. An Sueton, jedenfalls an dessen Schrift *de viris illustribus* kann nicht gedacht werden [24]). Die Annahme, dass Sueton etwa als eine Art Nachtrag dazu eine selbständige *vita Juvenalis* verfasst habe, würde das Zeitverhältnis beider Männer zwar gestatten, aber es fehlt wenigstens an jeder Spur. Wahrscheinlicher ist, dass die Biographie gleich von Haus aus als Bestandteil eines Kommentars zu Juvenal verfasst worden ist, sei es nun eines, wie neuerdings angenommen worden ist [25]), schon im 2. Jahrhundert verfassten oder aber des im 4. Jahrhundert oder früher entstandenen Kerns unseres sog. Probuskommentars, in welchem Fall also, wie schon oben angedeutet wurde, *vita* I als der echteste Abkömmling der Urbiographie zu betrachten wäre.

Unter den Quellen des Biographen ist natürlich auch der Dichter selbst. Dass jedoch sämtliche Angaben der *vitae* aus seinen Satiren herausgeklügelt seien, ist zwar wiederholt be-

---

schiedenen Motivierungen von Juvenals Übergang zur satirischen Poesie (I b, II b c d; alles im Anschluss an die erste Satire).

[23]) Ribbeck a. O. S. XII.

[24]) Vgl. Reifferscheid *Quaest. Sueton.* p. 371. 404. 422. Teuffel R.L.G. 347,7.

[25]) Matthias a. O. S. 260 ff.

hauptet [26]), aber niemals auch nur wahrscheinlich gemacht, geschweige denn bewiesen worden, und die künstlichen, oft wunderlichen Erklärungsversuche sprechen mehr gegen, als für das, was sie beweisen sollen. Jene Annahme ist, wie mir scheint, nicht zum mindesten unter dem Einfluss des überhaupt ungünstigen Urteils über den Wert und die Glaubwürdigkeit der *vitae* entstanden, welches seinerseits wieder auf den gegenseitigen Widersprüchen derselben beruhte. Liegt aber, wie ich erwiesen zu haben glaube, allen *vitae* eine Quelle zu Grund, und sind diese Widersprüche durch Verderbnis der ursprünglichen Darstellung des Biographen entstanden, so fällt dieses Bedenken weg: der Biograph bietet eine in sich zusammenhängende, widerspruchsfreie Darstellung, innere Bedenken gegen die Annahme, dass er auf wirklicher Überlieferung fusst, sind nicht vorhanden. Dass die späteren Schreiber und Scholiasten, die Verfasser der uns vorliegenden *vitae*, willkürlich aus dem Dichter mancherlei herausgeklügelt haben, ist oben nachgewiesen; dass diese Dinge auf ihre eigene Rechnung kommen, also Interpolationen sind, nicht schon der ursprünglichen Biographie angehörten, zeigen die Widersprüche solcher Angaben unter einander und ihr alberner, mit der sonstigen Erzählung der Biographie kontrastierender Inhalt. Auch der Biograph selbst hat vielleicht manches bloss aus dem Dichter entnommen. Aber in allen diesen Fällen liegt der Anschluss an bestimmte Stellen deutlich vor, und die Gedankenarbeit, welche solche Angaben zu Tag gefördert hat, ist keine sehr tiefgehende. Dagegen setzt die

in Rede stehende Annahme ausser einer genauen Vertrautheit mit dem Dichter nicht bloss eine blühende Phantasie, sondern auch eine, ich möchte sagen, methodisch vorgehende, verschiedene weit auseinander liegende Andeutungen geschickt verknüpfende Kombination voraus, mit der wir gewiss auch dem Biographen zuviel Ehre anthun [27]). Selbst der moderne Philologe stelle sich einmal unbefangen nicht an das Ende des Wegs und vor die Aufgabe, die zusammenhängende Darstellung der Lebensgeschichte in ihre vermeintlichen Elemente aufzulösen, sondern an den Anfang des Weges und vor die Aufgabe, aus den „*disiecta membra poetae*", aus den Stellen, die man als Anhaltspunkte für die angeblichen Kombinationen des Biographen namhaft macht, das Ganze der Lebensbeschreibung, wie sie uns vorliegt, beziehungsweise aus den abgeleiteten Darstellungen zu rekonstruieren ist, zu stand zu bringen, und frage sich, ob und wie er wohl diese Aufgabe lösen würde! Was sich aus dem Dichter selbst für seine Lebensgeschichte gewinnen lässt, ist fast durchgehends so wenig bestimmt, dass man bei unbefangener Beurteilung gerade für das eigentlich Wesentliche, Charakteristische in den Angaben des Biographen darin einen Anhaltspunkt nicht erblicken kann. Ferner ist für gewisse Nachrichten der Biographie (Geburtsjahr Juvenals, seine Familienverhältnisse, seine Erhebung in den Ritterstand, sein Kommando in Britannien) Zurückführung auf wirkliche geschichtliche Überlieferung geradezu unabweisbar und zum Teil von den Vertretern jener Ansicht selbst zugestanden [28]), endlich wenigstens

---

[26]) Früher von Francke, Düntzer, Kempf, neuerdings ebenso zuversichtlich als leichtfertig von Strack *de Jur. exilio* (Gymn.-Progr. Laubach 1880), dem sich sodann Seehaus *de Jur. vita* (Halle Diss. 1887. vgl. dazu Friedländer Berl. Phil. Wochenschr. 1887. S. 1049) anschliesst, und speziell für den Bericht über die Verbannung Juvenals von Vahlen Juvenal und Paris (Sitzungsberichte der Berl. Akad. 1883.).

[27]) Als bestätigender Vergleich ist auch instruktiv die Analyse der Elaborate der Humanisten, wie sie an einem Beispiel unten in Beilage D durchgeführt ist. Auch hier sind die eigenen Kombinationen des Verfassers sehr einfach und durchsichtig.

[28]) Vahlen a. O. S. 1189: „Da davon dass Juvenal Tribun oder Präfect einer *cohors Delmatarum*, vermutlich der ersten, von der anderweitig feststeht, dass sie in

für das Kommando in Britannien höchstwahrscheinlich eine authentische Bestätigung durch die Inschrift vorhanden. Ich glaube deshalb jene Annahme nicht bloss als unerwiesen, sondern auch als unrichtig zurückweisen und an der Ansicht festhalten zu müssen, **dass der Biograph zwar vielleicht manches aus dem Dichter selbst entnommen, in der Hauptsache aber seine Nachrichten aus guter alter Überlieferung geschöpft hat.** Weiteres lässt sich aber darüber nicht ausmachen. Denkbar ist, falls die Biographie erst im dritten oder vierten Jahrhundert entstanden ist', dass der in den Scholien (4,53) citierte Geschichtschreiber Marius Maximus (ca. 165—230 n. Chr.), dessen *vita Hadriani* bei ihrer hinreichend bekannten Tendenz [29]) die Verbannung Juvenals durch Hadrian gewiss erwähnt oder vielmehr bei der Weitläufigkeit seiner Darstellungen eingehend erzählt hat, eine Hauptquelle des Biographen war.

II. Das Leben Juvenals.

Der volle **Name** des Dichters lautet in der Subscription des ersten Buches seiner Satiren in dem zwar der geringeren Handschriftenklasse angehörigen, aber gewiss in diesem Punkt zuverlässigen *codex Laurentianus 34, 42 (saec. XI)* und in anderen späteren Handschriften derselben Klasse: *Decimus Junius Juvenalis.* Ob die in mehreren Handschriften des Cornutuskommentars in der Einleitung sich findende alberne Auseinandersetzung über die Bedeutung der Namen Decimus und Junius schon ursprünglich diesem Kommentar angehörte, in welchem Fall wir also schon aus dem 9. Jahrhundert ein Zeugnis für den Namen hätten, oder erst durch spätere Interpolation hereingekommen ist, kann ich nach dem mir vorliegenden Material nicht entscheiden; soweit ich sehe, ist das letztere der Fall. Wenn *vita V* dem Dichter den Vornamen Marcus giebt, so ist dies sicherlich eigene Erfindung des betr. Schreibers, vielleicht in Anknüpfung an die ihm bekannten

M. Junius Brutus. Auf der Inschrift ist von dem Namen nur erhalten : ......nius Juvenalis [30]).

Das **Geburtsjahr** Juvenals ist nach der zwar erst in der Humanistenzeit entstandenen, aber in diesem Punkt indirekt aus guter Überlieferung, aus der Biographie schöpfenden *vita* des *Anonymus Barberinus* das Jahr 55 n. Chr.: *Claudio Nerone et L. Antistio coss.* Mit dieser Angabe stimmen zunächst die übrigen Angaben des Biographen. Nach demselben wurde Juvenal 80jährig, also unter Hadrian (117—138) verbannt und starb *anno aetatis suae altero et octogesimo* unter Antoninus Pius (138—161). Sein 80. Lebensjahr ist 134/5, sein 82. 136/7. Die letztere Angabe müssen wir also dahin verstehen, dass Juvenal nicht im 82. Jahr, sondern mit 82 Jahren, d. h. nach vollendetem 82. Jahr im 83., also im Lauf des J. 137/8 gestorben ist; und zwar ist, da Antoninus Pius am 10. Juli 138 zur Regierung kam, Juvenals Tod in die zweite Hälfte des J. 138, seine Geburt in die zweite Hälfte des J. 55 zu setzen. Es stimmt damit die weitere Angabe, dass

Hadrianischer Zeit in Britannien stand, eine dunkle Kunde auch zu den Biographen Juvenals gelangt sein konnte, so war auch Schottland entfernt genug, dorthin die Verbannung zu legen."

[29]) Vgl. meine Schrift: die Reisen des Kaisers Hadrian (Abhandlungen des archäol.-epigraphischen Seminars zu Wien 1881) S. 12 ff. 78.

[30]) Der Vorname ist in den Handschriften häufig in Decius entstellt. Ob in dem *cod. mus. Brit. add.* 15 600 aus dem 9. Jahrh. wirklich, wie Rühl (Jahrbb. f. Phil. 109, 868) angiebt, steht: [*Deci*]*mi Juvenalis* und nicht vielmehr: [*Ju*]*nii Juvenalis*, ist mir zweifelhaft.

3

1

Juvenal erst um die *media aetas* von der Rhetorik zur Poesie überging; denn die Abfassung und Veröffentlichung der ersten Satire, seines poetischen Programms, fällt etwa um das J. 105 oder wenig später, um welche Zeit der Dichter ein Fünfziger war. Dass Juvenal in der That damals schon in gereiftem Alter war, zeigt der ganze Ton der Satire [31]). Diese Angabe des Biographen selbst kann freilich entstanden sein aus richtiger Kombination der Nachrichten über Geburts- und Todesjahr mit der aus den Satiren augenscheinlich zu erschliessenden Thatsache, dass Juvenal jedenfalls erst nach Domitians Tod als Satiriker aufgetreten ist. Auch die weiteren aus den Gedichten sich ergebenden chronologischen Indicien stimmen mit jenem Ansatz seiner Lebenszeit. In einer seiner spätesten Satiren bezeichnet er ein Ereignis des J. 127 als erfolgt „*nuper consule Iunco*" [32]). Wenn ferner, wie mir wahrscheinlich ist, die in derselben Satire sich findende Anspielung auf die Mysterien [33]) auf die von Hadrian in Rom eingeführten eleusinischen Mysterien geht, die dieser Kaiser wahrscheinlich erst nachdem er von seiner zweiten grossen Reise, auf welcher er im J. 129 in Athen selbst die zweite Stufe der Weihen erhalten hatte, im J. 134 nach Rom zurückgekehrt war, hier einführte [34]), so hätten wir damit in Juvenals eigenen Gedichten einen Beweis für seinen Aufenthalt in Rom bis in die Mitte der dreissiger Jahre des zweiten Jahrhunderts. Die Annahme von Friedländer [35]), dass unter dem Greis, von dem es in *sat.* 13,16 f. heisst:

„*stupet haec, qui iam post terga reliquit sexaginta annos, Fonteio consule natus?*"

Juvenal sich selbst meine, nicht, wie sonst allgemein angenommen wird, den Adressaten der Epistel, seinen Freund Calvinus, und dass somit Juvenals Geburt in das J. 67 zu setzen sei, hat mit Recht nirgends Anklang gefunden, da jene Erklärung sprachlich keineswegs notwendig, sogar unwahrscheinlich, dem Zusammenhang nach aber unangemessen ist.

Dass sein G e b u r t s o r t Aquinum war, sagt Juvenal selbst, indem er sich zu einer Zeit, wo er bereits in Rom seinen Wohnsitz aufgeschlagen hatte und nur zu kürzerem Aufenthalt nach seinem aquinatischen Landgut kam, durch seinen Freund Umbricius also anreden lässt [36]):

„*ergo vale nostri memor, et, quotiens te Roma tuo refici properantem reddet Aquino, Me quoque ad Helvinam Cererem vestramque converte a Cumis.*" [*Dianam*

Dort wurde auch, wie schon bemerkt, die Weihinschrift des Dichters für die eben in dieser Stelle erwähnte Ceres gefunden. Der Biograph, sowie Über- und Unterschriften der Satiren in den Handschriften bezeichnen ausdrücklich Aquinum als seine Heimat [37]), freilich vielleicht selbst nur auf Grund jener eigenen Angabe des Dichters [38]). Aquinum war Bürgerkolonie, wahrscheinlich von den Triumvirn gegründet [39]). Dass Juvenal auch wirklich Bürgerrecht in Aquinum besass, zeigt die Bekleidung munizipaler Ämter daselbst, wozu in der Regel nur *municipes* gelangten, *incolae*

---

[31]) vgl. 1,25.

[32]) 15,27. vgl. Borghesi *oeuvres*, 5,49 ff.

[33]) 15,140 ff.

[34]) Aur. Vict. *Caes.* 14. vgl. Dürr die Reisen Hadrians S. 42 ff., 59 ff. 124.

[35]) Friedländer *dissert. de Juv. vitae temporibus* Königsberg 1875; Sittengeschichte 3⁵, 458 ff.

[36]) 3,318 ff. vgl. 6,57.

[37]) Wenn *vita* II a sagt: „*de Aquino oppido oriundus et natus,*" so wird darin natürlich niemand eine etwa auf den Biographen zurückzuführende genaue Unterscheidung von rechtlicher *origo* und faktischem Geburtsort suchen, sondern lediglich eine Tautologie.

[38]) Über die einfältige Bemerkung des Scholiasten zu 1,1: „*Juvenalem aliqui Gallum propter corporis magnitudinem, aliqui Aquinatem dicunt*" vgl. Matthias a. O. S. 265.

[39]) vgl. Mommsen Hermes 17,175. 193. C. J. L. X. p. 530.

äusserst selten und nur durch kaiserliches Privilegium [40]).

Schwierig ist die Frage nach dem Stand Juvenals. Sein Name [41]), der von ihm selbst erwähnte Besitz eines väterlichen Erbguts [42]), die Bekleidung von Offizierstellen und von munizipalen Ämtern in der Bürgerkolonie Aquinum, seine Erhebung in den Ritterstand [43]) bezeugen, dass er jedenfalls im Mannesalter die Ingenuität und zwar in ihrer vollen Gestalt, als Ingenuität im dritten Glied, besass. Wahrscheinlich aber hat er diese erst durch verschiedene rechtliche Akte erworben. Was der Biograph über Herkunft und Stand des Dichters berichtete, ist uns in verschiedenen Stücken in den einzelnen *vitae* erhalten. Seine spätere Erhebung in den Ritterstand berichtet *vita* IV. Die Namen seiner Eltern und seiner Schwester giebt der *Anonymus Barberinus*. Besonders wichtig ist die Nachricht, die in der bestimmten Fassung der *vitae* I a b (darnach auch bei II c) lautet: *„libertini locupletis incertum filius an alumnus"*, in *vita* V in ungenauer Kürze: *„ordinis ut fertur libertinorum"*. Diese Angabe in ihrer formellen Genauigkeit, aber inhaltlichen Unbestimmtheit ist in gleicher Weise ein Zeugnis für die Gewissenhaftigkeit des Biographen, wie für die verhältnismässige Dürftigkeit der ihm zu Gebot stehenden Überlieferung. Die Annahme, dass diese Nachricht Kombi-

nation der Verfasser der *vitae* aus gewissen Stellen der Satiren sei, wo der Dichter von Freigelassenen redet, ist selbst unter der Voraussetzung eines bedeutenden Masses nicht nur von Phantasie, sondern auch von Scharfsinn nicht einleuchtend. Man wusste also, dass Juvenal in nahem Verhältnis zu einem Freigelassenen stand, und zwar entweder dessen leiblicher Sohn oder sein Pflegesohn, *alumnus*, war. Dies Schwanken der Überlieferung erklärt sich einigermassen schon durch den Umstand, dass Juvenal aus der Landstadt Aquinum stammte, als Dichter aber erst in Rom auftrat, und erst nachdem er schon jahrelang dort gelebt hatte, in einem Alter, wo niemand mehr grosses Interesse hatte, nach seiner Geburt sich zu erkundigen. Indes muss doch auch das Verhältnis selbst so beschaffen gewesen sein, dass es zu jener doppelten Überlieferung Anlass geben konnte. Wäre es nun so einfach gewesen, wie die erste Version es darstellt, nach welcher Juvenal jenes Freigelassenen Sohn war, dann wäre die Entstehung der anderen nicht begreiflich. Es ist also gewiss die andere Angabe, dass er jenes Freigelassenen *alumnus* war, die richtige. Der Begriff *alumnus* [44]) bezeichnet ähnlich, wie unser Ausdruck „Pflegesohn" persönliche Beziehungen, Pietätsverhältnisse verschiedener Art und Entstehung, ohne an sich irgend einen Hinweis auf die persönliche Rechts-

---

[40]) vgl. Mommsen zu C. J. L. V, 875. (= Wilmanns *Exempla inscriptionum* 691 Anm. 10); O. Hirschfeld Göttinger Gel. Anz. 1870 S. 1105 f.; Marquardt Röm. Staatsverw. 1,466. 510 f.

[41]) Die Führung eines römischen Cognomens ist Freigelassenen nur auf Grund kaiserlichen Privilegiums gestattet, vgl. Mommsen Staatsrecht 2², 857. A. 2.; Friedländer Sittengesch. 1⁵, 177 f.

[42]) 6,57. Wer seinen Vater beerbt, hat im Rechtssinn einen Vater, kann also nicht Freigelassener sein.

[43]) Ingenuität wird als Qualifikation zur Bekleidung munizipaler Ämter gefordert von der *lex Malacitana* c. 54. (dazu Mommsen Stadtrechte S. 416; vgl. auch Staatsrecht 1², 459 ff.) Besitz der wirklichen oder fiktiven

Ingenuität im dritten Glied ist Vorbedingung für den Besitz der Ritterwürde (vgl. Plin. h. n. 33, 32; Mommsen Staatsrecht 1², 459 A 3; 2¹, 857; Friedländer Sittengesch. 1⁵, 248 f.) und damit natürlich auch der *militiae equestres* (Marquardt Staatsverwaltung 2, 356).

[44]) Die genaueren Ausführungen über Begriff und Stellung der *alumni*, die ich ursprünglich in einem Exkurs zu der vorliegenden Abhandlung zu geben beabsichtigte, muss ich mit Rücksicht auf den Raum einem besonderen, demnächst anderweitig zu veröffentlichenden Aufsatz vorbehalten. Ich gebe daher hier zunächst nur die wichtigsten Belegstellen: Plin. *Epp. ad Trai.* 65.66. Gaius 1,19. Dig. 20, 1, 8; 40, 2, 14 pr. Cod. Just. 8, 51, 3. Suet. *de gramm.* 7. 11. 21 vgl. Marquardt Privataltert. S. 3. 81.

stellung des *alumnus* einzuschliessen. In technischer Weise aber werden damit die Findelkinder bezeichnet. Von Haus aus meist freigeboren, wurden diese Kinder, die als ausgesetzte im Rechtssinn einen Vater nicht hatten, wenn sie ein anderer aufnahm und aufzog, rechtlich dessen Sklaven. Sie hatten freilich meist in der Familie eine, auch vom Recht anerkannte, bevorzugte, der Stellung der Hauskinder sich nähernde Stellung, erhielten häufig, und zwar gewöhnlich durch ihre Pflegemutter, die Freilassung, für welche in diesem Fall die beschränkenden Bestimmungen der *lex Aelia Sentia* nicht galten, und wurden gewiss nicht selten auch von ihren Pflegeeltern adoptiert. Ob nun freilich die Bezeichnung *alumnus* auf Juvenal von dem Biographen in diesem technischen Sinn angewendet ist, lässt sich nicht entscheiden, doch ist es mir wahrscheinlich, weil es sich eben hier um Stand und Herkunft des Dichters handelt, jener *libertinus* geradezu als Stellvertreter des Vaters erscheint. Ohne also behaupten zu wollen, dass diese Annahme sicher sei, will ich im folgenden ausführen, wie wir uns unter der Voraussetzung, dass der Biograph den Ausdruck *alumnus* im technischen Sinn gebraucht habe und Juvenal also ein Findelkind gewesen sei, die weitere Entwicklung seiner persönlichen Rechtsstellung zu denken haben. Als, ursprünglich wohl freigeborenes, Findelkind durch die Aufnahme von seiten seiner Pflegeeltern zum Sklaven derselben geworden, müsste Juvenal in verhältnismässig jungen Jahren, jedenfalls vor dem Eintritt in den Militärdienst mit 17 Jahren, zunächst von denselben freigelassen und weiterhin adoptiert worden sein. Damit erhielt er dann auch den vollen römischen Namen; durch die Adoption von seiten des *libertinus* galt er selbst dann als *ingenuus*. Die volle Ingenuität im dritten Glied, die er jedenfalls vor seiner Erhebung in den Ritterstand besessen haben muss, erhielt er durch kaiserliche *natalium*

restitutio. [45]) Diese mochte ihm um so leichter gewährt werden, wenn er die Präsumption thatsächlich freier Geburt für sich geltend machen konnte, seine Beziehung zu jenem Freigelassenen nicht durch das Blut, sondern durch zufällige äussere Umstände bedingt war. Aus demselben Grund sind dann auch die abfälligen Bemerkungen des Dichters über die Freigelassenen, namentlich die freigelassenen Emporkömmlinge, psychologisch leichter zu verstehen.

Über Juvenals Familie berichtet der *Anonymus Barberinus: „Junio Juvenale patre, matre vero Septumuleia natus est. Sororem habuit Septumuleiam quae Fuscino nupsit."* Ich bin zu der Annahme geneigt, dass uns auch hier ein Stück guter Überlieferung vorliegt. Denn was der Namen der Eltern oder Pflegeeltern und der Schwester des Dichters betrifft, so kann zwar der Name des Vaters von dem Berichterstatter nach dem Namen des Sohnes und ebenso der der Tochter nach dem der Mutter erfunden sein. Aber hinsichtlich des Namens der Mutter ist nirgends ein Anhaltspunkt für eine Kombination gegeben, und für die Annahme autoschediastischer Erfindung ist der Name zu selten. [46]) Mit der Angabe, dass Juvenal eine Schwester gehabt und diese den *Fuscinus*, der von dem Dichter, jedoch ohne irgend welche Nebenbeziehung angeredet wird, [47]) geheiratet habe, verhält es sich ähnlich. Für Angaben, gegen die nach Inhalt und Herkunft ein bestimmtes Bedenken nicht vorliegt, eigene Erfindung durch den Biographen oder die Verfasser unserer *vitae* anzunehmen, halte ich nach dem früher Bemerkten nicht für gerechtfertigt.

Über Juvenals Jugenderziehung wissen wir nichts weiter, als was er selbst in reiferen Jahren in seiner ersten Satire scher-

45) vgl. Mommsen Staatsrecht 2³, 857; 1³, 460 f.
46) vgl. Thédenat in den *Mélanges Graux* S. 516 f.
47) 14,1.

zend erwähnt[48]), dass er, wie es damals bei den Söhnen besserer Häuser üblich war, grammatischen und rhetorischen Unterricht genoss, vielleicht beide, jedenfalls aber wohl den letzteren in Rom und nicht in Aquinum. In der verhältnismässig unbedeutenden Landstadt werden wir, zumal bei der Nähe der Hauptstadt schwerlich öffentliche oder private Schulen voraussetzen dürfen oder doch wenigstens keine Rhetorschule[49]). Der grammatische Unterricht gehört jedenfalls der Knabenzeit Juvenals an; den rhetorischen hat er, wenn er ihn überhaupt schon vor dem Eintritt in den Militärdienst begonnen hat, in reiferen Jahren in Rom fortgesetzt.

Über die militärische und politische Laufbahn Juvenals belehrt uns die Aquinatische Inschrift, die weit mehr Ausbeute gewährt, als man bisher daraus entnommen hat. Mit den von Mommsen vorgeschlagenen und gerechtfertigten Ergänzungen lautet dieselbe:

[cere]RI · SACRVM
[d. iu]NIVS · IVVENALIS
[trib.] COH· [I] DELMATARVM
II· VIR· QVINQ· FLAMEN
DIVI· VESPASIANI
VOVIT · DEDICAV[itq]VE
SVA PEC

Worin die Dedikation bestand, ist nicht zu sagen; der eine der Gewährsmänner, die Abschriften der Inschrift geben, bezeichnet den Stein als eine Marmortafel, der andere als eine Basis, auf deren Nebenseite eine andere Inschrift stand. In Z. 1 hat Mommsen die Lesart des besseren Gewährsmannes: SACRVM beibehalten, statt die des anderen: SEDEM in AEDEM zu ändern. Der Stein stand wohl, wie Mommsen richtig annimmt, ursprünglich

bei dem Tempel der Ceres, deren durch Juvenal bezeugter Beiname Helvina (oder vielleicht richtiger Elvina) daher zu stammen scheint, dass ein Mitglied der in Inschriften jener Gegenden vorkommenden gens Elvia ihr das Heiligtum stiftete. In Z. 3 ist: TRIB. und die Zahl I, ebenso in Z. 4: VIR nicht sicher, aber sehr wahrscheinlich.

Die Beziehung der Inschrift auf unseren Dichter ist oben gerechtfertigt. Über die Zeit derselben lässt sich zunächst nur sagen, dass sie nach dem J. 79, dem Todesjahr des Kaisers Vespasian, der als divus bezeichnet wird, gesetzt ist. Ob durch den Zusatz vovit dedicatvitque sua pecunia ausdrücklich angedeutet werden soll, dass Juvenal die Dedikation auch pecunia publica, also in magistratischer Stellung hätte machen können, woraus folgen würde, dass die Inschrift in dem Jahre seines duoviratus quinquennalis gesetzt ist, ist nicht sicher, aber deshalb nicht unwahrscheinlich, weil herkömmlicherweise die Munizipalbeamten Aufwendungen für öffentliche Zwecke, Bauten u. dergl. machen mussten. Die Inschrift erwähnt nur je das höchste militärische, politische und priesterliche Amt, das Juvenal bis dahin bekleidet hatte.

Was zunächst seine politische Laufbahn betrifft, so war für die Munizipalämter, wie für die hauptstädtischen, ein certus ordo, jedoch nicht wie bei diesen ein Intervall zwischen den einzelnen Ämtern vorgeschrieben[50]). Juvenal muss also vor dem duoviratus quinquennalis die Quaestur und die Aedilität in Aquinum bekleidet haben. Ebenso setzt der tribunatus cohortis die Bekleidung bestimmter anderer Chargen voraus.

Die Art wie Martial in zwei dem J. 91 oder 92 angehörigen Epigrammen[51]) von Ju-

---

[48] I, 15 ff.

[49] In Venusia gab es, als Horaz in die Schule kommen sollte, nur den „ludus Flavi magistri" (sat. 1, 6, 72 ff); unter Traian hatte Comum noch keinen Lehrer der Beredsamkeit (Plin. epp. 4,13.)

[50] Marquardt Staatsverwaltung 1,498.

[51] Mart. 7,24. 91. Martials 6. Buch ist im Sommer 90 veröffentlicht, das 7. im Dezember 92 (Friedländer Sittengeschichte 3⁵, 432 f.) Das letztere enthält also wohl die Gedichte der Jahre 91 und 92.

4

venal redet, zeigt, dass dieser damals und wohl schon seit einiger Zeit sich zu dauerndem Aufenthalt in Rom angesiedelt hatte; aller Wahrscheinlichkeit nach hatte er damals, also etwa um das J. 90, seine militärische und seine Ämterlaufbahn abgeschlossen. Für den Beginn der hauptstädtischen, wie der munizipalen Ämterlaufbahn war nach einer allgemeinen Vorschrift des Augustus ein Alter von 25 Jahren erforderlich, und zwar wurde dabei das begonnene 25. Lebensjahr als voll gerechnet [32]). Im allgemeinen begann man wohl auch mit diesem Termin, jedenfalls nicht viel später die Ämterlaufbahn. Juvenals 25. Lebensjahr ist 79/80; also ist seine Ämterlaufbahn in das Jahrzehnt von 80—90 zu verlegen.

Seine militärische Laufbahn begann Juvenal wohl gleich mit dem Eintritt ins dienstfähige Alter, nach zurückgelegtem 17. Jahr[53]), also im J. 72; und vermutlich hatte er sie um das Jahr 90 beschlossen. Die verhältnismässig kurze Zeit, die darnach für seinen Militärdienst bis zur Stufe des *tribunatus cohortis* bleibt, und die glaubwürdige Nachricht des Biographen, dass er *sua virtute* sich die Ritterwürde erworben habe, machen es wahrscheinlich, dass er als *petitor militae equestris* in das Heer eintrat. Es ist bekannt[34]), dass in der Kaiserzeit junge Leute, welche auf Avancement dienen wollten, mit besonderer kaiserlicher Erlaubnis, ohne das *tirocinium* als Gemeine zu machen, ihren Dienst als Centurionen begannen und der Reihe nach die vier Posten des *primipilus*, des *praefectus cohortis*, des *tribunus legionis* und des *praefectus alae* bekleideten, um dann den Dienst zu verlassen und gewöhnlich in die Laufbahn der ritterlichen Verwaltungsbeamten überzutreten. Der in unserer Inschrift erwähnte *tribunatus cohortis* rangierte mit dem *tribunatus legionis*[55]), ist also als die dritte Stufe in der

militärischen Laufbahn Juvenals zu betrachten. Ob er nachher noch eine *praefectura alae* bekleidet hat, wissen wir nicht; es ist wohl möglich, dass er auch vor Vollendung der üblichen Laufbahn die Ritterwürde erlangt hat. Diese letztere hatte er zur Zeit, da die Inschrift gesetzt ist, offenbar noch nicht erlangt, da sie sonst gewiss erwähnt wäre. Die *cohors I Delmatarum*, welche Juvenal als Tribun kommandierte, stand in den Jahren 106 und 124 nachweislich in Britannien[56]); der Annahme, dass sie schon längere Zeit vorher dort stationiert war und Juvenal also jenes Tribunat in Britannien bekleidete, steht nichts im Weg. Nun ist aus dem Biographen eine Nachricht erhalten, die sich auf dieselbe Sache zu beziehen scheint, freilich so, wie sie uns vorliegt, in falschen Zusammenhang eingereiht ist. Alle *vitae* berichten, dass Juvenal unter dem Schein eines militärischen Kommandos verbannt wurde, alle, dass die Veranlassung dazu der Zorn des Kaisers über die bekannten Spottverse auf den Pantomimen Paris war; die genaueren erzählen, dass Juvenal diese Verse zuerst als Epigramm unter Domitian gedichtet und erst später, unter einem anderen Kaiser, durch Aufnahme in die 7. Satire veröffentlicht habe, und bringen die Verbannung erst mit dieser Veröffentlichung in Zusammenhang. Während nun die anderen *vitae* als Ort der Verbannung Ägypten angeben, bezeichnet *vita IV*, die zwar auch die erste selbständige Abfassung jener Verse und die spätere Einfügung in die 7. Satire unterscheidet, aber dann weiterhin doch nicht bestimmt die Verbannung mit dieser letzteren in Zusammenhang bringt, Britannien als Ort der Verbannung (*fecit eum praefectum militum contra Scotos*). Im Hinblick auf den in der Inschrift gegebenen Fingerzeig erscheint als die einfachste Lösung dieses Widerspruchs die Annahme, dass zwei

---

[32]) Mommsen Staatsrecht 1[2], 554.
[33]) Mommsen Staatsrecht 1[2], 487 f. 553 f
[54]) Marquardt Staatsverwaltung 2,366 ff.

[55]) Marquardt Staatsverwaltung 2,459.
[56]) Vgl. Hübner im Rhein. Mus. 11,30; im Hermes 16,566.

zeitlich und sachlich getrennte, aber doch in einer gewissen inneren Beziehung stehende Ereignisse, über die der Biograph richtig berichtete, in *vita* IV zusammengeworfen sind. Vermutlich hat der Biograph, wie ich dies in der Rekonstruktion seines Berichtes dargestellt habe, unmittelbar nach der Erwähnung der Abfassung jener Spottverse dem zeitlichen Zusammenhang der Ereignisse folgend die militärische Verwendung Juvenals in Britannien erzählt und an späterer Stelle die Einfügung jener Verse in die 7. Satire als Ursache seiner unter dem Schein eines militärischen Kommandos erfolgten Verbannung nach Ägypten erwähnt. Dass bei flüchtigem Excerpieren beides zusammengeworfen werden und so die Angabe von der Verbannung des Dichters nach Britannien *contra Scotos* entstehen konnte, ist wohl begreiflich. Nun wird man annehmen dürfen, dass Juvenal jene Verse, die nach der Angabe des Biographen sein erster dichterischer Versuch waren, aus unmittelbarer eigener Anschauung des verderblichen Einflusses des Pantomimen Paris auf Domitian verfasst hat, also in Rom und in den Jahren 81—83, in welchen Paris jene Rolle am Hof spielte; im J. 83 wurde er auf Domitians Befehl wegen des Verdachts ehebrecherischen Umgangs mit der Kaiserin ermordet[57]). Vielleicht gehört auch die gewiss historische, von Juvenal in der 4. Satire geschilderte possenhafte Ratssitzung, die spätestens in das J. 87 gesetzt werden kann[58]), schon in die ersten Jahre Domitians; die anschauliche, lebensvolle, mit individuellen Zügen ausgestattete Schilderung des Dichters legt den Gedanken nahe, dass er die Sache aus der Nähe selbst miterlebt, die beteiligten Personen genau gekannt hat. Es würde also Juvenals Kommando etwa in den Jahren 82—84 begonnen haben. Ohne

Zweifel dauerte es mehrere Jahre. Bekanntlich war in den Jahren 78—84 Julius Agricola Statthalter von Britannien, und mit der Angabe des Biographen, dass Juvenal geschickt worden sei *„contra Scotos, qui bellum contra Romanos moverant"*, hat es also seine Richtigkeit. In welcher Eigenschaft Juvenal in den ersten Jahren der Regierung Domitians (81—96), vor seinem britannischen Kommando, in Rom weilte, darüber wage ich kaum eine Vermutung aufzustellen. Es kann sein, dass er nach Bekleidung eines oder zweier der Aquinatischen Ämter zu vorübergehendem Aufenthalt in Erwartung einer militärischen Verwendung in der Hauptstadt weilte; vielleicht aber könnte er auch in Rom selbst eine militärische Stellung, etwa die eines *tribunus vigilum*, die ungefähr dem *tribunatus legionis* und *tribunatus cohortis* gleichgestanden zu haben scheint[59]), bekleidet haben. Ich gestehe, dass ich das reiche einschlägige epigraphische Material, aus dem eine genauere Kenntnis der üblichen militärischen Laufbahn zu gewinnen wäre, nicht genügend beherrsche. Natürlich steht auch nichts der Annahme im Weg, dass Juvenal die munizipalen Ämter überhaupt erst nach Abschluss seines Militärdienstes bekleidet hat.

Das in der Inschrift erwähnte Priestertum eines *flamen divi Vespasiani* ist sicherlich ein munizipales[60]), und zwar nach der Analogie anderer, ein jähriges[61]). Die Zeit der Bekleidung desselben durch Juvenal lässt sich nicht genauer bestimmen; denn weder bestand dafür eine Altersvorschrift, noch giebt die Stellung in der Inschrift einen Anhalt; einen *certus ordo* in den Priestertümern gab es nicht, und Kumulierung mit politischen Ämtern war statthaft.

Es ergibt sich also mit einiger Wahrscheinlichkeit folgende, im einzelnen

---

[57]) Dio Cass. *Epit.* 67, 3. Suet. *Dom.* 3.
[58]) O. Hirschfeld Untersuchungen auf dem Gebiet der römischen Verwaltungsgeschichte 8. 223. vgl. Borghesi *oeuvres* 5,513 ff.

[59]) Vgl. Marquardt Staatsverwaltung 2,468 f.
[60]) Vgl. Mommsen Hermes 3,100.
[61]) Vgl. Wilmanns *Exempla inscriptionum latinarum* Index 8. 486 ff.

verschiedene Möglichkeiten offen
lassende Anordnung der öffentlichen
Laufbahn des Dichters. Mit 17 Jahren,
im J. 72 oder 73, als *petitor militiae equestris*
in das Heer eingetreten, bekleidete Juvenal
etwa bis zum Jahre 80 die Stellungen eines
primipilus und darnach eines *praefectus cohortis*.
Mit 25 Jahren, etwa im Jahre 80[62]), bekleidete
er vielleicht in seiner Vaterstadt Aquinum die
Quaestur oder die Aedilität[63]), möglicherweise
auch beide Ämter nacheinander; er verweilte
darauf, sei es als Privatmann für kürzere Zeit,
oder in einer militärischen Stellung, etwa als
tribunus cohortis vigilum für mehrere Jahre in
Rom, in der Zeit, da der Pantomime Paris bei
Domitian allmächtig war; darauf wurde er,
etwa zwischen den Jahren 82—84, als *tribunus
cohortis I Delmatarum* nach Britannien geschickt und blieb wohl mehrere Jahre in dieser
Stellung. Ob er auch noch die höhere Stufe
der *praefectura alae* bekleidet hat, ist zweifelhaft. Nach mehreren Jahren in die Heimat
zurückgekehrt, verwaltete er in seiner Vaterstadt die bisher noch nicht bekleideten Ämter,
jedenfalls erst jetzt gegen Ende der achtziger
Jahre[64]) den *duoviratus quinquennalis*. Wann er
das munizipale, ohne Zweifel jährige Priestertum eines *flamen divi Vespasiani* bekleidete,
wissen wir nicht, natürlich nur während seines
persönlichen Aufenthalts in Aquinum. Um

diese Zeit erhielt er dann vom Kaiser die durch
seine militärische Laufbahn verdiente Ritterwürde. Ob er je einmal daran gedacht hat, in
den ritterlichen Verwaltungsdienst überzutreten,
wissen wir nicht, bekleidet hat er jedenfalls
eine solche Stellung nicht.

Etwa um das Jahr 90 erfolgte Juvenals
Übersiedlung nach Rom zu dauerndem
Aufenthalt. Was des Dichters persönliche
Beziehungen daselbst betrifft, so bezeugen
uns seinen freundschaftlichen Verkehr mit
Martial die erwähnten zwei dem Jahre 91
oder 92 angehörigen Epigramme des letzteren.
Martial schickt im Dezember dem Freund von
seinem kleinen Landgut Nüsse als Saturnaliengruss. Eine *perfida lingua* versucht zwar das
Verhältnis beider Dichter zu stören, wird aber
von Martial mit bitteren Worten zurechtge-
wiesen. Das freundschaftliche Verhältnis blieb
auch bestehen, als Martial Rom verlassen hatte.
Noch im Jahre 101, kurz vor seinem Tod,
sendet der letztere aus Bilbilis dem in dem
aufregenden und verpflichtungsreichen Treiben
der Hauptstadt abgehetzten Freund einen poetischen Gruss[65]). Über die sonstigen persönlichen Beziehungen Juvenals in Rom wissen
wir nichts. Die in seinen Gedichten als Bekannte erwähnten Personen sind für uns bloss
Namen.

Über Juvenals gesellschaftliche Stel-

---

[62]) Der Antrittstag war wohl für die sämtlichen
Ämter eines Munizipiums derselbe, aber für die verschiedenen Munizipien verschieden, vgl. Mommsen Hermes 3,81.
Für Aquinum denselben zu bestimmen, fehlt es an uns
bis jetzt an Anhaltspunkten.

[63]) Die Quaestur hat, wie an manchen Orten, so auch
in Aquinum keine feste Stellung in dem *ordo honorum*
vgl. Mommsen C. J. L. X. p. 530; Stadtrechte von Sal-
pensa und Malaca S. 416.

[64]) Dass in der Kaiserzeit, wenigstens im ersten
Jahrhundert, in den einzelnen italischen Gemeinden der
Census, wie der Name der damit betrauten Beamten
besagt, regelmässig alle 5 Jahre gehalten wurde, ist
wahrscheinlich, nicht so, dass er in allen gleichzeitig

stattfand (Mommsen Staatsrecht 2², 409.) Was Aquinum
betrifft, so scheint dem J. 27 oder 28 nach Chr. der
duoviratus quinquennalis des Nero Caesar, des Sohnes
des Germanicus (Wilmanns *Exempla inscr.* 2046) anzugehören. Nero, der wahrscheinlich im J. 7 geboren war
und das Recht erhalten hatte, 5 Jahre vor der gesetz-
lichen Frist Ämter zu bekleiden, konnte also zuerst im
J. 27 ein Amt bekleiden; im J. 29 aber war er bereits
vor dem Senat angeklagt (vgl. Wilmanns zu n. 2046. 890;
Mommsen die Familie des Germanicus Hermes 13,245 ff.).
Regelmässige Censusperioden vorausgesetzt, würden also
für das J. 87 oder 88 *duoviri quinquennales* in Aquinum
anzusetzen sein. Doch ist diese Berechnung freilich sehr
unsicher.

[65]) Mart. 12, 18.

lung in Rom ergiebt sich aus seinen eigenen
Gedichten und anderweitigen Nachrichten
mancherlei. Den Besitz eines vom Vater er-
erbten Landgutes in Aquinum und eines
anderen in Tibur erwähnt Juvenal selbst [66]).
Die Angabe des Biographen, der jenen Freigelassenen, des Dichters Pflegevater, als *locuples*
bezeichnet, beruht vielleicht nur auf diesen Andeutungen. Indes eine jedenfalls für Aquinatische Verhältnisse nicht unbedeutende Wohl-
habenheit Juvenals, die doch wohl in der Hauptsache durch das väterliche Vermögen begründet
war, bezeugen auch andere Umstände. Die
Bekleidung öffentlicher Ämter war in den
Munizipien wie in Rom an einen gewissen
Census gebunden, dessen Höhe für Aquinum
wir allerdings nicht kennen, und erforderte
ausserdem die Erlegung gewisser gesetzlich
normierter Geldsummen als Antrittsgeld in die
Stadtkasse und herkömmlich freiwillige Aufwendungen für öffentliche Zwecke, namentlich
Spiele und Bauten [67]). Vielleicht ist das durch
die Inschrift der Göttin Ceres geweihte „Heiligtum" eben eine in diesem Sinn aufzufassende
Leistung des Dichters in seinem *duoviratus
quinquennalis*. Sodann ist bekannt, dass für
die Erwerbung der Ritterwürde ein Census
von 400 000 HS. gesetzlich erforderlich war [68]).
Freilich in Rom scheinen des Dichters ökono-
mische Verhältnisse bei dem Luxus, dem sich
auch Minderbemittelte, wenn sie gesellschaft-
lich einigermassen etwas gelten wollten, nicht
entziehen konnten, und bei den hohen Preisen
verhältnismässig kümmerliche gewesen zu sein.
Er scheint in der Subura, dem Plebejerquartier
seine Wohnung gehabt zu haben [69]) und die
Klagen, die er in der dritten Satire dem Umbricius in den Mund legt [70]), scheinen Stoss-

seufzer seines eigenen Gemütes zu sein. Ja
seine eigenen Andeutungen und Martials An-
spielungen [71]) lassen keinen Zweifel, dass er
ebenso wie jener es nicht verschmäht hat, sich
in die Klientel vornehmer Häuser zu begeben.
Nur sind wir gewiss zu der Annahme berech-
tigt, dass Juvenal sich nie in dieser gemeinen
Weise erniedrigt und weggeworfen hat, wie
der Speichellecker Martial.

Über Juvenals Beschäftigung in Rom
nach dem Abschluss seiner militärischen und
politischen Laufbahn bis zu seinem erst unter
Traian im Jahre 105 oder wenig später erfolgten öffentlichen Auftreten als Dichter berichtet der Biograph, dass er sich jahrelang
mit rhetorischen Deklamationen beschäftigt habe [72]). Diese Angabe bestätigt
Martial durch die Anrede: „*facunde Juvenalis*" in
dem erwähnten poetischen Saturnaliengruss. Dass
nur Liebhaberei und das Streben nach geistiger
Förderung überhaupt, nicht aber die Absicht
praktisch seine Fähigkeiten als Lehrer der
Beredsamkeit oder als Anwalt zu verwerten, für
Juvenal das Motiv war, sich in schon vorge-
rückten Jahren nochmals der Rhetorik zuzu-
wenden, hat der Biograph vielleicht selbst nur
aus der Thatsache, dass Juvenal später ganz
zur Dichtkunst überging, geschlossen, jedenfalls
also von einer solchen praktischen Thätigkeit
nichts überliefert gefunden. Auch der von
Martial auf Juvenal angewendete Ausdruck
facundus ist weder ein Beweis für [73]), noch
gegen eine öffentliche praktische Thätigkeit,
so wenig als die bitteren Schilderungen des
Dichters in seiner 7. Satire [74]) über die geringen Erfolge der Sachwalter und der Rhetoren.

Erst unter Traian, etwa als Fünfziger,

---

[66]) 6, 57. 11, 65.
[67]) Marquardt, Staatsverwaltung 1, 498 f.
[68]) Vgl. Friedländer, Sittengeschichte 1³, 243 ff.
[69]) Vgl. Mart. 12, 18. Juv. sat. 3, 5.
[70]) 3, 126—189. 223 ff.

[71]) *Sat.* 1, 100 f. vgl. 4, 98. Mart. 12, 18.
[72]) „*ad mediam fere aetatem declamavit, animi magis causa quam quod scholae se aut foro praepararet.*"
[73]) Dies nimmt Weidner (in der Einleitung seiner Ausgabe S. 6) an.
[74]) 7, 105 ff. 150 ff.

5

trat Juvenal öffentlich als satirischer Dichter auf. Dass er sich schon früher neben der Rhetorik im Stillen mit dichterischen Versuchen abgegeben hat, dass einzelne kleinere oder grössere poetische Stücke, die später, wie jenes Epigramm auf Paris, in seine Satiren eingefügt wurden, schon unter Domitian, Nerva und in den ersten Jahren Traians verfasst sind, halte ich für wahrscheinlich. Doch ist hier nicht der Ort, näher darauf einzugehen. Sein poetisches Programm ist die erste Satire, die etwa zwischen den Jahren 105 — 108 [73]) abgefasst ist. Die Veröffentlichung seiner Gedichte erfolgte ohne Zweifel dem damaligen Brauch entsprechend gewöhnlich in zweifacher Weise, zuerst durch Rezitation vor einem geladenen privaten Kreis von Personen der besseren Gesellschaft, worauf auch einzelne Spuren in seinen Gedichten hinzudeuten scheinen [76]), und dann durch buchmässige Herausgabe. Nach der Angabe des Biographen fanden seine Gedichte anfangs wenig Anklang, dann aber solchen Beifall, dass er zwei- und dreimal dieselbe Vorlesung halten musste. Die Einteilung der Satiren in 5 Bücher geht auf den Dichter selbst zurück, die Anordnung ist die nach der Zeitfolge. Die genaue Erörterung der Frage nach Art und Zeit der Abfassung der einzelnen Satiren muss ich einem anderen Ort vorbehalten. Nur hinsichtlich der 7. Satire will ich hier bemerken, dass meiner Überzeugung nach Friedländer[77]) mit vollem Recht annimmt, dass der im wesentlichen schon unter Traian gedichteten eigentlichen Satire (V. 36— 243) eine dazu gar nicht passende Einleitung (V. 1—35) zum Preis des neuen Kaisers Hadrian vorgesetzt ist. Die Angabe des Biographen,

dass die Aufnahme der Spottverse auf Paris in diese Satire Veranlassung zur Verbannung des Dichters gab, müssen wir, wollen wir nicht den ganzen, in sich zusammenhängenden und vertrauenerweckenden Bericht unseres Gewährsmannes über den Haufen werfen, auf eine spätere Neuherausgabe dieser Satire beziehen. Auf eine in seinen späteren Jahren in Rom begonnene, in der Verbannung fortgesetzte Neubearbeitung seiner Gedichte überhaupt [78]) weist ja ausdrücklich die unverdächtige Angabe des Biographen: „in exilio ampliavit satiras et pleraque mutavit", und weisen vielleicht auch Spuren in den Satiren selbst, und irgend ein positives Argument steht unserer Annahme nicht entgegen.

Nachdem Juvenal als Fünfziger das seiner Begabung und seiner Charakteranlage angemessene Gebiet der satirischen Poesie betreten und etwa 30 Jahre lang unter dem lebhaften Beifall seiner Zeitgenossen gepflegt hatte, traf ihn als 80jährigen Greis ein harter Schlag, durch die von dem Kaiser Hadrian unter dem Schein eines militärischen Kommandos verfügte Verbannung nach Ägypten. Was uns darüber in den vitae aus dem Biographen erhalten ist, ist voll von Widersprüchen und Unmöglichkeiten; indessen lässt sich doch daraus der echte gute Kern von Überlieferung herausschälen, der durch wiederholte Excerpierung und Interpolierung verwirrt, entstellt und verfälscht ist. Die Thatsache der Verbannung und zwar unter dem Schein eines militärischen Kommandos ist ein durch die Übereinstimmung der vitae feststehendes Element des ursprünglichen Berichts. Die Veranlassung bilden nach allen vitae jene unter dem unmittel-

---

[75]) Von den Gründen für diese Ansetzung erwähne ich hier nur einen. Die Anspielung auf den gefährlichen Angeber M. Aquilius Regulus (V. 33 ff.) hat Juvenal, eingedenk seines in eben dieser Satire ausgesprochenen Grundsatzes (V. 170 f.), gewiss erst nach dessen zwischen den Jahren 105—107 erfolgtem Tod (vgl. Mommsen Index Plinianus S. 401 f.) gewagt.

[76]) 1, 21, überhaupt die ganze Einleitung der ersten Satire; 3, 60.

[77]) Sittengeschichte 3⁵, 461 f.

[78]) Diese nehmen auch Teuffel (Studien und Charakteristiken S. 424 ff.) und Ribbeck (Einleitung seiner Ausg. S. XII; „Der echte und der unechte Juvenal" S. 70) an.

baren Eindruck der Sache selbst verfassten Spottverse auf den Pantomimen Paris [79]), nach den einen direkt, nach den anderen indirekt, indem ihre spätere Einfügung in die 7. Satire in einer Zeit, wo wiederum ein Schauspieler grossen Einfluss bei dem Kaiser besass, als boshafte, versteckte Anspielung auf die Gegenwart aufgefasst wurde. Dass diese letztere Darstellung die genauere, die erstere nur eine ungenaue Wiedergabe des ursprünglichen Berichtes des Biographen ist, kann nicht wohl bezweifelt werden. Dass der Biograph unter jenem Paris den Pantomimen des Domitian, nicht den gleichnamigen des Nero, verstanden, und auch schon ausdrücklich als solchen bezeichnet hat, ist klar. Über den Urheber der Verbannung aber gehen die Berichte sehr auseinander: sie nennen teils Nero, teils Domitian, teils Traian, teils auch nennen sie überhaupt an dieser Stelle oder an beiden gar keinen Namen des Kaisers. Welchen Kaiser der Biograph als Urheber der Verbannung Juvenals genannt hat, geht aus der in einigen vitae erhaltenen Notiz hervor, dass Juvenal 80jährig verbannt worden sei. Gerade daraus, dass in den betreffenden vitae diese Notiz im inneren Widerspruch mit den übrigen Angaben derselben steht, geht deutlich hervor, dass sie ein selbständiges Element der Überlieferung ist. Also war nach dem Biographen Hadrian der Kaiser, der Juvenal verbannte. Als Verbannungsort bezeichnete derselbe Ägypten; dies nennen alle vitae mit Ausnahme von vita IV, welche infolge einer oben besprochenen Verwirrung Britannien nennt. Die Entstehung der uns vorliegenden Darstellung von der Verbannung des Dichters aus dem so rekonstruierten Bericht des Biographen kann man sich etwa in folgender Weise denken. War zunächst beim Excerpieren der Urheber der Verbannung nicht mehr ausdrücklich mit seinem

Namen Hadrian, sondern nur noch als *imperator* bezeichnet, so war der nächste Schritt, dass jene beiden zwar in Beziehung zu einander stehenden, aber durch einen langen Zeitraum getrennten und auch in dem ursprünglichen Bericht genau auseinander gehaltenen Ereignisse in ungenauer Weise zeitlich zusammengerückt und beide unter Domitian verlegt wurden, in einzelnen *vitae* mit Beibehaltung der im Widerspruch damit stehenden Notiz, dass der Dichter bei seiner Verbannung 80 Jahre alt war. Der weitere Schritt war dann, dass sie überhaupt zu einer unmittelbar innerlich zusammenhängenden Gruppe von Ereignissen zusammengeworfen wurden. Hier setzte dann auch die Verwechslung des britannischen und des ägyptischen Kommandos an. Verschwand dann vollends unter den Händen des folgenden Excerptors der Name Domitians, wie dies uns noch in *vita* I a vorliegt, so war für den Nachfolger die Bahn frei, aus eigener Weisheit diese Lücke wieder durch Einführung Neros, des Gönners des früheren Paris, oder Traians, des vermeintlichen Caesars der 7. Satire, auszufüllen.

Ist diese Auffassung von der Entstehung der Widersprüche der *vitae* und von der ursprünglichen, ihren Berichten zu Grund liegenden Darstellung des Biographen richtig, so fragt sich, welcher Wert, welche Glaubwürdigkeit dieser Darstellung beizumessen ist. Noch neuerdings ist von Vahlen [80]) der Versuch gemacht worden, diesen ganzen Bericht von der Verbannung Juvenals als das Ergebnis phantasievoller Klügeleien der Verfasser unserer *vitae* oder ihrer Quelle zu erweisen. Indes zu den oben entwickelten allgemeinen Gründen gegen diese Annahme glaube ich hier noch folgende spezielle hinzufügen zu dürfen. Der Kernpunkt des Berichts des Biographen, die Thatsache der Verbannung wegen der Verse

---

[79]) 7,88 ff.

[80]) In der früher angeführten Abhandlung: Juvenal und Paris (Sitzungsberichte der Berliner Akademie 1883 S. 1175 ff.)

auf Paris ist anderweitig zwiefach beglaubigt, durch Johannes Malalas [81]) und Sidonius Apollinaris [82]). Beide können nach dem früher über die mutmassliche Zeit des Biographen Entwickelten schon aus chronologischen Gründen nicht Quelle desselben sein; den umgekehrten Fall, dass der Biograph Quelle der anderen gewesen sei, nimmt, wie es scheint, auch Vahlen nicht an. So hätten wir also drei von einander unabhängige Zeugen für die Thatsache der Verbannung. Zwar ist Malalas' Bericht durch gröbliche Personenverwechslung entstellt und die Anspielung bei Sidonius ohne Namen gegeben; aber der Kern des Berichts bei ersterem ist glaubhaft und die Beziehung der Anspielung des letzteren auf Juvenal bezweifelt niemand. Auch Vahlen nimmt an, dass „der Grundstock der Tradition, eine Nachricht, Juvenal sei durch den Schauspieler Paris in die Verbannung getrieben worden, aus älterer Zeit bis auf Sidonius und Malalas sich fortgepflanzt habe." [83]) Welche Gründe sind denn

nun beigebracht, um die Unglaubwürdigkeit dieser Tradition zu erweisen? Soweit ich sehe, kein wirklich stichhaltiger, keiner, der nicht bloss die *vitae*, sondern auch den ursprünglichen Bericht des Biographen treffen würde. Es scheint mir, dass das, was eigentlich bewiesen werden sollte, die Unglaubwürdigkeit der Tradition, vielmehr vorausgesetzt ist und unter dieser Voraussetzung die Entstehung der Tradition zu erklären versucht wird [84]). Und meines Erachtens reicht, was in dieser Richtung als Grundlage der Kombinationen angeführt wird, dafür in der That nicht aus und wird mit jener Annahme eben doch „der früh beginnenden Deuteleiensucht antiker Erklärung zu viel zugemutet." [85])

Aus der Verbindung der uns erhaltenen Nachrichten ergiebt sich etwa folgende Vorstel-

---

[81]) p. 262 f. Dind. ὁ δὲ αὐτὸς βασιλεὺς Δομετιανὸς ἐφίλει τὸν ὀρχηστὴν τοῦ πρασίνου μέρους τῆς Ῥώμης, τὸν λεγόμενον Πάριδα. περὶ οὗ καὶ ἐλοιδορεῖτο ἀπὸ τῆς συγκλήτου Ῥώμης καὶ Ἰουβεναλίου τοῦ ποιητοῦ τοῦ Ῥωμαίου, ὡς χαίρων εἰς τὸ πράσινον. ὅστις βασιλεὺς ἐξώρισε τὸν αὐτὸν Ἰουβενάλιον τὸν ποιητὴν ἐν Πενταπόλει ἐπὶ τὴν Λιβύην, τὸν δὲ ὀρχηστὴν πλουτίσας ἔπεμψεν ἐν Ἀντιοχείᾳ τῇ μεγάλῃ ἐπὶ τὸ οἰκεῖν αὐτὸν ἔξω τῆς πόλεως. ὅστις Πάρις ὀρχηστὴς ἐκεῖ ἀπελθὼν ᾤκει ἔξω τῆς αὐτῆς πόλεως κτίσας ἑαυτῷ οἶκον προάστειον καὶ λοῦτρον, ὅπερ ἐστὶν ἕως τῆς νῦν τὸ λεγόμενον Παράδεισος καὶ ὁ οἶκος· κἀκεῖ τελευτήσας κεῖται ἐν σορῷ ὄπισθεν τοῦ οἴκου ἐν τοῖς κήποις αὐτοῦ. Verkürzt giebt denselben Bericht Suidas v. Ἰουβεναλιος.

[82]) *Carm.* 9,267 ff.
Non qui tempore Caesaris secundi
Aeterno incoluit Tomos reatu.
Non qui consimili deinde casu
Ad vulgi tenuem strepentis auram
Irati fuit histrionis exul.

[83]) Vahlen a. O. S. 1191.

[84]) Vahlen S. 1187: „Wir fragen nicht, was ist Wahres an der Sache, sondern wir fragen nur, wie sollen wir diesen Thatbestand der Überlieferung erklären. Denn das leuchtet ein, dass eine feste Tradition über Juvenals Verbannung diesen Angaben der *vitae* nicht zu Grunde liegt, aber das ist auch nicht zu verkennen, dass ein gemeinsamer Kern durch alle Nachrichten hindurchgeht, der Aufklärung verlangt." S. 1191: „Wer diesen Grundstock der Tradition, so wie er ist, für wahr halten will, kann mit Gründen nicht widerlegt werden."

[85]) Vahlens Resultat ist (S. 1192): „Die Vermutung drängt sich auf, dass diese Verse (7,88—92) die Wurzel hergegeben für die ganze Tradition über die Verbannung des Dichters, in doppeltem Gange, einmal in älterer Zeit, so dass die Angabe, Juvenal sei durch Paris verwiesen worden, angesehen werde als Resultat von Combinationen, die von allgemeinen Erwägungen über die Juvenalische Satire und deren dem Dichter selbst wohl bewusste Gefährlichkeit ausgehend, ihre besondere Färbung aus unserer Stelle gezogen, die mit dem Angriff auf den einflussreichen Günstling Domitians und der gleich folgenden Erinnerung an Fabius und Cotta, die um den verbannten Ovid, an Lentulus, der um den verbannten Cicero sich mühte, den Gedanken nahe legen konnte, Juvenal sei selbst einmal einem ähnlichen Schicksal anheimgefallen; und von Neuem durch Vermittlung und Anregung der Verse des Sidonius in ⟨·⟩ confusen und albernen Erzählungen der Biographen und Scholiasten."

lung von der Verbannung des Dichters. Als Juvenal im J. 135 oder 136 von der zuerst im Anfang der Regierung Hadrians veröffentlichten 7. Satire eine neue Ausgabe veranstaltete, fügte er das einst in seiner Jugend auf Paris, den Günstling Domitians, gedichtete, aber nicht veröffentlichte Epigramm ein. Nun scheint damals bei Hadrian, der, in diesen seinen letzten Jahren körperlich leidend, geistig und gemütlich verdüstert, die frühere Selbstbeherrschung verloren hatte [86]), ein Schauspieler grossen Einfluss besessen zu haben. Das Volk erblickte, mit Recht oder Unrecht, in jenen Versen Juvenals eine indirekte Anspielung auf die Gegenwart und verhöhnte damit, sei es im gewöhnlichen Stadtgespräch oder etwa bei einer theatralischen Aufführung [87]), jenen Schauspieler. Der ergrimmte Kaiser rächte sich an dem Dichter, verbannte ihn, jedoch nicht offen, sondern indem er dem Achtzigjährigen zum Hohn ein militärisches Kommando in Ägypten übertrug. Zu Hadrians Charakter, zumal seiner Gemütsstimmung in jenen letzten Jahren seines Lebens passt diese Art von Bestrafung sehr gut. Wo die vitae dieses Kommando genauer bezeichnen, nennen sie dasselbe, wie es scheint, eine praefectura cohortis; nach dem früher über Juvenals militärische Laufbahn Entwickelten dürfte es

sich eher um einen tribunatus cohortis oder aber eine praefectura alae handeln. Mit boshafter Anspielung schrieb der Imperator in das Bestallungsdekret: „Et te Philomela promovit." Der Ort der Verbannung war, wie die genaueren vitae angeben, gelegen in der extrema pars Aegypti; gemeint ist damit wohl, wie die Scholien direkt angeben, die grosse Oase, die wohl auch Malalas im Auge hat, wenn er irrtümlich die libysche Pentapolis, d. h. die gleichfalls eine Oase bildende Landschaft Cyrenaica angiebt. Dass in der Oase eine militärische Abteilung stationiert war, ist zwar, soviel ich weiss, nirgends überliefert, aber ganz glaublich.

In der Verbannung mag Juvenal, wie der Biograph andeutet, die Neubearbeitung seiner Satiren fortgesetzt haben und jedenfalls wird wohl in diese Zeit, wo nicht die ganze fünfzehnte Satire, doch die darin sich findende Bemerkung, dass er Aegypten aus eigener Anschauung kennt [88]), zu setzen sein.

Juvenals Tod erfolgte, wie der Biograph erzählt, „angore ac taedio vitae" bald darauf, in der allerersten Zeit der Regierung des Kaisers Antoninus Pius, nachdem er ein Alter von 82 Jahren erlangt hatte, also in der zweiten Hälfte des J. 138.

III. Beilagen.
A. Zusammenstellung der alten vitas Juvenalis.

Im folgenden sind die sämtlichen teils schon gedruckten, teils mir bloss handschriftlich bekannt gewordenen alten vitae Juvenalis zusammengestellt. Ausgeschlossen sind unter den noch nicht veröffentlichten diejenigen, die ich für Elaborate der Humanistenzeit glaube halten zu müssen; vielleicht findet sich einmal anderweitig Gelegenheit zu ihrer Publikation.

Ich erwähne überall zunächst die schon von anderen benützten Handschriften, dann die weiteren, in denen ich die betreffende vita gefunden habe. Auf eine kritische Feststellung des Textes kommt es mir hier nicht an, sondern nur darauf, dem Leser durch übersichtliche Zusammenstellung des Materials die Prüfung und Beurteilung der Folgerungen und Ergebnisse meiner Abhandlung zu erleichtern.

---

[86]) Vgl. Spart. vit. Hadr. 23 ff.
[87]) Vgl. Teuffel Studien und Charakteristiken S. 412.
[88]) 15,45.

6

Ich gebe deshalb wenigstens bei den schon von Jahn herausgegebenen *vitae* einfach dessen Text und merke überall nur einzelne bedeutende Varianten an.

I a. (= Jahn I).

„*tamquam Probi edidit Valla, P in fine recentiore manu ascriptam habet. habent cod. Alexandrinus bibl. Vatic. 2029 saec. X, Fauchetii bibl. Parisinae 8070 saec. XI, Mazarineus apud Achaintre, codd. Vaticani 2810 saec. XIII., Urb. 342.*"

Dieselbe *vita* findet sich ausser in diesen sieben auch noch in folgenden Handschriften:

8) *cod. mus. Brit. add. 15600 saec. IX.* (Rühl Jahrbb. f. Philol. 109 (1874) S. 868 Nr. 1).

9) *cod. Regius 15 B. XVIII. mus. brit. saec. XI.* (Rühl a. O. No. 2.)

10) *Urbinas (bibl. Vatic.)* 661 (No. 1.)

11) *Urb.* 672.

12) *Palatinus (bibl. Vatic.)* 1701 (No. 1.)

13) *Pal.* 1708 (Nr. 1.; interpoliert.)

14) *Ottobonianus (bibl. Vatic.)* 1031 (No. 2.)

15) *Neapol. IV. F.* 45 *(bibl. naz.) saec. XII. s. XIII.* (No. 1.)

16) *Medic. XXXIV, 42 (saec. XI.)*

Iunius Iuvenalis, libertini locupletis incertum filius an alumnus, ad mediam fere aetatem declamavit animi magis causa quam quod scholae se aut foro praepararet, et dein paucorum versuum satyra non absurde composita in Paridem pantomimum poetamque semenstribus militiolis enitantem genus scripturae industrie excoluit, et tamen bene diu ne modico quidem auditorio quicquam committere est ausus, mox magna frequentia tantoque successu bis aut ter auditus est, ut ea quoque quae prima fecerat inferciret novis scriptis: „quod non dant proceres, dabit histrio. tu Camerinos et Bareas, tu nobilium magna atria curas? praefectos Pelopea facit, Philomela tribunos." erat tunc in deliciis aulae, multique fautorum eius quottidie provehebantur. venit ergo Iuvenalis in suspicionem quasi tempora figura notasset, ac statim per honorem militiae quamquam octogenarius urbe summotus est missusque ad praefecturam cohortis in extremam Aegypti partem tendentis. id supplicii genus placuit, ut levi atque ioculari

delicto par esset. verum intra brevissimum tempus angore ac taedio periit.

Z. 7. haben fast alle Handschriften „*tumentem*".

Z. 16. „*aulae histrio*" fast alle Handschriften.

Z. 19. „*militae, cum non auderet eum imperator publice damnare quamquam*" 13.

Z. 21. hat cod. Pith.: „*in extrema parte Aegypti*".

Z. 23. *par esset. Unde hic cum non posset carere consuetis spectaculis et ludis quae Romae fiebant intra* 13. offenbare Interpolation vgl. III c.

I b. (= Jahn II).

„*E cod. Is. Vossii ed. Henninius*".

Iunius Iuvenalis, libertini locupletis incertum filius an alumnus, ex Aquinio Volscorum oppido oriundus temporibus Claudii Neronis, ad mediam fere aetatem declamavit animi magis causa quam quod scholae se aut foro praepararet, et postquam diu tacuit, uberiori vitiorum iam gliscente contagione ab indignatione incepit: „semper ego auditor tantum." dehinc paucorum versuum satyra non absurde in Paridem Domitiani pantomimum et aulae histrionem semestribus tumentem vibrata poetamque P. Statium composita, hoc genus scripturae industrie excoluit, et tamen diu ne modico quidem auditorio quicqum committere est ausus, mox magna frequentia magnoque successu bis ac ter auditus est, ut ea quoque quae prima fecerat inferciret novis scriptis: „ille et militiae multis largitur honorem. quod non dant proceres dabit histrio." erat tum in deliciis aulae histrio, multique fautorum eius quotidie provehebantur. venit ergo Iuvenalis in suspicionem quasi tempora praesentia figura notasset, ac statim per honorem militiolae quamquam octogenarius urbe summotus missusque ad praefecturam cohortis in extrema Aegypti parte tendentis. id supplicii genus placuit, ut leui atque ioculari delicto par esset. verum intra brevissimum tempus θεὸς αὐτός adscribitur divorum choro, revertiturque Iuvenalis Romam, qui tandem ad Nervae. et Traiani principatum supervivens senio et taedio vitae confectus properantem spiritum cum tussi exspuit.

II a (= Rühl a. O. No. 3.)

1) *cod. Harleianus* 3301. *chart. saec.* XV. (Rühl).
2) *Lipsius epist. quaest.* IV, 20 aus einem *codex Divaei* (Jahn S. 390).
3) *Urb.* 664.
4) *Vatic.* 2813.
5) *Regin. (bibl. Vat.)* 1380.
6) *Palat.* 1706.
7) *Chig. H. V.* 175 *saec.* XIII. (Rom Palazzo Chigi).
8) *Neap. IV. F.* 38 *saec.* XIII *s.* XIV. (interpoliert).
9) *Medic. XXXIV,* 24. *saec.* XV.

Den Text gebe ich der Einfachheit halber nach Rühl, jedoch mit Verbesserung der von demselben beanstandeten Stellen aus den anderen Handschriften.

Iunius Iuvenalis Aquinas id est de Aquino oppido oriundus et natus, qui ad mediam fere aetatem satirice declamavit et in Paridem pantomimum apud aulam imperatoris Domitiani sese in deliciis habentem quosdam versus non absurde composuit hos scilicet:

„quod non dant proceres dahit histrio. tu
                                      Camerinos
Tu Bareas, tu nobilium magna atria curas?
Praefectos Pelopea facit, Philomena tribunos."

Paris iste carmina irrecitata emebat et suum titulum apponebat et pro suis recitabat. Hii versus per aliquantulum temporis aures imperatoris latuerunt. Sed postea cum hoc opus aggrederetur Iuvenalis, occasione accepta in quadam satira, hac scilicet: „Et spes et ratio", satis competenter eosdem versus interseruit. Quibus publicatis Domitianus sua tempora sentiens denotari pudore et ira correptus qualiter Iuvenalem deprimeret apud se excogitavit, sed cum tantae auctoritatis virum publice punire non auderet militibus Romanis in extremas partes Aegypti tendentibus in expeditionem quasi sub obtentu honoris, sub·dignitatis simulatione illum praefecit, ut, si aliquo modo periret, sub specie dilectionis animi malignitas compleretur. Iuvenalis vero hoc opus primum peregit. Unde in ultima satira multa *de* militaribus commodis scripsit, ut sic *in exercitum* ituros animaret. Deinde hoc opere *completo* eo profectus tandem

causa profectionis comperta taedio et angore vitam finivit.

Z. 1 ff. „*Aquinas fuit id est de Aquino oppido oriundus. Romae studuit. In prima aetate tacuit. in secunda declamavit. in tertia scripsit. In prima tacuit, quia pertinet adolescentium discere et non docere, tacere et non declamare. In secunda declamavit, quia declamare maximus labor est, virilis autem aetas patiens est laboris. In tertia scripsit, quia senilis aetas dedicata est sapientiae. Unde et senes sapientes dicuntur. Reprehendit autem ipsum Neronem et in Paridem pantomimum qui erat amasius ipsius Neronis qui emebat libros poetarum intactos non absurde hos composuit versus etc.* 8.

Z. 3. „*satirice*" fehlt in 4. 5. 7. 9.

Z. 4. „*Domitiani imperatoris XIIa Julio Caesare*" 7.

Z. 10 f. den Satz „*Paris iste . . . . recitabat*", haben ausser 1. nur 3. 6., und zwar haben sie, wie schon Löwe (*Acta sem. Lips.* 4,364) richtig conjiciert hatte: „*irrecitata*" und „*pro suis*" (Rühl: „*suas competenti*")

Z. 16 „*satis competenter*" alle Handschriften; ebenso Z. 17 „*publicatis*". (Rühl: „*publicans*".)

Z. 17. „*Nero sentiens*" 8

Z. 26. „*ut sic in exercitum ituros animaret*" alle Handschriften (Rühl: „*se in exercitum retentos curaret(?)*")

II b (= Jahn VII.)

1) „*ex cod. Vaticano* 2810 *descripsit Theod. Mommsen.*"
2) *cod. Regius mus. brit.* 15 B XVIII (Rühl a. O. Nr. 2.)
3) *Urb.* 661 (No. 2.)
4) *Pal.* 1708 (No. 2.)
5) *Ottob.* 1031 (No. 3.)
6) *Regin. (bibl. Vatic.)* 2029 (No. 2.)
7) *Barberin.* VIII, 105. *saec.* XIV (Rom Pal. Barber.)
8) *Medic.* XXXIV, 39 *saec.* XII (No. 2.)

Iuvenalis satyricus Aquinates fuit, id est de Aquino oppido. hic suo tempore videns nimiam luxuriam scribentium proposuit et ipse scribere satyram, in qua nemini pepercit, sed omnium carpsit vicia. ideo autem hanc materiam scribere voluit, quia Claudii Neronis tempore numerositas omnium viciorum plurimum viguit, maxime luxuries. unde cum Claudius audiret, quod iste sua tempora notasset, fecit eum exulare sub optentu militiae et cum exercitu ad Egiptum proficiscentem eum direxit, ubi angore et taedio periit. maxime autem ideo damnatus est, quia hos versus in Paridem pantomimum scripsit:

„quod non dant proceres dahit histrio. tu Camerinos et Bareas, tu nobilium magna atria curas? praefectos Pelopea facit, Philomela tribunos." hic pantomimus dolator erat pessimus et per hoc gratiam obtinuerat principis cum factione, et hic accusatus damnatus est.

II c.

Cod. Regin. 1828. *chart.*

Iuvenalis fuit Aquinas id est de Aquino oppido. Incertum est, an fuerit filius liberti locupletis an alumnus. Iste vero suo tempore videns superfluitatem scriptorum et multa vitia Romae pollere applicuit animum suum ad scribendum et maxime ad satiram scribendam. Unde cum notasset tempora Augusti Claudii Neronis et quosdam versus in Paridem pantomimum scripsisset, sub obtentu militiae missus est ab ipso Caesare cum exercitu ad Aegyptum proficiscente, ubi taedio et langore periit.

II d.

Cod. Barber. IX. 3. *chart.*

Iuvenalis proprium nomen. Aquinas natu. Hic suo tempore videns luxuriam scribentium nimiam, licet usque ad dimidiam aetatem suae tacuisset vitae, tamen satiras describere statuit, in quibus nemini pepercit, sed omnium vitia carpsit et, ut sibi liberius facere liceret, a suamet ipsius redargutione incipit sic dicens: semper ego auditor? Praecipue vero damnatus est propter supradictos versus, quos fecit de pantomimo.

III a.

1) „*Cramer ex msc. Vindobonensi*" (Synnerberg)
2) *Vatic.* 3288
3) *Urb.* 342 (No. 2.)
4) *Pal.* 1701 (No. 2.)
5) *Neapol.* IV F. 45 *saec.* XII. *s.* XIII. (No. 2)
Text nach *Urb.* 342.

Iuvenalis iste Aquinates fuit id est de Aquino oppido temporibus Neronis Claudii imperatoris. Prima aetate siluit, ad mediam fere aetatem declamavit, unde et quasi diu tacens ab indignatione coepit sic dicens: „Semper ego auditor tantum." Fecit quosdam versus in Paridem pantomimum, qui tunc apud imperatorem

plurimum poterat. Hac de causa venit in suspicionem quasi ipsius imperatoris tempora notasset sicque sub obtentu militiae pulsus est urbe. Ita tristitia et angore periit.

III b (= Jahn III.)

„exstat in cod. msc. Is. Vossii v. cl. auctoremque praefert Ael. Donatum, sed uidetur tamen potius ex superiori vita expressa per Cornutum aut Probum aut Asperum aut Euanthium aut similem compilatorem grammaticum." Henninius.

Nach Stephan *de Pithoeanis in Iuvenalem scholiis* S. 9. A. steht dieselbe *vita* auch im *codex Pithoeanus.*

Iuvenalis iste Aquinatis fuit, id est ex Aquinio oppido, temporibus Neronis Claudii imperatoris. prima aetate siluit, ad mediam fere aetatem declamavit, unde et quasi diu tacuit. fecit quosdam versus in Paridem pantomimum, qui tunc temporis apud imperatorem plurimum poterat. hac de causa venit in suspicionem, quasi istius imperatoris tempora notasset. sic obtentu militiae pulsus urbe tandem Romam cum veniret et Martialem suum non videret, ita tristitia et angore periit anno aetatis suae altero et octuagesimo.

III c.

1) Aus einem *Cod. Rehdigeranus* herausgeg. von Pinzger Archiv f. Philol. 14 (1835) S. 267. f.
2) *Pal.* 1708 (No. 3.)
3) *Vat.* 5204.
4) *Vatic.* 2810 (No. 3.)
5) *Ottob.* 1031 (No. 1.)
6) *Urb.* 661 (No. 3.)
7) *Barber.* VIII, 105 *saec.* XIV.
8) *Medic.* XXXIV, 39 *saec.* XII. (No. 3)
Text nach *Pal.* 1708.

Iuvenalis proprium illi fuit nomen. Fuit enim Aquinas id est de Aquino oppido. Qui prima aetate tacuit, media vero declamavit temporibus Claudii Neronis imperatoris. Primum in Paridem pantomimum imperatoris, qui fautores multos habebat, hos versus edidit: „Quod non dant proceres etc." Propter quos versus cum non auderet eum imperator publice damnare, pepulit eum Roma quasi sub obtentu militiae dignitatis cum octogenarius esset factoque principe unius cohortis destinavit eum ad ultimas partes Aegypti. Unde hic cum careret consuetis spectaculis et ludis, qui Romae fiebant, angore et taedio periit.

III d.

„Excussis non ita pridem armariolis nostris et schedis reperimus inter varia manuscripta cetera Persii Iuvenalis et Sulpiciae satiras cum veteribus commentariis e bibliotheca P. Pithoei Lutetiae 1585 vulgatas. Nostrum editionis illius exemplum olim, quod nomen et manus testatur, Petri fuit Scriverii, qui quia multa non contemnenda isti adscripsit ego autem alienis ornare me nolim hic ea fores dare constitui. In fine libri sui haec manu notavit Scriverius: Nomen Iuvenalis etc." Crenius.

Nomen Iuvenalis proprium illi, fuit enim de Aquino oppido. Prima aetate tacuit, media declamavit temporibus Claudii Neronis imperatoris primumque in Paridem pantomimum, qui fautores multos habebat, hos versus edidit: „Quod non dant proceres, dabit histrio etc." Propter quos versus publice ab imperatore damnatus et Roma pulsus est et quasi sub obtentu militiae devectus esset cum cohorte militum tendentium ad Aegyptum. Laudat ultima satira studium militare.

IV (= Jahn V. VI.)

„E cod. Bodleiano can. 35. chartaceo descripsit O. Müller. exstat teste Achaintre in cod. Mediolanensi 112—353."

3) *Vatic.* 2710.

4) *Regin. (bibl. Vat.)* 1724.

5) *„ex cod. Omniboni e monasterio Sancti Salvatoris de Bononia n. 110—40 e ed. Achaintre"* (= Jahn VI.)

6) Muccioli *Catalogus codicum manuscriptorum Malatestianae Caesenatis bibliothecae* (1780. 1784) II. p. 147: „Cod. II. Titulus est: „„Incipiunt commentarii magistri Omniboni supra satyras Iunii Iuvenalis Aquinatis."" *Prooemium hos anteit commentarios, quod ita se habet:* „„.... vita huius modi est. Cum ex Aquino municipio etc."" Diese von Omnibonus offenbar einfach nach dem Wortlaut einer Handschrift gegebene *vita* ist verschieden von der von Achaintre citierten und stimmt im wesentlichen überein mit allen übrigen.

Cum ex Aquino municipio Romam se contulisset et ad dignitatem equestris ordinis pervenire sua virtute meruisset, ad mediam fere aetatem declamavit et in Paridem pantomimum, qui in deliciis apud imperatorem habebatur,

quaedam carmina fecit, quae deinde inseruit in eam satyram: „et spes et ratio." sunt autem haec: „quod non dant proceres dabit histrio. tu Camerinos, tu Bareas, tu nobilium magna atria curas? praefectos Pelopea facit, Philomela tribunos." quae cum ad aures tyranni venissent, sui temporis vitia carpi intellexit. qua ex re commotus, nulla alia occasione reperta struendae mortis in Iuvenalem, sub honoris praetextu fecit eum praefectum militis contra Scotos, qui bellum contra Romanos moverant, ut ibi interficeretur Iuvenalis. sed tamen paulo post, ut sciret sibi iratum principem, in codicillis suis ad eum in exercitu mittendis inseruit: „et te philomela promouit." quo effectum est ut ipse animo consternatus ex mentis aegritudine diem suum obierit.

Z. 2 f. *„et venisset sua virtute ad equestris ordinis dignitatem"* 5; *„ad dignitatem equestris ordinis perrenit cum sua virtute meruisset"* 6.

Z. 5. *„apud Traianum imperatorem"* 2 (cod. Mediol.), 5; *„in deliciis apud Traianum imperatorem victitantem"* 4. 6.

Z. 11. *„Traiani"* 2. 4. 6; *Quibus Traianus* (*„Hadriani"* cj. Achaintre) *intellegens vitia carpi sui temporis ira pa cito praetextu honoris hoc modo poetae mortis instruendae opportunitatem invenit. Fecit"* 5.

Z. 15. *„militum"* 3. 4. 5.; *„militiae"* 6.

Z. 16. *„Gotos"* 4.

Z. 17 ff. *„sed tamen .... promorit"* fehlt in 5.

V (= Jahn IV).

„E cod. Kulenkampii ed. Ruperti."

M. Iunius Iuvenalis, ex municipio Aquinati, ordinis ut fertur libertinorum, Romae literis operam dedit. declamavit non mediocri fama, ut ipse scribit: „et nos consilium dedimus Syllae." extremis Domitiani temporibus missus in exilium expertus est quantum unius histrionis ira valeret. exulavit in Aegypto sub specie honoris nec inde a novis principibus revocatus est. in exilio ampliavit satyras et pleraque mutavit, invehiturque in cineres Domitiani. decessit longo senio confectus exul Antonino Pio imperatore.

VI. Scholia.

a) 1,1: „Iuvenalem aliqui Gallum propter

7

corporis magnitudinem, aliqui Aquinatem dicunt.
ea tempora Domiciani tyranni, quibus etiam
ipse vixit, eo quod in aula ipsius plus striones
quam bonae vitae homines possent, graviter
carpsit. hos autem libros in exilium missus ad
civitatem ultimam Aegypti Hoasim ab ipso
Domiciano scripsit. ideo autem in exilium missus
est, quia dixit versum illum [VII,90], „quod
non dant proceres, dabit strio." nunc autem
hoc inducit per figuras, quasi carptus sit a
miseris poetis, qui nil novum sed omnibus notas
fabulas recitarent. et dicit magis ideo saturam
se scribere, ut possit mores illius temporis
demonstrando notare."

4,38: „Hoc convicium in Fl. Domicianum,
Titi fratrem, Vespasiani filium, iactat, qui calvus
fuit. propterea quod Iuvenalis sub specie

honoris relegatus est ad cohortis curam in
Aegypto Hoasa; ubi mortuus est."

7,92: „Neronem significat, qui scenicis ob
turpem libidinem haec petentibus praestabat.
propter hunc versum missus est in exilio a
Claudio Nerone."

b) „cod. Bibl. reg. Brit. 15. B. XVIII olim Bonga-
rianus exhibet hoc scholion ad 7, 93, quod nobiscum
communicavit Oehler" K. F. Hermann.

Hic autem tangit Traianum et dicit quod
cantoribus eius praefecturas et tribunatus daret.
Quod Traianus sic ultus est, ut ipsi Iuvenali
daret praepositoram belli („galli" cod.) Scotici
et numquam dedit ei successorem qui eum iu-
varet. Ubi cotidie incursus Scotorum est.
Atque ut sciret iratum principem dans ei codi-
cillos dixit: „Ecce et te Philomela promovit."

B. Versuch einer Rekonstruktion der alten Biographie.

(Die von mir vorgeschlagenen Ergänzungen sind in Klammern gesetzt.)

Iunius Iuvenalis ex Aquino municipio
oriundus fuit, Iunii Iuvenalis libertini locupletis et Septumuleiae incertum filius an alumnus.
Claudio Nerone et L. Antistio consulibus natus
est. Sororem habuit Septumuleiam quae Fuscino nupait. Romae litteris operam dedit.
Prima aetate siluit; primum fecit quosdam versus in Paridem pantomimum, qui apud Domi-
tianum imperatorem tum plurimum poterat.
Deinde missus est [ad tribunatum cohortis]
contra Scotos, qui bellum contra Romanos moverant. [Inde reversus] cum ex Aquino Romam se contulisset et ad dignitatem equestris
ordinis sua virtute pervenisset ad mediam fere
aetatem declamavit animi magis causa, quam
quod scholae se aut foro praepararet. Deinde
ad poeticen se applicavit [et olim] paucorum
versuum satira non absurde in Paridem composita [tum] hoc genus scripturae industrie
excoluit. Tamen diu ne modico quidem auditorio quicquam committere est ausus, mox magna
frequentia magnoque successu bis ac ter auditus est. Extremis [vitae? Hadriani?] tempo-

ribus, [cum] ea, quae primum fecerat inseruis-
set satirae illi: „Et spes et ratio":

„Quod non dant proceres, dabit histrio: tu
Camerinos
et Baream, tu nobilium magna atria curas?
praefectos Pelopea facit, Philomela tribunos."
expertus est quantum unius histrionis ira valeret.
Erat tum in deliciis aulae histrio multique
fautorum eius quotidie provehebantur. Venit
ergo Iuvenalis in suspicionem quasi tempora
praesentia figura notasset. Et cum imperator
[Hadrianus] ira percitus tantae auctoritatis
virum publice damnare non auderet, sub obtentu militiae quamquam octogenarius urbe
summotus et missus est ad praefecturam cohortis
[alae?] in extrema Aegypti parte tendentis.
Et, ut sciret iratum sibi principem, in codicillis
ad eum in exercitu mittendis inseruit: „Et te
Philomela promovit." Ita causa profectionis
comperta paulo post in exilio senio confectus
angore et taedio periit Antonino Pio imperatore
anno aetatis suae altero et octogesimo. In
exilio ampliavit satiras et pleraque mutavit.

C. Proben aus dem Cornutus-Kommentar.

Aus dem Cornutuskommentar zu Juvenal sind schon anderweitig einzelne Proben [1]) veröffentlicht; den ganzen Kommentar herauszugeben wird sich bei seiner grossen Weitschweifigkeit und seiner geringen Ergiebigkeit für die Erklärung des Dichters selbst, wie für andere litterarhistorische oder antiquarische Fragen kaum je empfehlen. Ich gebe im folgenden die Einleitung die für die Zwecke unserer Abhandlung über Juvenals Leben von einigem Wert ist, nicht sowohl für die Sache selbst, als weil sie in die Entstehung eines Teils der uns vorliegenden Überlieferung einen Einblick gestattet; es wurde schon früher bemerkt (S. 3.), dass mehrere der uns vorliegenden *vitae* aus verschiedenen Stücken des Cornutuskommentars zusammengestoppelt zu sein scheinen. Leider habe ich seinerzeit im Drange der raschen Durchsicht und Excerpierung zahlreicher Handschriften für meine Zwecke die Bedeutung und den inneren Zusammenhang des so gesammelten Materials, namentlich die Zugehörigkeit der Rühlschen *vita* zu dem Cornutuskommentar während der Arbeit auf den Bibliotheken selbst nicht gleich erkannt, und finde so jetzt bei der Durcharbeitung des Materials manche Lücken. So habe ich auch von dem, was ich hier veröffentliche, aus keiner der von mir eingesehenen Handschriften eine vollständige, zusammenhängende Abschrift genommen. Immerhin reichen aber meine Notizen aus, um in gegenseitiger Ergänzung im grossen Ganzen den Zusammenhang der Einleitung herzustellen, wie er fast wörtlich übereinstimmend in zahlreichen Handschriften sich

findet. Indem ich für dieses wenig angemessene Verfahren um Nachsicht bitte, wage ich hier zu bieten, was ich bieten kann. Wo in meinen Aufzeichnungen eine Lücke ist, habe ich im Text mehrere Punkte gesetzt. benützten

Die von mir für das Folgende b Handschriften sind:

1) *Urbinas (bibl. Vatic.)* 664.
2) *Palatinus (bibl. Vatic.)* 1706.
3) *Vatic.* 2813.
4) *Regin. (bibl. Vatic.)* 1380.
5) *Regin.* 1828.
6) *Chig. H. V.* 175 *saec.* XIII. (Rom Pa lazzo Chigi.)
7) *Neapol. (bibl. nazion.)* IV. F. 38 *saec.* XII s. XIV.)
8) *Medic.* 34,24.
9) *Harleian.* 3301 *saec.* XV (Rühl a. O.)

Cornuti grammatici commentum in satyras Iuvenalis (1). Iunius Iuvenalis Aquinas etc. (*vita* II a: 1. 2. 3. 4. 6. 7. 8. 9). Et haec de illius vita ad praesens sufficiant; nunc ad ea, quae circa hunc librum inquirenda sunt, accedamus. haec sunt: causa compositionis operis, quae materia, quae intentio, quae utilitas, cui parti philosophiae supponatur, quis titulus. Causa itaque compositionis talis est, quod cum Iuvenalis tempore Domitiani (Neronis 7.) imperatoris Romae studens ibi vidisset vitia dominari virtutem subiacere et nullum existere correctorem animum suum ad scribendum hunc librum applicuit. Materia vero huius operis est illa communis omnium satirarum scilicet vitiorum redargutio et per oppositum suasio virtutum. Intentio omnium satirarum communis esse dicitur virtutem persuadere et vitia reprehendere spe correctionis et non spe malevolentiae. utilitas . . . . . Ethicae supponitur. Titulus talis est: Iunii Iuvenalis satirarum primus liber incipit. Iunius nomen est auctoris, sicut et Iuvenalis; fuit enim binomius. Bene dicitur primus, quia sequitur secundus, sunt enim quinque. Satyra

---

[1]) **Schopen** Unedierte Scholien zu Juvenals 3. Satire. Progr. Bonn 1847; **Jahn** *Prolegg. ad Persium* p. 116 ff. K. F. **Hermann** *Schediasma de Scholiorum ad Juv. genere deteriore* Göttingen 1849; **Gigoh** *Apparatus criticus ad Juv.* (Leiden 1849) und *Tria capita ad Juv. eiusque scholiastae* (1850) sind mir nicht zugänglich. Vgl. Schönaich a. O. S. 5 ff.

est carmen reprehensorium et dicitur satyra a
satura quadam lance deorum quae in sacrificiis
diversis replebatur ferculis super altare poneba-
tur ...... Nunc ad litteram accedamus. Expositio
q. rnuti super libros Iunii Iuvenalis (et Persii
cai aterrani) incipit feliciter (1.)
civi
Domicid Schluss des Kommentars: „Finit expo-
est, quia di'i super toto libro Iuvenalis" (1.)
non dant pr ht am Schluss im cod. Regin. 1828
hoc induci Bemerkung: „Explicit commentum
miseris p' nalis Aquinatis exceptum a Cornuto
fabulas , tamento magistri."
se so Nr. 6 und 7, sowie in verschiedenen
dem en Handschriften von Kommentaren, die
uren Einleitungen neben anderen Erörter-
gen zwar auch mancherlei Verwandtes und
Übereinstimmendes mit dem Cornutuskommentar bieten, aber in anderer Auswahl und Reihen-

folge und eine andere vita als II a, findet sich
bei dem Abschnitt, der von dem Namen des
Dichters handelt, eine einfältige Auseinandersetzung über die Namen Decimus und Iunius,
z. B. „Decimi dicebantur apud antiquos qui
hoc calendarii die nascebantur vel quamlibet
dignitatem promerebantur" (Barber. VIII,105;
ähnlich Medic. 34,39)
„Iunius dictus est quia Iunio mense natus
est vel quod melius quia binomius fuit." (6.7.)
Iunius dictus vel a Iunio mense quo aut
consul fuerit factus aut natus vel hinc poetari
vel aliquod opus inchoaverat vel in Iunio reci-
tavit suas satiras." (Barb. IX,3. Medic. 34,39).
Eine derartige Auseinandersetzung über die
Namen des Dichters scheint ursprünglich dem
Cornutuskommentar nicht angehört zu haben,
sondern spätere Interpolation zu sein (oben S. 9).

D. Unedierte vita Juvenalis des Cod. Barberinus VIII, 18.

In einer dem 15. Jahrhundert angehörigen
Pergamenthandschrift der Satiren Juvenals in
der Bibliothek des Palazzo Barberini in Rom,
bezeichnet VIII,18 N(umerus) A(ntiquus) 2174,
ist am Schluss von anderer Hand folgende vita
Juvenalis nachgetragen.

„Iunius Iuvenalis Aquinas Iunio Iuvenale
patre, matre vero Septumuleia ex Aquinati
municipio Claudio Nerone et L. Antistio consulibus natus est. Sororem habuit Septumuleiam,
quae Fuscino nupsit. Sub Berutio Probo gram-
matico celeberrimo profecit ex rhetoribus maxime. Frequentavit M. Antonium Liberalem,
distulit Palaemonem, quia cum Antonio maxi-
mas exercuit inimicitias. Sub Frontone declamasse traditur, quem coluisset unice, si intra
epycureum dogma non constitisset. De Quin-
tiliano nihil consentio. nam in urbe septimo Domitiani imperii anno profiteri coepit, licet longe
antea a Galba fuisset in urbem adductus. Amicos
habuit praecipuos L. Gallum et Volusium Bithy-
nicum. Genus dicendi Luciana (= Luciliana)
libertate maxime probasset, si temporum ratio

suasisset, quibus nec etiam tuta erant silentia.
Satiras quattuordecim mortuorum solum taxatione ediderat, cum perinde ac eo commente
sua notasset tempora in Domitiani suspicionem
venerit. Incertum profecto id Paridis panto-
mimi odio, qui erat principi gratissimus, an
ipsius imperatoris offensa factum sit. Tamen qui
Martiali tribuunt vitasseque (?) invidiam volunt
eo epigrammate: „Cum Juvenale meo quid tu
comittere tentas?" Utcunque fuerit, sub honoris
specie in Aegyptum cohortis praefectus mittitur
in exilium, ubi duas edidit alias. In libros quinque
partitus est universas. Illorum opinionem omnino
non probo, qui hanc librorum distinctionem sub-
stulerunt. Nam si Ennius, si Lucilius satiras,
si Varro suas quas alii Menippeas a Menippo
servo, alii cinicas a mordacitate nuncuparunt,
in volumina distinxisse gravissimi auctores pro-
diderunt, quid est quod Juvenalis suas partiri
noluerit? Martialis praeterea in libros distingui
satiras probat saepissime (?) cum dicit:

„Saepius in libro laudatur Persius uno
Quam levis in tota Marsus Amazonide."

In exilio non multo post interiit. Vixit annos ferme quinquaginta. Miror qui octogenarium in exilium actum tradiderunt, cum ab Antistii consulatu, conatus (= quo natus) est ad Traiani principatum, quo interiit, si quis diligenter supputaverit, vix agi annos inveniet quinquaginta. Ad hoc si diutius vixisset, credibile est, plura ingenii monumenta posteris fuisse relicta." Der ganze Ton und die Darstellungsweise dieser *vita* entspricht der Art der humanistischen Elaborate überhaupt. Mit viel Phantasie und Willkür wird aus den überkommenen Nachrichten eine neue eigene Darstellung zurechtgemacht unter kritischer Bezugnahme auf andere gleichzeitige Darstellungen. Die Quellen, aus denen unser *Anonymus* schöpft, sind Juvenals Satiren, Martial, eine alte *vita Juvenalis*, die Chronik des Hieronymus und vielleicht Gellius oder Macrobius. Aus Juvenal selbst ist zunächst entnommen die Notiz von der Freundschaft des Dichters mit L. Gallus und Volusius Bithynicus; an den ersteren ist die 16., an den letzteren die 15. Satire gerichtet. Des Gallus, oder, wie er im *codex Pithoeanus* heisst, Gallius Vorname Lucius ist frei erfunden. Ebenso ist die folgende Bemerkung, dass Juvenal sich eine Einschränkung seines satirischen Freimuts mit Rücksicht auf die Zeitverhältnisse auferlegt habe, ersichtlich nur kurze Wiedergabe des von dem Dichter selbst im Epilog seiner ersten Satire (V. 148—171) ausgeführten Gedankens. Die Angabe ferner, dass Juvenal 14 Satiren in Rom „*mortuorum solum taxatione*", die zwei letzten in der Verbannung geschrieben habe, ist entstanden aus der naheliegenden Kombination der in der *vita* überlieferten Nachricht von des Dichters Verbannung nach Ägypten mit dessen eigener Angabe in der fünfzehnten Satire (15,45), dass er Ägypten selbst aus Anschauung kennt. Die Angabe „*Sub Frontone declamasse traditur, quem coluisset unice si intra epycureum dogma non constitisset*" knüpft an die in der ersten Satire

(1,12) sich findende Erwähnung eines Fronto an, in dessen Halle die Rezitationen stattfinden. Diesen Fronto identifiziert der *Anonymus* wahrscheinlich, wie auch andere Humanisten, mit dem bekannten Rhetor M. Cornelius Fronto aus Cirta. Das Motiv, das Juvenals Verehrung für diesen Mann beeinträchtigt haben soll, ist natürlich freie Erfindung, jedoch nicht einmal recht klar, da man nicht weiss, wer der Epikureer sein soll, ob Juvenal oder Fronto. Meint der *Anonymus* Juvenal selbst, so mag er diese Weisheit aus den Stellen, wo der Dichter sich abfällig über die Stoiker, die philosophischen Antipoden der Epikureer, äussert [1]), geschöpft haben und auf den Gegensatz der philosophischen Anschauung desselben zu der des Fronto dadurch gekommen sein, dass er sich den Erzieher des Marc Aurel, des stoischen Philosophen auf dem Kaiserthron, selbst als Stoiker dachte. Ist aber nach der Meinung des *Anonymus* Fronto der Epikureer, so könnte er dabei möglicherweise an das Scholion zu 1,12: „*Frontonis platani: in Horatiana domo*" angeknüpft haben, den wohlhabenden, überdies ähnlich wie Epikur selbst situierten [2]) Besitzer der *domus Horatiana* auch zum Nachfolger der Lebensanschauung und Lebensweise des epikureischen Dichters Horaz [3]) gemacht haben; andererseits kann man Juvenal mit Rücksicht auf seine bittere, pessimistische Lebensauffassung, seine scharfe Satire, seine kümmerlichen Verhältnisse, endlich im Hinblick auf eine bestimmte Stelle [4]) leicht zu einem Gegner epikureischer Lehre stempeln. Die weiteren Angaben über Juvenals Jugenderziehung sind, ganz in der Manier vieler alter Litterahistoriker, aus dem Be-

---

[1]) 2,64 f. 3,116. 13,120 ff.

[2]) Vgl. Juv. sat. 1,12: „*Frontonis platani convulsaque marmora clamant*"; 13,122 f.: „*non Epicurum Suspicit exigui laetum plantaribus horti*".

[3]) Horaz bezeichnet sich bekanntlich (*Epist.* 1,4,16) selbst humoristisch als „*Epicuri de grege porcum.*"

[4]) 15,106 f.: „*Melius nos Zenonis praecepta monent.*"

streben hervorgegangen, den berühmten Dichter mit anderen berühmten, älteren Zeitgenossen durch Statuierung des Schülerverhältnisses in Beziehung zu bringen. Das Material hat der *Anonymus* im grossen, meist wörtlich, aus der Chronik des Hieronymus entnommen [5]), das Detail *(prófecit maxime; frequentavit — distulit)* ist eigene Erfindung. Weiter hat er, oder haben vielmehr andere Ungenannte, aus einem der bekannten, Juvenals Freundschaft mit Martial bezeugenden Epigramme des letzteren (7, 24) eine, allerdings auch wegen der unsicheren Lesart nicht recht verständliche Angabe herausgeklügelt. Der Wortlaut, und damit auch der Sinn des Citats ist verändert [6]), und es wird nun dies Gedicht in Zusammenhang gebracht mit dem durch die Spottverse auf Paris erregten Zorn dieses Pantomimen selber oder seines kaiserlichen Gönners auf Juvenal, wie es scheint in dem Sinn, dass Martial die ihn selbst bedrohende *invidia* von sich auf Juvenal abzulenken versucht habe. Ein anderes Epigramm Martials (4, 29) wird neben anderen *gravissimi auctores*, vermutlich Gellius oder Macrobius [7]), citiert als Beleg für die bei den römischen Satirikern übliche Einteilung ihrer Werke in Bücher. Aus der alten *vita* hat der *Anonymus* zunächst die Nachricht von der wegen jener Verse durch Domitian unter dem Schein eines militärischen Kommandos verfügten Verbannung des Dichters nach Ägypten

entnommen; damit ergab sich ihm dann, da er, wie fast alle *vitae*, Juvenal bald darauf in der Verbannung sterben lässt, die Ansetzung seines Todes unter Traian und seines Lebensalters auf ungefähr 50 Jahre unter ausdrücklicher Abweisung der von ihm in seiner Quelle vorgefundenen Nachricht, dass Juvenal bei seiner Verbannung 80 Jahre alt gewesen sei. Endlich aber hat der *Anonymus* aller Wahrscheinlichkeit nach aus der ihm vorliegenden alten *vita* auch die am Anfang stehenden Angaben über Juvenals Geburtsjahr (55 n. Chr.) und über seine Familie entnommen. Die Genauigkeit jener, am Schluss wiederholten chronologischen Angabe, die Unmöglichkeit, in den Satiren Juvenals oder anderweitigen Nachrichten irgend einen Anhaltspunkt für Erschliessung oder willkürliche Erfindung derselben zu entdecken, ihr treffliches Zusammenstimmen mit den sonstigen Nachrichten über Juvenals Leben, endlich die wohlberechtigte Annahme, dass den Humanisten des 15. Jahrhunderts noch eine oder die andere alte *vita* vorgelegen haben mag, die wir nicht mehr haben, — alles das zusammen führt zu der Annahme, dass die genaue Angabe von Juvenals Geburtsjahr und ebenso, wie schon oben (S. 12) ausgeführt wurde, die Nachrichten über die Familie des Dichters von dem *Anonymus* aus seiner alten Quelle entnommen und von dieser aus echter guter Überlieferung geschöpft sind.

> „Cum Juvenale meo quae me committere tentas,
> Quid non audebis, perfida lingua, loqui?"

Der *Anonymus* citiert:

> „Cum Juvenale meo quid tu committere tentas?

[7]) Gellius 2, 18, 6 f.: „Alii quoque non pauci servi fuerunt, qui post philosophi clari extiterunt. Ex quibus ille Menippus fuit, cuius libros M. Varro in satiris aemulatus est, quas alii cynicas, ipse appellat Menippeas." Dieselbe Bemerkung wörtlich ausgeschrieben bei Macrob. Saturn. 1, 11.

---

[5]) Hieronym. z. d. J. Abr. 2064: „Palaemon insignis grammaticus Romae habetur". „M. Antonius Liberalis Latinus rhetor gravissimas inimicitias cum Palaemone exercet." Abr. 2072: „Probus Berytius eruditissimus grammaticorum Romae agnoscitur." Abr. 2084: „M. Fabius Quintilianus Romam a Galba perducitur." Abr. 2104: „Quintilianus primus Romae publicam scholam et salarium e fisco accepit et claruit."

[6]) Mart. 7, 24, 1 f.:

CPSIA information can be obtained
at www.ICGtesting.com
Printed in the USA
LVHW021505261118
598291LV00012B/1281

9 781334 613357